INTRODUCTION TO THE MECHANICS OF A CONTINUOUS MEDIUM

ADIWES INTERNATIONAL SERIES
IN THE ENGINEERING SCIENCES

ADDISON-WESLEY SERIES IN
MECHANICS AND THERMODYNAMICS

BERNARD BUDIANSKY AND HOWARD EMMONS
Consulting Editors

INTRODUCTION TO THE MECHANICS OF A CONTINUOUS MEDIUM

LEONID IVANOVICH SEDOV

TRANSLATED FROM THE RUSSIAN BY SCRIPTA TECHNICA, INC.

ADDISON-WESLEY PUBLISHING COMPANY, INC.

READING, MASSACHUSETTS • PALO ALTO • LONDON

ORIGINALLY PUBLISHED AS:
VVEDENIE V MEKHANIKU SPLOSHNOI SREDY
STATE PHYSICS AND MATHEMATICS PRESS, MOSCOW, 1962

PRINTED IN THE NETHERLANDS
BY N.V. DRUKKERIJ D. REIDEL, DORDRECHT

Library of Congress Catalog Card No. 64-16909

PREFACE TO THE ENGLISH EDITION

The ever increasing use of various models of continuous media has created a need for a deeper and clearer understanding of existing theories and has forced the development of new theories based on modern methematical and physical concepts, methods, and procedures.

The rules of development of science (which are clearly evident from the history of science) show that all truly fundamental progress arises from, and is closely related to, the creation, development, and application of new or improved methods, both theoretical and experimental.

In the present book the author attempted to present a simple, clear, and precise – yet detailed – treatment of the fundamental classical results and to acquaint the reader with modern methods and theories of models used in mechanics of continuous media. In a number of cases, both the material itself and its treatment represent an original contribution of the author. The book is intended to provide a means for understanding the relationship of mechanics to geometry and thermodynamics, and to impart some momentum to the further development of macroscopic theories.

After the publication of the original (Russian) edition, the author and his collaborators wrote several articles that may be considered a logical continuation of the present work. These are:

L. I. Sedov and M. E. Eglit, "Construction of anholonomic models of continuous media, taking into consideration finite deformations and certain physicochemical processes," *Dokl. Akad. Nauk SSSE, 142*, No. 1, 1962.
V. V. Lokhin and L. I. Sedov, "Nonlinear tensor functions of several tensor arguments," *Prikl. Mat. Mekh.*, No. 3, 1963. B. S. Kogarko, "One model of a cavitating liquid," *Dokl. Akad. Nauk SSSR, 137*, No. 6, 1961.

The first of the above papers treats the mechanical and thermodynamic theory of models of continuous media as applied to hypoelastic bodies and bodies exhibiting creep properties. In both cases finite deformations were taken into account. The second article presents methods for setting up symmetric groups by using tensors and gives simple tensor systems governing symmetric orientation- and all point-crystal groups. Computation of symmetry in tensor equations is accomplished by introducing tensors describing the corresponding symmetry groups as parametric arguments. Thus, the structure of tensor functions of various rank, which are dependent on several tensors of arbitrary rank, is established. The corresponding formulas necessary for the applications are also given. These formulas represent a significant generalization and development of formulas in Sections 5 and 6 of Chapter I.

The third paper presents the construction of a somewhat unusual concrete model of a continuous medium – a fluid whose free energy is a function not only of temperature and density, but also of the time derivative of density.

Obviously, the future development of mechanics of continuous media will involve construction of various models for solids, fluids, and gases, taking into consideration the effects of temperature, electromagnetic effects, phase and chemical transformations, and, in certain cases, quantum effects at low temperatures, etc.

Recently, some research has been done on models of material media for which the internal stress tensor contains nonsymmetric components.

Of the interesting recent developments, the theory of continuous dislocations and the theory of plastic properties of solids appear to be very promising. The latter uses the properties of non-Euclidean and non-Riemannian geometric manifolds. These manifolds are introduced as ideal states in analogy with the initial states in Euclidean space, when such states for a given solid are possible in the absence of internal stresses and internal defects (Kondo, Bilby, Kröner, and others.)

Theoretical treatment of models and motion of continuous media within the framework of the special theory of relativity is becoming more and more popular. It is obvious that relativistic theories require the most intensive application of tensor calculus, group theory, and differential geometry.

At the present time, the construction of macroscopic models for low-pressure gases and plasma is often directly related to the methods of the kinetic theory of gases. In statistical physics certain aspects and cases of setting up functional equations, and finding their solution or representation as partial differential equations in several variables require additional treatment.

The author hopes that he will be able to write additional chapters treating the above developments and, in particular, presenting that extensive and important field of mechanics which is concerned with the study of weak and strong discontinuities in media with multiple properties and various transformations. The above theory has been enriched during the past few years by many new results and important applications.

L. I. Sedov

7 December, 1963.

PREFACE

In the theoretical and experimental study of motions and the various physical and chemical processes in deformed solids, we introduce, explore, and utilize many special concepts, mathematical methods of description, and the laws of nature, finally formulating closed systems of equations. We should keep in mind, however, that the formulation and solution of problems describing theoretically the phenomena in the world about us always involve the introduction of schematic models and ideal processes, which correspond to observations and experiments on actual bodies to the extent required by the problems under study.

A system of differential or general functional equations is said to be closed, of course, when the number of independent equations is equal to the number of unknowns or functions. If we isolate fixed closed systems of equations, we can establish and study many classes of problems. The theoretical solution of a specific problem generally operates on the closed system of equations and on the various types of supplementary conditions, such as initial and boundary conditions, stability conditions, steady-state and discontinuity conditions, conditions at infinity, etc. An explicit formulation of all the equations and supplementary conditions determining a unique solution – answers to the questions which are posed – forms the basis of the problem. The correct statement of the problem is an important step in guaranteeing the success of the observations. Insufficiently precise conditions can lead to a nonunique solution and to all sorts of "paradoxes"; conversely, excessive strictness or the presence of unnecessary requirements can lead to a situation where the required solution does not exist.

The task of correctly stating the problem is difficult in many cases and is the primary object of investigation.

In this book, we present the theoretical apparatus, the basic physical concepts, and principles, which will be used to establish models of material bodies that fill space in an uninterrupted manner, i.e., as continua. Various examples of continua and typical processes will be examined, although the properties of individual processes and the solutions of particular problems on the motion of continuous media will not be given.

A restriction of this type, explicitly assumed, permits us to define the principles of mechanics of a continuum in a unique manner and to isolate problems related to the establishment of the problems of mechanics of a continuum from the methods and results of solving these problems. For the solution of particular problems at the present time, we have numerous observations applicable in practice only to certain limited classes of problems and, further, only to certain special problems.

The essential characteristic of the development of the theories in the text is the absence of any assumption about the geometrical smallness of the deformation of the particles in the medium, an assumption which is usually exploited to a high degree in the theories of elasticity, plasticity, and other phenomena.

Taking into account the finiteness of deformations complicates the theory to a great extent. In many contemporary practical problems, however, this complication is indispensable, and therefore in this book geometrically and dynamically nonlinear mechanics are developed.

Consideration of the finiteness of relative displacements and deformations of the particles in bodies is necessary for the investigation of some problems in the theory of elasticity for solids such as rubber, for plastic flow in solids, for establishing the deformation of plastics, and very frequently for liquids and gases, etc.

Our treatment of the geometric and kinematic characteristics of motion with finite deformations contains both in form and quality certain innovations. In particular, we examine in an explicit form the definition of different tensors in various spaces, determined by a succession of deformed states. We consider the tensors as invariants, represented as symbolic sums of the type

$$\boldsymbol{T} = T^{\alpha\cdot\gamma}_{\cdot\beta\cdot}\boldsymbol{\ni}_\alpha\boldsymbol{\ni}^\beta\boldsymbol{\ni}_\gamma, \tag{1}$$

where $T^{\alpha\cdot\gamma}_{\cdot\beta\cdot}$ are the components of the tensor and $\boldsymbol{\ni}_\alpha$ and $\boldsymbol{\ni}^\alpha$ $(\alpha = 1, 2, 3)$ are the covariant and contravariant vectors of the coordinate basis.

This is the normal vector representation. A similar representation for dyad-tensors of second rank has been widely used by M. Lagally [69]. The use of a tensor representation of type (1) leads to a substantial simplification in the development of the theory of tensor operators, particularly in the theory of differentiation of tensors with respect to coordinates or scalar parameters, when the vector bases change and, in particular, when we investigate simultaneously a given tensor for different bases moving with respect to one another.

The first two chapters deal with the tensor theory and its application to kinematic problems, while special care is devoted to the little-known theory of nonlinear tensor functions.

A significant part of the related theory, has, until now, been published only in specialized journals, and some of the results are being published here for the first time.

The dynamic and thermodynamic laws are treated in the third chapter. A reader who is already generally familiar with tensor theories can omit the first two chapters and should be able to go on to Chapter III without much difficulty.

Those who wish to do research on the further development of dynamic and thermodynamic theory or who wish to solve specific theoretical problems on the motion of continua with finite deformations will find it necessary to study the material of the first two chapters.

The book does not contain a historical description of the subject, nor is the list of references to the topics discussed exhaustive.*

As illustrations which are of independent interest, the book presents some examples of classical applications and newly developed continuum models for gases, liquids, and solids. In particular, the current problem of establishment of a continuum model for a plastic body is considered.

Many important specific models are not considered in this book because we did not think it necessary to give a complete review of the existing models or of models being developed.

The present book has come about as a result of lectures for a special course entitled "Introduction to Continuum Mechanics" given by the author at the Moscow State University from 1955 to 1958. (These lectures were first issued as reproductions from typescript in 1959.)

In conclusion, the author would like to express his sincere gratitude to N. S. Mel'nikova and V. V. Rozantseva, who gave much help in the editing and preparation of the manuscript prior to printing.

L. I. Sedov

Moscow, 1961

---

* We limit ourselves to the following brief summary. The theory of finite deformations and the corresponding general geometric and dynamic relationships and equations were studied from the very start of continuum mechanics. Kirchhoff [65] advanced these theories considerably. The results of the work in the 19th and early part of the 20th centuries are described in the well-known book of Love [20]. Subsequently, further developments and applications of the theory of finite deformations were noted, both in the theory of elasticity and in theories of models of continua having irreversible processes. A significant contribution to the development of the nonlinear theory of elasticity is mentioned in the works of F. D. Murnaghan [73, 74], A. Signorini [92], and V. V. Novozhilov [23].

The development of nonlinear tensor function theory and a full historical account of the theoretical work published up to 1953 are to be found in the memoirs of C. Truesdell [96]. Recently, the theory of nonlinear tensor bonds was developed in the works of R. S. Rivlin [85, 86], J. L. Ericksen [51, 52], A. E. Green [54], M. Reiner [82, 83], and many other authors.

Rheological, thermodynamic, and statistical investigations are dealt with in a huge number of scientific works, some of which are indicated in the bibliography at the end of the book. (This list is in no way complete.) The noteworthy course in continuum mechanics by M. Roy [88] is worth mentioning, where a close connection between mechanics and macroscopic thermodynamics is established.

CONTENTS

CHAPTER I. *The Elements of Tensor Analysis* 1

1. Curvilinear coordinate systems 1
2. Transformation of coordinates 8
3. The concept of tensors and the fundamentals of tensor algebra 11
4. Second-rank tensors 19
5. Tensor functions 32
6. Functions of certain tensors 48
7. Potential tensor functions 52
8. Differentiation of a tensor with respect to the space coordinates . . . 57
9. The Riemann-Christoffel tensor 61
10. Differentiation of tensors with respect to a parameter 65

CHAPTER II. *The Kinematics of a Deformed Medium* 78

1. General properties of continuous deformations 78
2. Affine deformations 81
3. Continuous finite displacements of a continuum 87
4. The tensor characteristics of a deformation 90
5. The rotation vector of the axes of deformation 99
6. Kinematic tensors characterizing a deformation 101
7. The differentiation of nonlinear tensor functions 106
8. Compatibility conditions 112

CHAPTER III. *Dynamic and Thermodynamic Equations* 115

1. Physical foundations 115
2. The concept of a material continuum 118
3. The continuity equations 120
4. The dynamic equations 124
5. The kinetic energy theorem and the work of internal surface forces . . 136
6. Thermodynamic systems and cycles, equations of the law of the conservation of energy, and the concept of the internal energy of a system . . 139
7. Basic principles and consequences of the second law of thermodynamics 148
8. Ideal liquids and gases 155
9. The simplest ideal processes 165
10. Special examples of ideal compressible media 170

11. The equations of motion for gaseous mixtures with physico-chemical interactions among the components 175
12. Viscous liquids and gases 195
13. Turbulent motion in continua 197
14. A model of an elastic body 201
15. Thermoelastic isotropic media 218
16. Notes on mechanical models with irreversible processes 225
17. Plastic, elastic, and complete deformations 230
18. The elastic region and loaded surface 236
19. The basic laws in the theories of plastic bodies 241
20. Models of plastic media whose loaded surfaces have angular points . . 254
Bibliography 261
Index 267

INTRODUCTION

Scientific description and investigation of the motion of various bodies have been based on the construction of theoretical models. Examples of such models which are satisfactory from a physical point of view and have many applications include the following ideal cases: a point mass, systems of a finite number of point masses with given laws of interaction, an absolutely rigid body, an ideal compressible liquid with certain known equations of state, a viscous liquid (or gas) of the Navier-Stokes type, and an elastic body which for small deformation follows Hooke's Law and for finite deformations follows some generalization of this law. To this list we could also add models of material bodies with more complex mechanical properties formulated to describe a narrow range of problems applicable to special practical questions.

Many contemporary mechanical problems, however, cannot possibly be solved on the basis of the collection of models currently in widespread use. The process of observation calls for new models with complicated physical and chemical properties which can accommodate the particular effects under study and permit the solution of important practical problems. Further scientific progress requires new models for studying the moving medium in relation to physical, chemical, and thermal processes. Dynamic, thermal, and physical interrelationships are important aspects of most present-day practical problems.

Let us consider some important fields of research in which new models for a continuum are needed to solve the new problems that have arisen.

The theory of motion of a plasma

The basic effects in a moving quasi-neutral plasma are essentially reducible to the interaction of the charge of the ions and electrons with an external electromagnetic field and with the natural electromagnetic field due to motion of the charges constituting the plasma. The characteristic condition in certain problems of plasma motion is the presence of a strong magnetic field and a high temperature. We need to develop a method for studying plasma motion by taking into account the physical and chemical conversion and emission.

Problems on the motion of highly compressed liquids and gases or, conversely, rarefied gases

In many important practical cases, one may also consider strongly rarefied gases as continua, but with properties different from those of a continuum of the ideal-gas type, such as is assumed in the classical problems of aerodynamics and gas dynamics.

We must remember that we are dealing with a continuum, i.e., a continuum model, when we describe motion or other processes with the aid of a closed system of differential equations or with the aid of functional equations containing continuous functions of the distribution of motion characteristics.

The motion of solid, liquid, and gaseous bodies with phase transitions and chemical reactions

The theory has been widely developed in this field for the case of ideal gases with reversible processes. However, for solids under the action of shearing stresses and in the general case of liquids and gases with irreversible processes, the corresponding theory is only in the first stage of its development.

To these problems, one should add *the problem of investigating the motions of mixtures.*

Problems of alloys, solutions, and mixtures have been considered thermodynamically in substance only in those cases in which there are no shearing stresses.

Within this range of problems, we can also pose important questions on the *motion of liquid suspensions and emulsions, on cavitation problems, on the formation and disappearance of bubbles in liquids, which bubbles are filled with gases and vapors of a liquid.*

The theory of plasticity

The concept of the elastic limit and the origin of a residual plastic deformation are closely related to physical changes in the microscopic structure of the solid. A study of plasticity ought to be bound up with the introduction of additional parameters characteristic of the known physical processes. In order to establish the laws governing the variation in these parameters, physical investigations or hypotheses of a thermodynamic nature are needed.

The theory of creep

The theory of creep and relaxation in solids is dependent on the fundamental relationship of the internal stresses to temperature and to the geometric and kinematic characteristics of the motion of the media. The present understanding of the phenomenon of aging and fatigue in materials is apparently possible only on a physical basis, provided that additional physical parameters are introduced, together with additional equations describing the characteristic internal physical and chemical processes taking place in solids under stressed conditions and closely related to temperature effects.

The problem of mechanical models for polymeric plastic materials has still been dealt with only briefly. In order to establish the appropriate models, it is apparently necessary to base them on the general notions of nonlinear elastic theory for finite deformations, and use the results of the theory of plasticity and creep.

At present we are still considering the various models of continua in application to *the problem of the mechanics of sandy and other types of soils*, and also to *subterranean hydrodynamics* or *gas dynamics for motion of liquids or gases in comparatively porous media.*

We shall not be dealing with any particular problems on continua from these standpoints. Our problem is to investigate the fundamental macroscopic relationships which are necessary in order to establish the desired models.

In essence, statistical physics and thermodynamics are required in the formulation of the basic macroscopic concepts and laws for different materials. Therefore, the introduction of thermodynamic and physical considerations connected with the molecular structure and the concept of the interaction between the molecules constituting the solid are most significant in the establishment of new models in contemporary mechanics.

Since it is necessary to take into consideration a large number of solids having different properties, many models will need to be constructed. In addition, in applications one must introduce a minimum number of new models, and these must necessarily have a complete description of the mechanical and thermal properties. Only in this case can one solve a wide range of problems. New models should be as simple as possible, rational, and useful for theoretical calculations.

The view is widely held that the models must possess the greatest simplicity permitting the development of suitable mathematical methods of solving the problems. This point of view may sometimes be extended and one can consider, within the limit of the physical accuracy of the problem in question, certain special models which allow solutions of certain standard problems to be used, for example, models for which "self-similar" solutions of a given type exist.

It is to be noted that the generally used theoretical models have always concerned themselves with methods applicable to the study and solution of established problems. It is sufficient to recall the basic universally accepted assumptions on a material continuum filling space, on continuous motion in time and space coordinates, on the differentiability of the functions adopted, etc. Without such assumptions, it is impossible to use the methods of differential and integral calculus.

We can recognize many examples of the interaction between the methods of investigation developed and the fixed properties of the model. This useful relationship is expedient not only for the extension and application in the construction of many general theories, but also in the solution of specific problems.

The method of consolidating the models and their properties is justified even in those cases in which a more complicated structure of molecules is already well known but which cannot be studied from the point of view of the general framework within which the theory is developed. To explain this, it is sufficient to recall the idea of a point mass. Under certain conditions and for completely defined problems, any mechanical system of finite mass can be thought of as a point mass, and on the basis of this, certain universal and extremely useful equations can be stated.

In many concrete cases, in spite of increased knowledge of the given material system and statement of new problems related to the impossibility of considering the system as a point mass, the general principles for the system regarded as a material point retain their significance. These ideas may be insufficient for describing all the effects which interest us, in which case the use of supplementary physical relationships is necessary.

Despite the fact that in the last hundred years our ideas on the structure of material bodies have changed radically, the models of continua and the formulation of basic continuum mechanics constructed by the founders of mechanics of continua (ideal liquids and gases, viscous liquids, elastic bodies, etc.) have an intrinsic significance even now.

Thus, to construct new, physically justified, and practically necessary models, one must understand the essence of the properties of matter; and when these are taken into account in the simplest possible manner, with certain deliberately neglected insignificant details noted experimentally, we obtain the relationships applicable to physically small particles. This in turn allows us to study the mechanical and physical phenomena taking place in finite bodies subjected to different particular conditions.

CHAPTER I

THE ELEMENTS OF TENSOR ANALYSIS

In order to construct continuum mechanics, various curvilinear coordinate systems are used, in particular, a moving deforming coordinate system considered as frozen into the medium (a satellite coordinate system). In connection with this, and also with the mathematical nature of the fundamental characteristics of continuum motion, it is always necessary to use either in an explicit or implicit form tensor concepts and ideas about functional relations between tensors.

The general theory of nonlinear relationships between tensors and the theory of finite deformations are described by a series of hypotheses and corollaries of tensor analysis, which are generally not described in elementary textbooks and are therefore not well known by a wide circle of specialists in mechanics.

In this short chapter, we shall state some basic facts of tensor calculus for a certain unique system which permits simplification in the treatment of the theory of mechanics.

In order to avoid a lengthy and detailed formulation of tensor analysis, we have assumed many elementary and common considerations, but a number of simple concepts, operations, and relationships will be mentioned in order to emphasize the introductory aspect of the treatment and to clarify basic ideas which will be used in various applications.

1. Curvilinear coordinate systems

The application of mathematical numerical methods to the description of geometric and mechanical phenomena is based on the introduction of a system of calculations, i.e., a coordinate system. Moreover, in order to handle particular numbers and to measure magnitudes (length, time, force, etc.), a system of unit dimensions must be fixed.

Coordinate systems and systems of units can assume various and diverse forms and are externally introduced as auxiliary means of investigation not having any direct connection with the effects and phenomena described.

Hence it follows that physical facts and laws are characterized by properties that are independent of the coordinate system and units chosen. The study of such properties, magnitudes, and laws is particularly important in mechanics.

By using a coordinate system, one can establish the relationship between numbers and points in space. In three-dimensional space, a point is described by three numbers, which are called the coordinates of the point.

We shall further bear in mind that the applications will be within the frame of Newtonian mechanics. In this case, we can limit ourselves to three-dimensional space. Of course, for Euclidean space one can introduce a single rectilinear cartesian system or a single curvilinear coordinate system, in which coordinates of the points can be described in the form of continuous functions of the cartesian coordinates.

Let us consider a curvilinear coordinate system in which the coordinates of the points in space are described by x^1, x^2, and x^3. The lines along which any two coordinates remain constant are called coordinate lines. For example, a line along which $x^2 = \text{const}$ and $x^3 = \text{const}$ defines the coordinate line x^1; along this line various points are defined by the value x^1 and the direction of increase of the coordinate x^1 defines the direction along this line.

Three coordinate lines can pass through every point in space. Tangents to the coordinate line through every point do not lie in the same plane, and form, in general, a nonorthogonal triad.

Let M and M_1 be two infinitesimally close points in space with coordinates x^1, x^2, x^3 and $x^1 + dx^1$, $x^2 + dx^2$, $x^3 + dx^3$. Points M and M_1 form an infinitesimally small directed segment $\boldsymbol{MM}_1 = d\boldsymbol{r}$, independent of the choice of the coordinate system. Segment $d\boldsymbol{r}$ can be expediently introduced as a separate geometric concept or as displacement vector. The length of segment $\boldsymbol{MM}_1$, which is denoted by ds, is called the modulus, or magnitude, of the displacement vector $d\boldsymbol{r}$. Together with $d\boldsymbol{r}$, we introduce another displacement vector $\boldsymbol{Э}$,* different from $d\boldsymbol{r}$ only in length. If the length of vector $\boldsymbol{Э}$ has unit length, then for all numbers $k > 0$, the symbol $k\boldsymbol{Э}$ means a vector directed along the element $\boldsymbol{MM}_1$ of length k, while $-k\boldsymbol{Э}$ is a vector of the same magnitude but oppositely directed, i.e., from M_1 to M.

Any desired length directed along MM_1 can be written in the form $k\boldsymbol{Э}$ by using the unit vector $\boldsymbol{Э}$. One can then write the relationship

$$d\boldsymbol{r} = ds\,\boldsymbol{Э}, \tag{1.1}$$

where ds is the distance between points M and M_1.

Proceeding along the coordinate lines from point M, we consider points

---

* To be consistent with the original Russian edition, the Russian "eh" has been retained in the English translation. It is pronounced as the *e* in *e*dge.

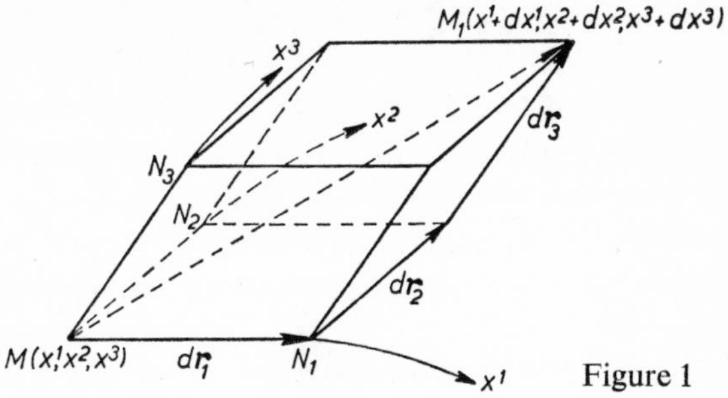

Figure 1

N_1, N_2, and N_3 on these lines, which points are defined by corresponding increments in only one of the coordinates by moving along the coordinate lines from point M to point M_1 (Fig. 1).

It is obvious that an infinitesimal segment MN_i is proportional to dx^i and we can therefore write

$$\begin{aligned} \boldsymbol{MN}_1 &= \boldsymbol{dr}_1 = dx^1 \mathbf{Э}_1, \\ \boldsymbol{MN}_2 &= \boldsymbol{dr}_2 = dx^2 \mathbf{Э}_2, \\ \boldsymbol{MN}_3 &= \boldsymbol{dr}_3 = dx^3 \mathbf{Э}_3, \end{aligned} \tag{1.2}$$

where $\mathbf{Э}_1$, $\mathbf{Э}_2$, $\mathbf{Э}_3$ are linearly independent displacement vectors directed tangentially to the coordinate lines with a length which, in general, is different from unity; the length of the vector $\mathbf{Э}_i$ is unity, if the increment dx^i is equal to the differential of the length of the arc along the coordinate line. Infinitesimal vectors $\boldsymbol{dr}_1$, $\boldsymbol{dr}_2$, $\boldsymbol{dr}_3$ form an infinitesimal parallelepiped of which vector $\boldsymbol{dr}$ is the diagonal.

A translation from point M to point M_1 can be achieved along the segment $\boldsymbol{dr}$ with a simultaneous change of all the coordinates or with a successive change of coordinates along the edges of the parallelepiped. The similarity of the results can be seen by writing the vector identities

$$\boldsymbol{dr} = \boldsymbol{dr}_1 + \boldsymbol{dr}_2 + \boldsymbol{dr}_3$$

or

$$\boldsymbol{dr} = ds\mathbf{Э} = dx^1 \mathbf{Э}_1 + dx^2 \mathbf{Э}_2 + dx^3 \mathbf{Э}_3 . \tag{1.3}$$

Equations (1.3) may be considered as the definition of vector addition. They show how any displacement vector $\boldsymbol{dr}$ can be represented as a sum of three other displacement vectors directed along the coordinate lines.

According to the definition and properties of a scalar product, it can be represented as

$$ds^2 = (\boldsymbol{dr}, \boldsymbol{dr}) = \sum_{\alpha,\beta=1}^{3} g_{\alpha\beta}\, dx^\alpha dx^\beta , \tag{1.4}$$

where

$$g_{ik} = (\vartheta_i, \vartheta_k) \qquad (i, k = 1, 2, 3). \tag{1.5}$$

In the right-hand side of formula (1.4), the summation is carried out with respect to the indices α and β, and for convenience the summation sign Σ will be omitted each time in the presence of the same index.

Also on the right of (1.4) we have the quadratic form of the differentials dx^i, the coefficients of these quadratic forms g_{ik} forming the symmetrical matrix g_*:

$$g_* = \begin{Vmatrix} g_{11} & g_{12} & g_{13} \\ g_{12} & g_{22} & g_{23} \\ g_{13} & g_{23} & g_{33} \end{Vmatrix} = \|(\vartheta_i, \vartheta_k)\| .$$

It is easy to show that the determinant of the matrix g_* is equal to the square of the quantity $V/dx^1\, dx^2\, dx^3$, where V is the volume of the parallelepiped formed by the three vectors $d\boldsymbol{r}_1 = dx^1\, \vartheta_1$, $d\boldsymbol{r}_2 = dx^2\, \vartheta_2$, $d\boldsymbol{r}_3 = dx^3\, \vartheta_3$. Indeed, the volume V of the parallelepiped defined by these three vectors can be represented by the scalar triple product

$$V = (\vartheta_1, [\vartheta_2, \vartheta_3])\, dx^1\, dx^2\, dx^3 ,$$

where the brackets denote the vector product. If an orthogonal coordinate system is introduced at the point M, then the scalar triple product for the ratio $V/dx^1\, dx^2\, dx^3$ can be represented in the form of a determinant. It is easy to see that a matrix equal to the product of the matrix of this determinant with its own transpose is identical with matrix g_*. Consequently, the following relationship holds:

$$\frac{V}{dx^1\, dx^2\, dx^3} = (\vartheta_1\, [\vartheta_2, \vartheta_3]) = \sqrt{|(\vartheta_i, \vartheta_j)|} = \sqrt{g}\,, \tag{1.6}$$

where the symbol g stands for the determinant of the matrix g_*: $g = |(\vartheta_i \vartheta_j)|$. Together with the trihedral $\vartheta_1, \vartheta_2, \vartheta_3$, we also introduce a reciprocal trihedral $\vartheta^1, \vartheta^2, \vartheta^3$ defined by

$$\vartheta^1 = \frac{[\vartheta_2, \vartheta_3]}{\sqrt{g}}, \qquad \vartheta^2 = \frac{[\vartheta_3, \vartheta_1]}{\sqrt{g}}, \qquad \vartheta^3 = \frac{[\vartheta_1, \vartheta_2]}{\sqrt{g}}. \tag{1.7}$$

The reciprocity follows from the immediately obvious formulas

$$(\vartheta^i, \vartheta_j) = \delta^i_j, \qquad \text{where} \qquad \delta^i_j = \begin{cases} 0, & i \neq j, \\ 1, & i = j \end{cases} \qquad (i, j = 1, 2, 3), \tag{1.8}$$

and

$$\vartheta_1 = \frac{[\vartheta^2, \vartheta^3]}{\sqrt{g_1}}, \qquad \vartheta_2 = \frac{[\vartheta^3, \vartheta^1]}{\sqrt{g_1}}, \qquad \vartheta_3 = \frac{[\vartheta^1, \vartheta^2]}{\sqrt{g_1}}, \tag{1.9}$$

where g_1 is the determinant of matrix $\|(\mathfrak{Э}^i, \mathfrak{Э}^j)\| = g^*$:

$$g_1 = |(\mathfrak{Э}^i, \mathfrak{Э}^j)|.$$

Equalities (1.7) and (1.9) follow from equations (1.8), whose solutions are unique, since the determinants made up of the components of vectors $\mathfrak{Э}_i$ or $\mathfrak{Э}^i$ are nonsingular. It is obvious that in an orthogonal cartesian coordinate system, the bases of the unit vectors $\mathfrak{Э}_i$ or $\mathfrak{Э}^i$ will coincide. Therefore, the distinction between quantities with upper and lower indices disappears. If the coordinate system used is orthogonal, the vectors of the bases $\mathfrak{Э}_i$ and $\mathfrak{Э}^i$ coincide in direction, but their magnitudes, in general, will differ because $\mathfrak{Э}_i = g_{ii}\mathfrak{Э}^i$.

An elementary vector $d\boldsymbol{r}$ can always be represented as the sum of three vectors having directions parallel to $\mathfrak{Э}^1, \mathfrak{Э}^2, \mathfrak{Э}^3$, in a form analogous to formula (1.3):

$$d\boldsymbol{r} = ds\mathfrak{Э} = dx_1\mathfrak{Э}^1 + dx_2\mathfrak{Э}^2 + dx_3\mathfrak{Э}^3, \tag{1.10}$$

where the infinitesimal quantities dx_1, dx_2, dx_3 are the counterparts of dx^1, dx^2, dx^3 in formula (1.3).

From (1.10) if follows that

$$ds^2 = g^{\alpha\beta}\, dx_\alpha\, dx_\beta, \tag{1.11}$$

where $g^{ik} = (\mathfrak{Э}^i, \mathfrak{Э}^k)$.

Moreover, from (1.3) and (1.10), by using relationship (1.8) and taking the scalar product on both sides, one obtains

$$ds^2 = dx^\alpha\, dx_\alpha = dx^1\, dx_1 + dx^2\, dx_2 + dx^3\, dx_3.$$

From the relationship

$$dx^\alpha\mathfrak{Э}_\alpha = dx_\beta\mathfrak{Э}^\beta$$

after taking the scalar product of both sides with either $\mathfrak{Э}_i$ or $\mathfrak{Э}^i$, one obtains

$$dx_i = g_{\alpha i}\, dx^\alpha \qquad \text{and} \qquad dx^i = g^{\beta i}\, dx_\beta\,; \tag{1.12}$$

moreover, the following formulas are immediately obvious:

$$\mathfrak{Э}_i = g_{\alpha i}\mathfrak{Э}^\alpha, \qquad \mathfrak{Э}^i = g^{\alpha i}\mathfrak{Э}_\alpha. \tag{1.13}$$

From (1.13), it follows that the matrices $g_* = \|g_{ik}\|$ and $g^* = \|g^{ik}\|$ are reciprocal. Consequently, $g_1 = 1/g$. The system of vectors $\mathfrak{Э}_i$ is called the covariant basis, and $\mathfrak{Э}^i$ the contravariant basis. The quantities dx_i are called the covariant components of the vector* $d\mathbf{r}$, and dx^i are called the contravariant components. Equations (1.12) define the transformation from covariant components to contravariant components and vice versa.

From formula (1.2), it follows that

$$\frac{\partial \mathbf{r}}{\partial x^i} = \mathbf{Э}_i . \tag{1.14}$$

On the basis of formulas (1.10), the analogous formulas are obvious:

$$\frac{\partial \mathbf{r}}{\partial x_i} = \mathbf{Э}^i . \tag{1.15}$$

The vectors of the basis $\mathbf{Э}_1$, $\mathbf{Э}_2$, $\mathbf{Э}_3$ generally depend on the position of the point M and define the coordinate trihedral about M. A change of position of point M will change the basis. A change in basis is characterized by the values of derivatives $\partial \mathbf{Э}_i / \partial x^j$.

It is clear, without any additional considerations, that in a Euclidean space, the derivative of a vector with respect to a variable scalar is also a vector, which may be represented by the sum of three other vectors parallel to the base vectors. Therefore, the following relation must hold:

$$\frac{\partial \mathbf{Э}_i}{\partial x^j} = \Gamma_{ij}^{\alpha} \mathbf{Э}_{\alpha} , \tag{1.16}$$

where the Γ_{ij}^{α} are certain values called Christoffel symbols. In Euclidean space, $\Gamma_{ij}^{\alpha} \equiv 0$ if the coordinate system is rectangular, and $\Gamma_{ij}^{\alpha} \neq 0$ if the coordinate system is curvilinear.

---

* In the general case, it is not permissible to consider the system of covariant components of vector $d\mathbf{r}$

$$dx_1 = g_{\alpha 1}\, dx^{\alpha}, \qquad dx_2 = g_{\alpha 2}\, dx^{\alpha}, \qquad dx_3 = g_{\alpha 3}\, dx^{\alpha}$$

as exact differentials for the corresponding functions of the coordinating points in the space x^1, x^2, x^3, because the conditions of integrability are not satisfied. For example, the conditions of integrability for all dx_i are not fulfilled in the spherical coordinate system when $x^1 = r$, $x^2 = \theta$, $x^3 = \phi$ and when

$$dx_1 = dr, \qquad dx_2 = r^2\, d\theta, \qquad dx_3 = r^2 \sin^2 \theta\, d\phi.$$

If the coordinate system is of the oblique cartesian type, then $g_{\alpha k} = \text{const}$, and the following holds true:

$$x_k = g_{\alpha k} x^{\alpha}.$$

In the general case of curvilinear coordinates, the quantities x_k cannot be defined as single-valued functions of the coordinates for all points of the space x^i.

In Euclidean space, if the radius vector of points of the space $\boldsymbol{r}(M)$ is introduced, then clearly

$$\frac{\partial \mathfrak{I}_i}{\partial x^j} = \frac{\partial^2 \boldsymbol{r}}{\partial x^i \partial x^j} = \Gamma^{\alpha}_{ij}\mathfrak{I}_{\alpha},$$

from which it follows that

$$\Gamma^{\alpha}_{ij} = \Gamma^{\alpha}_{ji}. \tag{1.17}$$

The coefficients Γ^{α}_{ij} can be expressed in terms of derivatives of g_{ik}. By taking the scalar product of (1.16) with $\mathfrak{I}_s$, we obtain

$$\frac{\partial g_{is}}{\partial x^j} - \mathfrak{I}_i \frac{\partial \mathfrak{I}_s}{\partial x^j} = \Gamma^{\alpha}_{ij} g_{\alpha s},$$

and by interchanging the indices i and j, we obtain

$$\frac{\partial g_{js}}{\partial x^i} - \mathfrak{I}_j \frac{\partial \mathfrak{I}_s}{\partial x^i} = \Gamma^{\alpha}_{ij} g_{\alpha s}.$$

Further, since

$$\frac{\partial g_{ij}}{\partial x^s} = \mathfrak{I}_i \frac{\partial \mathfrak{I}_j}{\partial x^s} + \mathfrak{I}_j \frac{\partial \mathfrak{I}_i}{\partial x^s} = \mathfrak{I}_i \frac{\partial \mathfrak{I}_s}{\partial x^j} + \mathfrak{I}_j \frac{\partial \mathfrak{I}_s}{\partial x^i},$$

we obtain

$$\frac{\partial g_{is}}{\partial x^j} + \frac{\partial g_{js}}{\partial x^i} - \frac{\partial g_{ij}}{\partial x^s} = 2\Gamma^{\alpha}_{ij} g_{\alpha s}. \tag{1.18}$$

Multiplying (1.18) by $g^{\beta s}$ and summing over s, we find

$$\Gamma^{\beta}_{ij} = \tfrac{1}{2} g^{\beta s}\left(\frac{\partial g_{is}}{\partial x^j} + \frac{\partial g_{js}}{\partial x^i} - \frac{\partial g_{ij}}{\partial x^s}\right). \tag{1.19}$$

It can be easily shown that the derivatives of the vectors of the contravariant basis $\partial \mathfrak{I}^i/\partial x^j$ can also be expressed in terms of the Γ^{β}_{ij} by formulas analogous to formula (1.16).

Differentiating the equality $(\mathfrak{I}^i, \mathfrak{I}_k) = \delta^i_k$, and making use of (1.16), we obtain

$$\left(\frac{\partial \mathfrak{I}^i}{\partial x^j}, \mathfrak{I}_k\right) = -\left(\mathfrak{I}^i, \frac{\partial \mathfrak{I}_k}{\partial x^j}\right) = -\Gamma^{i}_{kj},$$

which leads to

$$\frac{\partial \mathfrak{I}^i}{\partial x^j} = -\Gamma^{i}_{\alpha j}\mathfrak{I}^{\alpha}. \tag{1.20}$$

Further, on the basis of formulas (1.12), we have

$$\frac{\partial \mathfrak{I}_i}{\partial x_j} = \frac{\partial \mathfrak{I}_i}{\partial x^{\alpha}} \frac{\partial x^{\alpha}}{\partial x_j} = \frac{\partial \mathfrak{I}_i}{\partial x^{\alpha}} g^{j\alpha} = \Gamma^{\beta}_{i\alpha}\mathfrak{I}_{\beta} g^{j\alpha} \tag{1.21}$$

and, by a similar process, we obtain

$$\frac{\partial \mathbf{Э}^i}{\partial x_j} = -\Gamma^i_{\alpha\beta}\mathbf{Э}^\alpha g^{\beta j}.$$

The concept of a vector of infinitesimal displacement, the operations of scalar and vector multiplication, vectors with covariant and contravariant bases, the quantities g_{ik} and g^{ik}, the Christoffel symbols Γ^α_{ij}, and, in particular, formulas (1.16) through (1.21), which were introduced in this section for Euclidean space, are all retained, by definition, in the same form for Riemannian space.

2. Transformation of coordinates

The coordinates of space points, the coordinate lines, the vector trihedrals $\mathbf{Э}_i$ and $\mathbf{Э}^i$, and the quantities connected with them depend on the choice of coordinate system. Let us examine the transformation formulas used in changing from one coordinate system to another.

Consider two coordinate systems K and K'. In the system K, the coordinates of points of the space are denoted by x^1, x^2, x^3, and in K' by y^1, y^2, y^3, and the given functions

$$y^i = y^i(x^1, x^2, x^3) \qquad (i = 1, 2, 3). \tag{2.1}$$

It will be further supposed that the functions $y^i(x^1, x^2, x^3)$ are continuous and differentiable and that they define a one-to-one correspondence in the regions considered.

Naturally, in this case the Jacobians of the transformations are different from zero:

$$\Delta = \left|\frac{\partial y^i}{\partial x^k}\right| \neq 0 \qquad \text{and} \qquad \Delta^{-1} = \left|\frac{\partial x^i}{\partial y^k}\right| \neq 0. \tag{2.2}$$

Then the matrices corresponding to these determinants are inverse to each other. Formula (2.1) can be solved in the neighborhood of an arbitrary point in the regions referred to and can be put in the form

$$x^i = x^i(y^1, y^2, y^3).$$

Let $\mathbf{Э}_i$ and $\mathbf{Э}'_i$ $(i = 1, 2, 3)$ be the reference vectors for coordinates at the point M in the systems K and K', respectively. For an arbitrary displacement vector $d\mathbf{r}$, the following holds:

$$d\mathbf{r} = dx^1\mathbf{Э}_1 + dx^2\mathbf{Э}_2 + dx^3\mathbf{Э}_3 = dy^1\mathbf{Э}'_1 + dy^2\mathbf{Э}'_2 + dy^3\mathbf{Э}'_3.$$

From here, one can easily find formulas connecting $\mathfrak{Э}_i$ and $\mathfrak{Э}'_i$. Since

$$dx^i = \frac{\partial x^i}{\partial y^\alpha} dy^\alpha \qquad \text{and} \qquad dy^i = \frac{\partial y^i}{\partial x^\alpha} dx^\alpha, \tag{2.3}$$

where the summation is carried out over α, it follows that

$$dy^\alpha \frac{\partial x^\beta}{\partial y^\alpha} \mathfrak{Э}_\beta = dy^\alpha \mathfrak{Э}'_\alpha \qquad \text{and} \qquad dx^\alpha \mathfrak{Э}_\alpha = dx^\alpha \frac{\partial y^\beta}{\partial x^\alpha} \mathfrak{Э}'_\beta .$$

Consequently, we obtain

$$\mathfrak{Э}'_\alpha = \frac{\partial x^\beta}{\partial y^\alpha} \mathfrak{Э}_\beta, \qquad \mathfrak{Э}_\alpha = \frac{\partial y^\beta}{\partial x^\alpha} \mathfrak{Э}'_\beta . \tag{2.4}$$

If A denotes the matrix of the transformation, that is, if

$$A = \|a^{i\cdot}_{\cdot k}\| = \left\| \frac{\partial x^i}{\partial y^k} \right\| = \begin{Vmatrix} \dfrac{\partial x^1}{\partial y^1} & \dfrac{\partial x^1}{\partial y^2} & \dfrac{\partial x^1}{\partial y^3} \\ \dfrac{\partial x^2}{\partial y^1} & \dfrac{\partial x^2}{\partial y^2} & \dfrac{\partial x^2}{\partial y^3} \\ \dfrac{\partial x^3}{\partial y^1} & \dfrac{\partial x^3}{\partial y^2} & \dfrac{\partial x^3}{\partial y^3} \end{Vmatrix},$$

then

$$A^{-1} = \|b^{i\cdot}_{\cdot k}\| = \left\| \frac{\partial y^i}{\partial x^k} \right\|,$$

where the first index, i, refers to the row, and the second, k, to the column. Formulas (2.3) and (2.4) can be written symbolically as

$$dx^i = a^{i\cdot}_{\cdot k}\, dy^k, \qquad \mathfrak{Э}_k = \mathfrak{Э}'_i A^{-1} \quad \text{and} \quad dy^i = b^{i\cdot}_{\cdot k}\, dx^k, \qquad \mathfrak{Э}'_k = \mathfrak{Э}_i A . \tag{2.5}$$

In (2.5), one must pay attention to the order of the factors. In the summations $a^{i\cdot}_{\cdot k}\, dy^k, dy^1, dy^2, dy^3$ is convoluted with the various terms of a fixed row of the matrix A (summation over the lower index); in the summations $\mathfrak{Э}_i A$, the convolution of $\mathfrak{Э}_1, \mathfrak{Э}_2, \mathfrak{Э}_3$ is carried out with fixed elements of the column (summation over the upper index) of matrix A.

We have thus established the formulas for the transformation of the contravariant components dx^i, dy^i of the vector $d\boldsymbol{r}$ and the covariant base reference vectors $\mathfrak{Э}_i$ and $\mathfrak{Э}'_i$.

We now proceed to find the formulas for the transformation of the covariant components dx_i and dy_i and the contravariant basis reference vectors $\mathfrak{Э}^i$ and $\mathfrak{Э}'^i$.

Let us first consider the transformation formulas for g_{ik}. To this end, we have

$$g'_{ik} = (\mathfrak{Э}'_i, \mathfrak{Э}'_k) = \frac{\partial x^\alpha}{\partial y^i} \frac{\partial x^\beta}{\partial y^k} (\mathfrak{Э}_\alpha, \mathfrak{Э}_\beta) = \frac{\partial x^\alpha}{\partial y^i} \frac{\partial x^\beta}{\partial y^k} g_{\alpha\beta}, \tag{2.6}$$

and obviously the inverse formulas are of the form

$$g_{ik} = \frac{\partial y^\alpha}{\partial x^i}\frac{\partial y^\beta}{\partial x^k} g'_{\alpha\beta}.$$

From formulas (2.2) and (2.6) in particular, it follows that

$$g = \Delta^2 g' \qquad \text{and} \qquad g_1 = \Delta^{-2} g'_1, \tag{2.7}$$

where g' denotes the determinant of the matrix

$$g'_* = \|(\ni'_i, \ni'_j)\|, \qquad g' = |(\ni'_i, \ni'_j)|$$

and g'_1 the determinant of the matrix

$$g^{*\prime} = \|(\ni'^i, \ni'^j)\|, \qquad g'_1 = |(\ni'^i, \ni'^j)|.$$

Furthermore, since

$$dx_i = g_{is}\, dx^s \qquad \text{and} \qquad dy_k = g'_{kr}\, dy^r,$$

from formulas (2.3) and (2.7), we obtain

$$dx_i = \frac{\partial y^\alpha}{\partial x^i}\frac{\partial y^\beta}{\partial x^s} g'_{\alpha\beta} \frac{\partial x^s}{\partial y^r} dy^r = \frac{\partial y^\alpha}{\partial x^i} g'_{\alpha r}\, dy^r = \frac{\partial y^\alpha}{\partial x^i} dy_\alpha, \tag{2.8}$$

because

$$\frac{\partial y^\beta}{\partial x^s}\frac{\partial x^s}{\partial y^r} = \delta^\beta_r.$$

If we now use the relationship

$$dx_\alpha \ni^\alpha = dy_\beta \ni'^\beta,$$

together with (2.8), we obtain the transformation formula

$$\ni'^i = \frac{\partial y^i}{\partial x^\alpha} \ni^\alpha. \tag{2.9}$$

Finally, we obtain four more formulas in the following form:

$$dx_k = dy_i b^{i\cdot}_{\cdot k}, \qquad \ni^i = A \ni'^k$$

and

$$dy_k = dx_i a^{i\cdot}_{\cdot k}, \qquad \ni'^i = A^{-1} \ni^k. \tag{2.10}$$

In formulas (2.10), the order of the factors has the same significance as in (2.5).

Equations (2.5) and (2.10) give a complete set of formulas for either a direct or inverse transformation of the components of a displacement vector and the coordinate base vectors. The symmetry and the various laws of transformation for covariant and contravariant quantities are obvious from the structure of these formulas.

3. The concept of tensors and the fundamentals of tensor algebra

In the preceding section, formulas were derived to describe the transformation between the covariant and contravariant components of an infinitesimal vector $\boldsymbol{dr}$ and the vectors of the coordinate bases $\mathbf{Э}^i$ and $\mathbf{Э}_i$ subject to arbitrary coordinate transformation laws. These formulas were obtained as the simple consequence of the invariance of $\boldsymbol{dr}$, considered as being independent of the chosen coordinate system.

After establishing (2.5) and (2.10), one may ask whether there could be other quantities, like the elementary vector $\boldsymbol{dr}$, that can be regarded as invariant and independent of the coordinate system.

One can introduce as basic new objects the quantities $\mathbf{Э}_1$, $\mathbf{Э}_2$, $\mathbf{Э}_3$, and correspondingly, $\mathbf{Э}^1$, $\mathbf{Э}^2$, $\mathbf{Э}^3$, and define, with respect to these quantities, the operations of multiplication by a number, addition, scalar and vector multiplication, and the transformation from one coordinate system to another.

Furthermore, one may define a vector quite generally as a linear combination of the type

$$\boldsymbol{a} = a^1\mathbf{Э}_1 + a^2\mathbf{Э}_2 + a^3\mathbf{Э}_3 = a_1\mathbf{Э}^1 + a_2\mathbf{Э}^2 + a_3\mathbf{Э}^3 , \tag{3.1}$$

where the a^i and a_i can be regarded as the contravariant and covariant components of a vector $\boldsymbol{a}$, which in itself is an invariant, but the numbers a^i and a_i must be thought of as a system of components, analogous to the components dx^i and dx_i and transforming according to the same laws. For an arbitrary vector $\boldsymbol{a}$, having fixed units, considered invariant, and defined by formula (3.1), one can recognize only one sca ar invariant, i.e., the length of the vector, which is defined by the formula

$$a = \sqrt{(a, a)} = \sqrt{g_{\alpha\beta}a^\alpha a^\beta} = \sqrt{g^{\alpha\beta}a_\alpha a_\beta} = \sqrt{a^\alpha a_\alpha}\,.$$

As was noted above, the recognition and use of invariant quantities is of great significance, because this allows one to separate the externally applied theoretical methods of investigation from the essence of the problems under question.

Following the introduction of the vectorial bases $\mathbf{Э}_i$ and $\mathbf{Э}^i$, it is possible to generalize the vector concept and to examine invariants of the following general type:

$$\boldsymbol{T} = T_{\alpha\beta\cdots}^{\cdot\cdot\ \cdots\gamma\delta\cdots}\mathbf{Э}^\alpha\mathbf{Э}^\beta\ldots\mathbf{Э}_\gamma\mathbf{Э}_\delta\ldots . \tag{3.2}$$

The summation is carried out over all the indices α, β, ..., γ, δ, ..., and in each monomial, the product $\mathbf{Э}^\alpha\mathbf{Э}^\beta\ldots\mathbf{Э}_\gamma\mathbf{Э}_\delta$ on the right-hand side of (3.2) has a definite order and is regarded as a linearly independent quantity so far as the other monomials of the general sum are concerned.

The quantity T, which is determined by the components $T_{\alpha\beta\cdots\cdots}^{\cdot\cdot\ \gamma\delta\cdots}$, and can be considered independent of the choice of the coordinate system, is called a tensor. However, the components of a tensor depend on the coordinate system chosen. The total number of covariant and contravariant indices is called the rank of the tensor. The indices are arranged in a definite order so that the lower indices have nothing written above them, and the upper indices nothing below. In formula (3.2), the summation is carried out over the same indices from 1 to n, which is the number of dimensions of the space under consideration. A simultaneous interchange of the indices of the components and the vector symbols of the basis would leave equation (3.2) unaltered. If only the order of the indices of the components were changed, a new quantity would result which would be equal to the original quantity only if the initial components were respectively equal to the components with interchanged indices.

From the invariance of the tensor $\boldsymbol{T}$ and from the transformation formulas (2.5) and (2.6) for the basis vectors, one can easily derive the general transformation formulas for the components of a tensor of arbitrary rank.

The condition of invariance of a tensor $\boldsymbol{T}$ is equivalent to

$$\boldsymbol{T} = T_{\alpha\beta\cdots\cdots}^{\cdot\cdot\ \gamma\delta\cdots}\,\boldsymbol{\ni}^{\alpha}\boldsymbol{\ni}^{\beta}_{\cdots}\boldsymbol{\ni}_{\gamma}\boldsymbol{\ni}_{\delta}\ldots = T'^{\cdot\cdot\ ks\cdots}_{ij\cdots\cdots}\,\boldsymbol{\ni}'^{i}\boldsymbol{\ni}'^{j}_{\cdots}\boldsymbol{\ni}'_{k}\boldsymbol{\ni}'_{s}\ldots,$$

in which, for convenience, the indices of summation in the different coordinate systems are represented by different letters.

The following formulas are then immediately obvious:

$$T'^{\cdot\cdot\ ks\cdots}_{ij\cdots\cdots} = T_{\alpha\beta\cdots\cdots}^{\cdot\cdot\ \gamma\delta\cdots}\frac{\partial x^{\alpha}}{\partial y^{i}}\frac{\partial x^{\beta}}{\partial y^{j}}\cdots\frac{\partial y^{k}}{\partial x^{\gamma}}\frac{\partial y^{s}}{\partial x^{\delta}}\cdots. \tag{3.3}$$

Formulas (3.3) are equivalent to (3.2). Usually tensors are defined as a set of components obeying the transformation laws (3.3), without explicitly introducing the tensor quantity $\boldsymbol{T}$ into the argument. However, the explicit use of the idea of a vector as the quantity $\boldsymbol{a} = a_i\boldsymbol{\ni}^i$ is widely employed. The viewing of a tensor as an object in the sense of, for example, (3.2), just as is done with vectors, is especially suitable and convenient in tensor analysis for establishing better rules for differentiation with respect to the coordinates and variable parameters in various coordinate systems (time rates in different senses).

From the definition of a tensor, it follows that if all the components of the tensor are equal to zero in one coordinate system, the components will be zero in any other coordinate system.

From formula (3.3) it is also obvious that after interchanging any two *upper* or any two *lower* indices of the components of a given tensor, a new tensor is formed whose components, generally speaking, are not equal to the corresponding components of the original tensor.

If any pair of upper and lower indices are interchanged, and the tensor remains unaltered, it is said to be *symmetric* with respect to these indices.

If, because of an interchange of indices, the new tensor is different only in that the sign of components has changed, the tensor is said to be skew-symmetric with respect to these indices. It is clear that the components of a skew-symmetric tensor in which the interchangeable indices are identical are equal to zero.

The foregoing definitions of symmetry and skew-symmetry are invariant properties of a tensor, because if these properties are fulfilled in any one coordinate system, then from (3.3) it follows that they will be fulfilled in any other coordinate system.

The lower indices of the components of the tensor $T_{\alpha\beta\cdots\cdots}^{\cdot\cdot\;\gamma\delta\cdots}$ can be raised, and the upper ones lowered, by interchanging the corresponding basis vectors according to equation (1.13). Thus, for example, to raise the index α and lower the index δ, one can write

$$T = T_{\alpha\beta\cdots\cdots}^{\cdot\cdot\;\gamma\delta\cdots} g^{\alpha s} \mathbf{\ni}_s \mathbf{\ni}^\beta \ldots \mathbf{\ni}_\gamma g_{\delta r} \mathbf{\ni}^r \ldots = T_{\cdot\beta\cdots\cdot r}^{s\cdot\;\gamma\cdots} \mathbf{\ni}_s \mathbf{\ni}^\beta \ldots \mathbf{\ni}_\gamma \mathbf{\ni}^r \ldots, \tag{3.4}$$

where

$$T_{\cdot\beta\cdots\cdot r}^{s\cdot\;\gamma\cdots\cdot} = T_{\alpha\beta\cdots\cdots}^{\cdot\cdot\;\gamma\delta\cdots} g^{\alpha s} g_{\delta r}.$$

Formula (3.4) gives a general rule for "juggling" the indices.

For an orthogonal cartesian coordinate system, one should note that

$$g^{\alpha s} = \begin{cases} 1, & \alpha = s, \\ 0, & \alpha \neq s, \end{cases} \quad \text{and} \quad g_{\delta r} = \begin{cases} 1, & \delta = r, \\ 0, & \delta \neq r, \end{cases}$$

and therefore the components with the raised and lowered indices are equal to one another. Consequently, in an orthogonal cartesian coordinate system, the distinction between upper and lower indices vanishes.

It is to be noted that in accordance with the transformation formulas (2.6), the set of numbers g_{ik} forms a tensor G; thus, it is possible to write the equalities

$$G = g_{\alpha\beta} \mathbf{\ni}^\alpha \mathbf{\ni}^\beta = g^{\alpha\beta} \mathbf{\ni}_\alpha \mathbf{\ni}_\beta = \delta_\beta^\alpha \mathbf{\ni}_\alpha \mathbf{\ni}^\beta, \tag{3.5}$$

where

$$\delta_\beta^\alpha = \begin{cases} 0, & \alpha \neq \beta, \\ 1, & \alpha = \beta. \end{cases}$$

It is interesting to note that the components of the tensor $\boldsymbol{G}$ with mixed indices (covariant with respect to one index and contravariant with respect to the other) in a given coordinate system are all simply equal to δ^i_j. The tensor $\boldsymbol{G}$ is symmetric because $g_{ik} = g_{ki}$ and $g^{ik} = g^{ki}$.

For tensors, just as for vectors, one can define the operations of multiplication of tensors by scalars and addition of tensors.

Multiplication of a tensor by a number k results in another tensor which has all its components multiplied by k.

Tensor addition can be defined only for tensors of the same rank. To obtain the components of a tensor $\boldsymbol{T}$ equal to the sum $\boldsymbol{T}' + \boldsymbol{T}''$, it is necessary to make the components of $\boldsymbol{T}'$ and $\boldsymbol{T}''$ equal with respect to the arrangement of indices by raising or lowering the indices. When this is done, the components of the sum are simply equal to the sum of the components of the two tensors. The sum of the components forms a tensor because it transforms just as the summed components. The result of the addition does not depend on the structure of the indices of the components to be added.

Obviously, the rule of addition of two tensors can easily be extended to an arbitrary number of tensors.

From given tensors (or, in particular, vectors), it is easy to form new tensors by forming arrays of numbers from the products of the components

$$\boldsymbol{T} = \boldsymbol{T}'\boldsymbol{T}'' = T'^{\cdot\cdot\delta\gamma}_{\alpha\beta\cdot\cdot} T''^{\cdot s}_{\omega\cdot} \boldsymbol{\ni}^{\alpha} \boldsymbol{\ni}^{\beta} \boldsymbol{\ni}_{\delta} \boldsymbol{\ni}_{\gamma} \boldsymbol{\ni}^{\omega} \boldsymbol{\ni}_{s} . \tag{3.6}$$

The resulting tensor $\boldsymbol{T}$ formed in this manner depends on the order of the factors and is of rank equal to the sum of the ranks of the multiplied tensors $\boldsymbol{T}'$ and $\boldsymbol{T}''$.

From any two given tensors it is possible to form new tensors having a rank lower than the sum of their ranks by means of the invariant operation of scalar multiplication of any given pair of the three basis vectors corresponding to a definite index. For example, by using tensors $\boldsymbol{T}'$ and $\boldsymbol{T}''$, one may form a tensor equal to the following double scalar product:

$$\overset{*}{\boldsymbol{T}} = T'^{\cdot\cdot\delta\gamma}_{\alpha\beta\cdot\cdot} T''^{\cdot s}_{\omega\cdot} g^{\alpha\omega} \delta^{\beta}_{s} \boldsymbol{\ni}_{\delta} \boldsymbol{\ni}_{\gamma} = T'^{\cdot\cdot\delta\gamma}_{\alpha\beta\cdot\cdot} T''^{\alpha\beta} \boldsymbol{\ni}_{\delta} \boldsymbol{\ni}_{\gamma} . \tag{3.7}$$

In particular, for scalar multiplication of a given tensor by the fundamental tensor $\boldsymbol{G}$, defined by (3.5), we shall obtain another tensor. In the case of repeated multiplication by $\boldsymbol{G}$, using only one index in each of the multipliers of the tensor $\boldsymbol{G}$ in the scalar product, we shall obtain the original tensor, in which the new components can only have their indices moved from the top to the bottom or vice versa. Thus, the operation of "juggling" with the indices has the nature of a scalar multiplication in which the fundamental tensor $\boldsymbol{G}$ plays the role of a unit tensor.

By using both the indices of the tensor $\boldsymbol{G}$ in scalar multiplication, we obtain tensors of lower rank of the form

$$\mathring{\boldsymbol{T}} = \boldsymbol{T}\cdot\boldsymbol{G} = T_{mn\cdot\cdot}^{\cdot\cdot rs}\boldsymbol{\mathfrak{I}}^m\boldsymbol{\mathfrak{I}}_s\delta_\beta^\alpha\delta_\alpha^n\delta_r^\beta = T_{m\alpha\cdot\cdot}^{\cdot\cdot\alpha s}\boldsymbol{\mathfrak{I}}^m\boldsymbol{\mathfrak{I}}_s. \tag{3.8}$$

The scalar product in the above is formed over the indices n and r of the tensor $\boldsymbol{T}$. This invariant operation of transforming a tensor $\boldsymbol{T}$ into $\mathring{\boldsymbol{T}}$ is reduced to the summation of the components of the tensor $\boldsymbol{T}$ over the indices n and r with $n = r$ and is called the contraction of the corresponding upper and lower indices. By means of this process of contraction, it is always possible to obtain a tensor of lower rank.

In particular, for an arbitrary given tensor, one can form by this method scalar invariants from its components. For example, for any vector $\boldsymbol{a} = a^r\boldsymbol{\mathfrak{I}}_r$, we have the scalar invariant

$$a^2 = a^1a_1 + a^2a_2 + a^3a_3 = a^\alpha a_\alpha = a^\alpha a^\beta g_{\alpha\beta} = a_\alpha a_\beta g^{\alpha\beta}$$

equal to the square of its magnitude.

For a second-rank tensor $\boldsymbol{T} = T_{\cdot n}^{m\cdot}\boldsymbol{\mathfrak{I}}_m\boldsymbol{\mathfrak{I}}^n$, it is obvious that the following quantities are scalar invariants:

$$\begin{aligned}\mathcal{J}_1 &= T_{\cdot\alpha}^{\alpha\cdot},\\ \mathcal{J}_2^* &= T_{\cdot\beta}^{\alpha\cdot}T_{\cdot\alpha}^{\beta\cdot},\\ \mathcal{J}_3^* &= T_{\cdot\beta}^{\alpha\cdot}T_{\cdot\gamma}^{\beta\cdot}T_{\cdot\alpha}^{\gamma\cdot}.\end{aligned} \tag{3.9}$$

In this way it is possible to form invariant scalar sums of a higher order. It should be noted, however, that not all the invariants of this type are independent. For tensors of high order, the number of independent scalar invariants depends on the structure of the components of the tensor. Bearing in mind further applications, it is not necessary for us to examine this problem in the general case.

The process of vector multiplication of the basis vectors corresponding to one particular index in the first tensor and to another particular index in the second can be used to find the corresponding arrays of the vector product of two tensors. For the vector product of two vectors, from (1.9) we have

$$[\boldsymbol{a}, \boldsymbol{b}] = a_\alpha b_\beta[\boldsymbol{\mathfrak{I}}^\alpha, \boldsymbol{\mathfrak{I}}^\beta] = \sqrt{g_1}\,(a_\alpha b_\beta - a_\beta b_\alpha)\,\boldsymbol{\mathfrak{I}}_\gamma = c^\gamma\boldsymbol{\mathfrak{I}}_\gamma, \tag{3.10}$$

where

$$c^\gamma = \sqrt{g_1}\,(a_\alpha b_{\bar\beta} - a_\beta b_\alpha).$$

In every term of the sum on the right-hand side, the indices α, β, γ form one of the combinations of the indices 1, 2, 3 for a cyclic permutation of these indices.

In a similar way, one can define the vector product of two tensors of arbitrary rank for any two upper or lower indices of these tensors. It is obvious that the vector product of tensors depends on the order of the multiplication.

The process of forming new arrays by means of the vector product of the basis vectors, which produces tensors with rank lower than the sum of the ranks of the multiplied tensors, is closely related to the invariant process of alternation. This process can be applied to tensors with several indices (given directly or obtained from the product of several tensors), and, in this case, a lowering of the rank of the alternating tensor does not occur. We introduce the idea of alternation of tensors by using the operation of scalar multiplication. To this end, in addition to the tensor $\boldsymbol{G}$ having components δ^i_j, we introduce another tensor $\boldsymbol{S} = \delta^{ip}_{jq}\mathbf{Э}_i\mathbf{Э}_p\mathbf{Э}^j\mathbf{Э}^q$, where

$$\delta^{ip}_{jq} = \delta^i_j\delta^p_q - \delta^p_j\delta^i_q, \tag{3.11}$$

and a tensor $\boldsymbol{V} = \delta^{ijk}_{lmn}\mathbf{Э}_i\mathbf{Э}_j\mathbf{Э}_k\mathbf{Э}^l\mathbf{Э}^m\mathbf{Э}^n$ having components

$$\delta^{ijk}_{lmn} = \delta^i_l\delta^j_m\delta^k_n - \delta^j_l\delta^i_m\delta^k_n + \delta^j_l\delta^k_m\delta^i_n - \delta^k_l\delta^j_m\delta^l_n + \delta^k_l\delta^i_m\delta^j_n - \delta^i_l\delta^k_m\delta^j_n. \tag{3.12}$$

The arrays of the components of $\boldsymbol{S}$ and $\boldsymbol{V}$ are formed by the process of multiplication and addition from the fundamental tensor $\boldsymbol{G}$ and, therefore, they will also be tensors. From the structure of the right-hand sides of (3.11) and (3.12), it is clear that only one term can differ from zero, or else they all must be zero. Thus, depending on the value of the arrays of indices i, j, k and l, m, n, the components of a tensor with a given arrangement of indices are equal to $+1$, -1, or 0 in a given coordinate system.

Let us consider now two vectors $\boldsymbol{a} = a_i\mathbf{Э}^i$ and $\boldsymbol{b} = b_p\mathbf{Э}^p$ and let us form the tensor

$$\boldsymbol{C} = \boldsymbol{ab} = a_ib_p\mathbf{Э}^i\mathbf{Э}^p.$$

The scalar product of the tensors $\boldsymbol{S}$ and $\boldsymbol{C}$ with respect to indices i and p can be found by using (3.11), and has the form

$$\boldsymbol{S}\cdot\boldsymbol{C} = \delta^{ip}_{jq}a_ib_p\mathbf{Э}^j\mathbf{Э}^q = (a_jb_q - a_qb_j)\mathbf{Э}^j\mathbf{Э}^q. \tag{3.13}$$

The components of the second-rank tensor $\boldsymbol{S}\cdot\boldsymbol{C}$ differ in magnitude from the components of the vector product (3.10) only by a factor $\sqrt{g_1}$; in this connection, these components have the same sign for $j < q$, and opposite signs for $j > q$.

The formation of a new tensor by taking the scalar product of a given tensor of rank two or higher with the tensor $\boldsymbol{S}$ is called the operation of alternation with respect to two covariants or, by analogy, two contravariant indices.

In the formulas above, it is possible to write the tensor $\boldsymbol{C}$ in a more general form:

$$\boldsymbol{C} = C_{ip}\boldsymbol{Э}^i\boldsymbol{Э}^p;$$

then,

$$\boldsymbol{S}\cdot\boldsymbol{C} = (C_{jq} - C_{qj})\boldsymbol{Э}^j\boldsymbol{Э}^q = d_{jq}\boldsymbol{Э}^j\boldsymbol{Э}^q.$$

After performing the alternation of the second-rank tensor, we obtain a skew-symmetric tensor with components

$$d_{jq} = -\,d_{qj}.$$

Skew-symmetric tensors in general, and, more particularly, those formed from any arbitrary tensor by using the process of alternation with respect to any two indices, can, in three-dimensional spaces, be replaced by a tensor of next lower order. For example, if a given tensor

$$\boldsymbol{T} = T_{ik\cdot\beta}^{\cdot\cdot\alpha\cdot}\boldsymbol{Э}^i\boldsymbol{Э}^k\boldsymbol{Э}_\alpha\boldsymbol{Э}^\beta,$$

is skew-symmetric with respect to the covariant indices i, k, then for a three-dimensional space, we can introduce a tensor $\overset{*}{\boldsymbol{T}}$ defined by

$$\overset{*}{\boldsymbol{T}} = \overset{*}{T}{}^{j\alpha\cdot}_{\cdot\cdot\beta}\boldsymbol{Э}_j\boldsymbol{Э}_\alpha\boldsymbol{Э}^\beta,$$

where

$$\begin{aligned} \overset{*}{T}{}^{1\alpha\cdot}_{\cdot\cdot\beta} &= -\sqrt{g_1}\,T_{23\cdot\beta}^{\cdot\cdot\alpha\cdot} = \sqrt{g_1}\,T_{32\cdot\beta}^{\cdot\cdot\alpha\cdot}, \\ \overset{*}{T}{}^{2\alpha\cdot}_{\cdot\cdot\beta} &= \sqrt{g_1}\,T_{13\cdot\beta}^{\cdot\cdot\alpha\cdot} = -\sqrt{g_1}\,T_{31\cdot\beta}^{\cdot\cdot\alpha\cdot}, \\ \overset{*}{T}{}^{3\alpha\cdot}_{\cdot\cdot\beta} &= -\sqrt{g_1}\,T_{12\cdot\beta}^{\cdot\cdot\alpha\cdot} = \sqrt{g_1}\,T_{21\cdot\beta}^{\cdot\cdot\alpha\cdot}. \end{aligned} \tag{3.14}$$

Let us assume that by definition $\sqrt{g_1}$ is positive. Recalling relationship (2.6) and the fact that the matrices

$$\left\|\frac{\partial y^i}{\partial x^j}\right\| \quad \text{and} \quad \left\|\frac{\partial x^i}{\partial y^j}\right\|$$

are reversible, it is easy to show immediately that the tensor transformation formulas

$$T'^{\cdot\cdot\alpha\cdot}_{ik\cdot\beta} = T_{\lambda\mu\cdot\gamma}^{\cdot\cdot\nu\cdot\cdot}\frac{\partial x^\lambda}{\partial y^i}\frac{\partial x^\mu}{\partial y^\kappa}\frac{\partial y^\alpha}{\partial x^\nu}\frac{\partial x^\gamma}{\partial y^\beta},$$

in the presence of skew-symmetry with respect to the indices i and k are equivalent to the tensor transformation formulas

$$\overset{*}{T}{}'^{j\alpha\cdot}_{\cdot\cdot\beta} = \overset{*}{T}{}^{\omega\nu\cdot}_{\cdot\cdot\gamma}\frac{\partial y^j}{\partial x^\omega}\frac{\partial y^\alpha}{\partial x^\nu}\frac{\partial x^\gamma}{\partial y^\beta}.$$

The components of the tensor $\overset{*}{\boldsymbol{T}}$ are formed from the independent components of the tensor $\boldsymbol{T}$ and change their signs in going from a right-handed coordinate system to left-handed one when the determinant of the transformation Δ is negative. In particular, it follows that all skew-symmetric second-rank tensors can be thought of as axial vectors.

Let us now consider the process of alternation with respect to three indices. Let a tensor $\boldsymbol{T}$ exist in the general form and let its components be $T^{lmn\cdot\cdot}_{\cdots pq}$. We form the scalar product of the tensors $\boldsymbol{V}\cdot\boldsymbol{T}$ and obtain

$$\boldsymbol{V}\cdot\boldsymbol{T} = \delta^{ijk}_{lmn} T^{lmn\cdot\cdot}_{\cdots pq} Э_i Э_j Э_k Э^p Э^q .$$

Then, using (3.12), we find

$$\boldsymbol{V}\cdot\boldsymbol{T} = (T^{ijk\cdot\cdot}_{\cdots pq} - T^{jik\cdot\cdot}_{\cdots pq} + T^{jki\cdot\cdot}_{\cdots pq} - T^{kji\cdot\cdot}_{\cdots pq} + T^{kij\cdot\cdot}_{\cdots pq} - T^{ikj\cdot\cdot}_{\cdots pq}) Э_i Э_j Э_k Э^p Э^q . \quad (3.15)$$

It is obvious that the components of the tensor $\boldsymbol{V}\cdot\boldsymbol{T}$ are skew-symmetric for each of the two upper indices over which the alternation is carried out.

Let

$$\boldsymbol{T} = \boldsymbol{abc} = a^l b^m c^n Э_l Э_m Э_n ,$$

where

$$\boldsymbol{a} = a^l Э_l , \qquad \boldsymbol{b} = b^m Э_m , \qquad \boldsymbol{c} = c^n Э_n ;$$

then

$$\boldsymbol{V}\cdot\boldsymbol{T} = A^{ijk}_{\cdots} Э_i Э_j Э_k , \qquad \text{where} \qquad A^{ijk}_{\cdots} = \pm (\boldsymbol{a}, [\boldsymbol{b}, \boldsymbol{c}]) , \qquad (3.16)$$

because each component will be equal to the determinant of the components of vectors $\boldsymbol{a}$, $\boldsymbol{b}$, $\boldsymbol{c}$, taken in a definite order. On the right-hand side of (3.16), the plus sign is taken if the system of indices i, j, k is obtained from the system 1, 2, 3 by an even permutation, and the minus sign if by an odd permutation. After the process of alternation, the components with identical indices with respect to which the alternation was performed, are all equal to zero. In three-dimensional space, for tensors of fourth or higher ranks, alternation over four or more indices always results in zero identically, because each component has two equal indices.

Together with the tensor $\boldsymbol{G}$, we can use the tensors $\boldsymbol{S}$ and $\boldsymbol{V}$ to find scalar invariants of tensors. For example, given a tensor

$$\boldsymbol{T} = T^{m\cdot}_{\cdot n} Э_m Э^n ,$$

it is obvious that the following sums are invariant:

$$\mathscr{I}_1 = \delta^n_m T^{m\cdot}_{\cdot n} = T^{m\cdot}_{\cdot m} = g^{m\alpha} T_{\alpha m} = g_{m\alpha} T^{m\alpha} , \qquad (3.17a)$$

$$\begin{aligned} \mathscr{I}_2 &= \tfrac{1}{2}(\delta^{ip}_{jq} T^{j\cdot}_{\cdot i} T^{q2}_{\cdot p}) = \tfrac{1}{2}(T^{\alpha\cdot}_{\cdot\alpha} T^{\beta\cdot}_{\cdot\beta} - T^{\alpha\cdot}_{\cdot\beta} T^{\beta\cdot}_{\cdot\alpha}) \\ &= \left\{ \begin{vmatrix} T^{1\cdot}_{\cdot 1} & T^{1\cdot}_{\cdot 2} \\ T^{2\cdot}_{\cdot 1} & T^{2\cdot}_{\cdot 2} \end{vmatrix} + \begin{vmatrix} T^{2\cdot}_{\cdot 2} & T^{2\cdot}_{\cdot 3} \\ T^{3\cdot}_{\cdot 2} & T^{3\cdot}_{\cdot 3} \end{vmatrix} + \begin{vmatrix} T^{1\cdot}_{\cdot 1} & T^{1\cdot}_{\cdot 3} \\ T^{3\cdot}_{\cdot 1} & T^{3\cdot}_{\cdot 3} \end{vmatrix} \right\} \\ &= \tfrac{1}{2} g^{\alpha p} g^{\beta q} (T_{p\alpha} T_{q\beta} - T_{p\beta} T_{q\alpha}) = \tfrac{1}{2} g_{\alpha p} g_{\beta q} (T^{p\alpha} T^{q\beta} - T^{p\beta} T^{q\alpha}) , \end{aligned} \qquad (3.17b)$$

$$\mathscr{J}_3 = \tfrac{1}{6}\delta^{ijk}_{lmn} T^{l\cdot}_{\cdot i} T^{m\cdot}_{\cdot j} T^{n\cdot}_{\cdot k} = \begin{vmatrix} T^{1\cdot}_{\cdot 1} & T^{1\cdot}_{\cdot 2} & T^{1\cdot}_{\cdot 3} \\ T^{2\cdot}_{\cdot 1} & T^{2\cdot}_{\cdot 2} & T^{2\cdot}_{\cdot 3} \\ T^{3\cdot}_{\cdot 1} & T^{3\cdot}_{\cdot 2} & T^{3\cdot}_{\cdot 3} \end{vmatrix}$$

$$= |T^{i\alpha} g_{\alpha j}| = |g^{i\alpha} T_{\alpha j}| = g\,|T^{i\alpha}| = \frac{1}{g}|T_{\alpha j}|. \tag{3.17c}$$

The identity $\mathscr{J}_3 = |T^{i}_{\cdot j}|$ follows from the fact that each of the six terms of the sum in question is a determinant obtained from the fundamental one by a simultaneous interchange of two rows and two columns; therefore, all these determinants are equal to one another. The different expressions for $\mathscr{J}_1$, $\mathscr{J}_2$, and $\mathscr{J}_3$ in the right-hand sides of (3.17) are obtained by using the covariant, contravariant, and mixed components in an arbitrary coordinate system and for an arbitrary second-rank tensor.

By comparing (3.9) and (3.17) it is easy to show the validity of the formulas

$$\mathscr{J}^*_2 = \mathscr{J}^2_1 - 2\mathscr{J}_2 \qquad \text{and} \qquad \mathscr{J}^*_3 = 3\mathscr{J}_3 + \mathscr{J}^3_1 - 3\mathscr{J}_1\mathscr{J}_2.$$

It is obvious that the definition of tensors and the algebraic operations on them are directly connected with the definition and properties of and operations on the vectors of the covariant and contravariant bases $\mathbf{Э}_i$ and $\mathbf{Э}^i$.

In order to extend the previously examined concepts, we note that it is possible in some cases to introduce the basic quantities ϵ_i and ϵ^i, for which the fundamental operations and transformation formulas will differ in certain ways from the corresponding operations on $\mathbf{Э}_i$ and $\mathbf{Э}^i$. Therefore, by means of ϵ_i and ϵ^i, one can introduce, in accordance with the formulas (3.2), quantities analogous to tensors together with corresponding operations. Thus, in a four-dimensional space, one can introduce spinors and tensor-spinors.

Complex numbers, quarternions, and the operations on them can be defined and examined by analogous methods.

4. Second-rank tensors

A second-rank tensor in a three-dimensional space has nine components, which can be written in the form of a square matrix. In the general case for a given coordinate system, there correspond to one tensor the following four matrices:

$$\tau_1 = \begin{Vmatrix} T_{11} & T_{12} & T_{13} \\ T_{21} & T_{22} & T_{23} \\ T_{31} & T_{32} & T_{33} \end{Vmatrix}, \qquad \tau_2 = \begin{Vmatrix} T_{1\cdot}^{\cdot 1} & T_{1\cdot}^{\cdot 2} & T_{1\cdot}^{\cdot 3} \\ T_{2\cdot}^{\cdot 1} & T_{2\cdot}^{\cdot 2} & T_{2\cdot}^{\cdot 3} \\ T_{3\cdot}^{\cdot 1} & T_{3\cdot}^{\cdot 2} & T_{3\cdot}^{\cdot 3} \end{Vmatrix},$$

$$\tau_3 = \begin{Vmatrix} T^{1\cdot}_{\cdot 1} & T^{1\cdot}_{\cdot 2} & T^{1\cdot}_{\cdot 3} \\ T^{2\cdot}_{\cdot 1} & T^{2\cdot}_{\cdot 2} & T^{2\cdot}_{\cdot 3} \\ T^{3\cdot}_{\cdot 1} & T^{3\cdot}_{\cdot 2} & T^{3\cdot}_{\cdot 3} \end{Vmatrix}, \qquad \tau_4 = \begin{Vmatrix} T^{11} & T^{12} & T^{13} \\ T^{21} & T^{22} & T^{23} \\ T^{31} & T^{32} & T^{33} \end{Vmatrix}.$$

Whether it is at the top or at the bottom of the element of the matrix, the first index refers to the number of the row, and the second to the number of the column, at the intersection of which a given element occurs. Between these matrices, the following matrix identities hold:

$$\tau_1 = \tau_2 g_* = g_* \tau_3 = g_* \tau_4 g_*, \tag{4.1}$$

where g_* is the symmetric matrix of the fundamental tensor $\boldsymbol{G}$:

$$g_* = \begin{Vmatrix} g_{11} & g_{12} & g_{13} \\ g_{21} & g_{22} & g_{23} \\ g_{31} & g_{32} & g_{33} \end{Vmatrix}.$$

In formulas (4.1), the law of matrix multiplication is used, whereby the rows of the first factor are multiplied by the columns of the second. The operations of addition, multiplication by a number, and scalar multiplication for matrices correspond to those for a second-rank tensor. In connection with this, use of the methods and results of matrix algebra simplifies the development of the theory of tensor functions.

In the general case, both for symmetric and nonsymmetric tensors, the matrices τ_2 and τ_3 differ from each other. If the components T_{ik} and T^{ik} are symmetric (which condition is always satisfied simultaneously), the components of the matrices τ_2 and τ_3 are, in general, nonsymmetric, that is, $T_{i\cdot}^{\cdot k} \neq T_{k\cdot}^{\cdot i}$ and $T_{\cdot k}^{i\cdot} \neq T_{\cdot i}^{k\cdot}$; but because of the symmetry of T^{ik} and g_{ik}, the equations

$$T_{\cdot k}^{i\cdot} = T_{k\cdot}^{\cdot i}$$

hold. Therefore, for a symmetric T^{ik}, there will also hold the matrix equations

$$\tau_2 = \overset{*}{\tau}_3 \qquad \text{and} \qquad \overset{*}{\tau}_2 = \tau_3,$$

where $\overset{*}{\tau}_2$ and $\overset{*}{\tau}_3$ are the transposes of the matrices τ_2 and τ_3. They are obtained from τ_2 and τ_3, respectively, by interchanging the rows and the columns.

For any second-rank tensor and the matrix of its components, there will exist two corresponding linear vector functions

$$b^i = T_{\cdot \alpha}^{i\cdot} a^\alpha \qquad \text{and} \qquad b'^i = T_{\alpha\cdot}^{\cdot i} a^\alpha,$$

where

$$\boldsymbol{b} = \boldsymbol{T} \cdot \boldsymbol{a} \qquad \text{and} \qquad \boldsymbol{b}' = \boldsymbol{a} \cdot \boldsymbol{T}\ , \tag{4.2}$$

which define a transformation from the vector $\boldsymbol{a} = a^i \boldsymbol{\vartheta}_i$ to the vector $\boldsymbol{b} = b^i \boldsymbol{\vartheta}_i$ or to the vector $\boldsymbol{b}' = b'^i \boldsymbol{\vartheta}_i$. The vectors $\boldsymbol{b}$ and $\boldsymbol{b}'$ coincide if the tensor $\boldsymbol{T}$ is symmetric. Equations (4.2) define the invariant operations of transformation from a given vector $\boldsymbol{a}$ to the vector $\boldsymbol{b}$ or $\boldsymbol{b}'$. It is clear that defining the linear vector functions (4.2) is equivalent to defining the tensor.

It is possible to put a bilinear form, defined in terms of two vectors $\boldsymbol{x}$ and $\boldsymbol{y}$ by the equation

$$\mathscr{F}(x^i, y^i) = T_{\alpha\beta} x^\alpha y^\beta, \tag{4.3}$$

in correspondence with any second-rank tensor, where $\mathscr{F}$ is an invariant quantity depending only on the tensor $\boldsymbol{T}$ and the vectors $\boldsymbol{x}$ and $\boldsymbol{y}$. Defining the bilinear invariant form and defining the second-rank tensor are completely equivalent. Thus, the characteristics of a tensor, since it is an invariant quantity, coincide with the invariant properties of a matrix, a linear vector function, or a bilinear form.

Let us introduce a skew-symmetric tensor

$$\boldsymbol{\Omega} = \tfrac{1}{2}\boldsymbol{S}\cdot\boldsymbol{T} = \tfrac{1}{2}\delta_{ij}^{\alpha\beta} T_{\alpha\beta} \mathfrak{Э}^i \mathfrak{Э}^j = \tfrac{1}{2}(T_{ij} - T_{ji})\, \mathfrak{Э}^i \mathfrak{Э}^j \tag{4.4}$$

and a symmetric tensor N, defined as the difference

$$\boldsymbol{N} = \boldsymbol{T} - \boldsymbol{\Omega} = \tfrac{1}{2}(T_{ij} + T_{ji})\, \mathfrak{Э}^i \mathfrak{Э}^j = N^{i\cdot}_{\cdot j} \mathfrak{Э}_i \mathfrak{Э}^j. \tag{4.5}$$

Obviously, equations (4.4) and (4.5) define the relationship between the components of the tensors $\boldsymbol{T}$, $\boldsymbol{\Omega}$, and $\boldsymbol{N}$ which are valid in any coordinate system.

From formula (3.9), it is apparent that the array $\frac{1}{3}\mathscr{I}_1 g_{ik}$ forms a symmetric tensor $\boldsymbol{P}$, which can be written in the form

$$\boldsymbol{P} = \frac{\mathscr{I}_1}{3} \delta^i_k \mathfrak{Э}_i \mathfrak{Э}^k. \tag{4.6}$$

From (3.7), the tensor $\boldsymbol{P}$ has the invariants

$$\mathscr{I}_1^p = \mathscr{I}_1, \qquad \mathscr{I}_2^p = \frac{\mathscr{I}_1^2}{3}, \qquad \mathscr{I}_3^p = \frac{\mathscr{I}_1^3}{27}. \tag{4.7}$$

Let us define a symmetric tensor $\boldsymbol{D}$, equal to the difference $\boldsymbol{N} - \boldsymbol{P}$:

$$\boldsymbol{N} = \boldsymbol{P} + \boldsymbol{D}, \qquad \boldsymbol{D} = \mathscr{D}^{i\cdot}_{\cdot j} \mathfrak{Э}_i \mathfrak{Э}^j, \qquad \mathscr{D}^{i\cdot}_{\cdot j} = N^{i\cdot}_{\cdot j} - \tfrac{1}{3} T^{\alpha\cdot}_{\cdot\alpha} \delta^i_j. \tag{4.8}$$

It is obvious that the sum $\mathscr{D}^{\alpha\cdot}_{\cdot\alpha} = 0$. The tensor $\boldsymbol{D}$ is called the deviator of the tensor $\boldsymbol{T}$ or of the tensor N.

Any tensor can be represented in the form of sums of two or three tensors:

$$\boldsymbol{T} = \boldsymbol{N} + \boldsymbol{\Omega} = \boldsymbol{P} + \boldsymbol{D} + \boldsymbol{\Omega}. \tag{4.9}$$

This representation has an invariant character for any transformation of coordinates. In a transformation from one coordinate system to another, the tensors **P**, **D**, **Ω** are transformed independently and are expressed in the same way by a transformation of the components of the tensor **T**.

The matrix of the tensor **Ω** depends only on three components, which may be different from zero. If we introduce the quantities ω_1, ω_2, ω_3 according to the formulas

$$\omega_1 = \tfrac{1}{2}(T_{32} - T_{23}), \qquad \omega_2 = \tfrac{1}{2}(T_{13} - T_{31}), \qquad \omega_3 = \tfrac{1}{2}(T_{21} - T_{12}),$$

then the matrix of the tensor **Ω** can always be written in the form

$$\overset{*}{\omega} = \begin{Vmatrix} 0 & -\omega_3 & \omega_2 \\ \omega_3 & 0 & -\omega_1 \\ -\omega_2 & \omega_1 & 0 \end{Vmatrix},$$

where the quantities ω_1, ω_2, and ω_3 for $g_1 = g = 1$ can be regarded as the components of a vector.

Symmetric tensors have only six unequal components because the matrices corresponding to them are symmetric if the components are purely co- or contravariant. For a symmetric tensor, instead of the bilinear form (4.3), it is sufficient to examine the quadratic form

$$\mathscr{F}(x^i) = N_{\alpha\beta} x^\alpha x^\beta . \tag{4.10}$$

In the case of the tensor **P**, this quadratic form differs from the form

$$g_{\alpha\beta} x^\alpha x^\beta$$

only by the scalar invariant factor $\frac{1}{3} T^{\alpha \cdot}_{\cdot \alpha} = \frac{1}{3} \mathscr{I}_1$.

Let us suppose that we have a rectilinear cartesian coordinate system, and let x^i be the coordinates of the radius vector in Euclidean space. It follows that the equation

$$N_{\alpha\beta} x^\alpha x^\beta = \text{const} \tag{4.11}$$

defines a second-order surface which characterizes a symmetrical tensor and which is called a tensor surface. It is also obvious that the tensor surface

$$g_{\alpha\beta} x^\alpha x^\beta = \text{const}$$

is a sphere.

Of course, it is always possible to introduce rectilinear orthogonal cartesian coordinate axes which will coincide with the principal diameters of a tensor surface and for which equation (4.11) takes on the canonical form

$$N_1 x_1^2 + N_2 x_2^2 + N_3 x_3^2 = \text{const} . \tag{4.12}$$

These coordinate axes are called the principal axes of the tensor, and the real numbers N_1, N_2, N_3 are the principal components of the tensor $\boldsymbol{N}$. For the tensor $\boldsymbol{P}$, equation (4.12) defines a sphere; then for the principal components of the tensor $\boldsymbol{P}$, we have

$$P_1 = P_2 = P_3 = \tfrac{1}{3}\mathscr{I}_1, \tag{4.13}$$

where P_1, P_2, P_3 are the principal components of the tensor $\boldsymbol{P}$.

A tensor for which the surface (4.12) is a sphere is called spherical. Thus, the tensor $\boldsymbol{P}$ is a spherical tensor. A spherical tensor is similar to a scalar, because, in a given rectilinear cartesian coordinate system, its matrix assumes a diagonal form, and the nonzero components are equal to the scalar $\frac{1}{3}\mathscr{I}_1$. The axes in a orthogonal cartesian system act as the principal tensor axes for a spherical tensor.

In an arbitrary coordinate system, all the components of a symmetric tensor can be expressed by N_1, N_2, N_3 and by parameters defining the transformation from the arbitrary coordinate system to another system whose axes coincide with the principal axes of the tensor. Consequently, all numerical invariants of a symmetric tensor can be expressed in terms of the quantities N_1, N_2, and N_3, and, therefore, a symmetric second-rank tensor does not contain more than three independent scalar invariants.

Clearly, one may take six quantities as a complete system of the invariants of a nonsymmetric tensor: (the principal components of the tensor $\boldsymbol{N}$ N_1, N_2, N_3), and the three components of the tensor $\boldsymbol{\Omega}$ $(\omega_1, \omega_2, \omega_3)$ contained in the principal coordinate system for the tensor $\boldsymbol{N}$.

For the deviator $\boldsymbol{D}$, there exist no more than two independent scalar invariants, because, for the principal components of the deviator $\boldsymbol{D}$, the following holds:

$$\mathscr{D}_1 + \mathscr{D}_2 + \mathscr{D}_3 = 0.$$

It is obvious therefore that the principal axes of the symmetric tensor $\boldsymbol{N}$ and the corresponding deviator $\boldsymbol{D}$ coincide.

Let x^1, x^2, x^3 be the coordinates of points in space, with respect to the principal axes of the tensor $\boldsymbol{N}$, and let $y^1(x^1,x^2,x^3)$, $y^2(x^1,x^2,x^3)$, $y^3(x^1,x^2,x^3)$ be an arbitrary curvilinear coordinate system. From formulas (3.3), it follows that for the components of $\boldsymbol{N}$ in the coordinate system y^1, y^2, y^3, the following holds true:

$$N^{i\cdot}_{\cdot j} = N_1 \frac{\partial y^i}{\partial x^1}\frac{\partial x^1}{\partial y^j} + N_2 \frac{\partial y^i}{\partial x^2}\frac{\partial x^2}{\partial y^j} + N_3 \frac{\partial y^i}{\partial x^3}\frac{\partial x^3}{\partial y^j}. \tag{4.14}$$

It is not difficult to see that the cubic equation

$$\Delta(\lambda) = \begin{vmatrix} -N_1+\lambda & 0 & 0 \\ 0 & -N_2+\lambda & 0 \\ 0 & 0 & -N_3+\lambda \end{vmatrix} = 0 \tag{4.15}$$

or

$$\lambda^3 - \mathscr{I}_1^n \lambda^2 + \mathscr{I}_2^n \lambda - \mathscr{I}_3^n = 0,$$

after multiplying the matrix of the determinant $\Delta(\lambda)$ on the left and right by the Jacobian matrices

$$\frac{\mathscr{D}(y^1 y^2 y^3)}{\mathscr{D}(x^1 x^2 x^3)} \quad \text{and} \quad \frac{\mathscr{D}(x^1 x^2 x^3)}{\mathscr{D}(y^1 y^2 y^3)},$$

is, in accordance with (4.14), equivalent to the equation

$$\Delta(\lambda) = \begin{vmatrix} -N^{1\cdot}_{\cdot 1}+\lambda & -N^{1\cdot}_{\cdot 2} & -N^{1\cdot}_{\cdot 3} \\ -N^{2\cdot}_{\cdot 1} & -N^{2\cdot}_{\cdot 2}+\lambda & -N^{2\cdot}_{\cdot 3} \\ -N^{3\cdot}_{\cdot 1} & -N^{3\cdot}_{\cdot 2} & -N^{3\cdot}_{\cdot 3}+\lambda \end{vmatrix} = 0. \tag{4.15'}$$

It will be recalled that $N^{i\cdot}_{\cdot j} = N^{\cdot i}_{j\cdot}$ follows from the symmetry of the tensor $\boldsymbol{N}$. The invariant character of the coefficients of equation (4.15), which are expressed in an arbitrary coordinate system in terms of $N^{i\cdot}_{\cdot j}$ by

$$\mathscr{I}_1^n = N_1 + N_2 + N_3 = T^{i\cdot}_{\cdot j} = \mathscr{I}_1,$$
$$\mathscr{I}_2^n = N_1 N_2 + N_1 N_3 + N_2 N_3 = \tfrac{1}{2}(N^{\alpha\cdot}_{\cdot\alpha} N^{\beta\cdot}_{\cdot\beta} - N^{\alpha\cdot}_{\cdot\beta} N^{\beta\cdot}_{\cdot\alpha}),$$
$$\mathscr{I}_3^n = N_1 N_2 N_3 = |N^{i\cdot}_{\cdot k}|,$$

was established on page 18. This is also obvious from equation (4.15).

In addition to the cartesian coordinate system $X(x_1, x_2, x_3)$ directed along the principal axes of the tensor $\boldsymbol{N}$, let us also consider an arbitrary rectangular cartesian coordinate system $Y(y^1, y^2, y^3)$. The transformation formulas are of the form

$$y^i = l^{i\cdot}_{\cdot\alpha} x^\alpha, \quad \text{where} \quad l^{i\cdot}_{\cdot\alpha} = \cos(\widehat{y^i x^\alpha}). \tag{4.16}$$

The matrix of the coefficients of transformation

$$L = \| l^{i\cdot}_{\cdot\alpha} \|$$

is generally not symmetric, i.e., $l^{i\cdot}_{\cdot\alpha} \neq l^{\alpha\cdot}_{\cdot i}$. It is easy to see that the inverse matrix, $L^{-1} = \| p^{i\cdot}_{\cdot\alpha} \|$ corresponding to the inverse transformation

$$x^i = p^{i\cdot}_{\cdot\alpha} y^\alpha,$$

is obtained from the matrix L simply by interchanging the rows and columns (the first index corresponds to the rows), because

$$l^{i\cdot}_{\cdot\alpha} = \cos\left(\widehat{y^i x^\alpha}\right) = \cos\left(\widehat{x^\alpha y^i}\right) = p^{\alpha\cdot}_{\cdot i}.$$

Of course, the nine direction cosines $l^{i\cdot}_{\cdot j}$ can be represented by three independent parameters defining the orientation of the coordinate system Y with respect to the coordinate system X, for example, by means of the Eulerian angles. The six supplementary relationships between the $l^{i\cdot}_{\cdot j}$ can be written in the form

$$l^{i\cdot}_{\cdot 1} l^{j\cdot}_{\cdot 1} + l^{i\cdot}_{\cdot 2} l^{j\cdot}_{\cdot 2} + l^{i\cdot}_{\cdot 3} l^{j\cdot}_{\cdot 3} = \delta^i_j \qquad (i \leq j). \tag{4.17}$$

For $i > j$, we obtain similar equations which will not be independent of (4.17).

For the components $N^{i\cdot}_{\cdot j}$ in a coordinate system Y, formulas (4.14) give

$$N^{i\cdot}_{\cdot j} = N_1 l^{i\cdot}_{\cdot 1} p^{1\cdot}_{\cdot j} + N_2 l^{i\cdot}_{\cdot 2} p^{2\cdot}_{\cdot j} + N_3 l^{i\cdot}_{\cdot 3} p^{3\cdot}_{\cdot j}. \tag{4.18}$$

Let us now consider the extreme (stationary) values of the components $N^{i\cdot}_{\cdot j}$ for all possible coordinate systems Y while the values of the indices i and j are held fixed. Without any loss in generality, one can always assume that

$$N_1 \geq N_2 \geq N_3. \tag{4.19}$$

For simplicity, we consider the case when, instead of the inequality (4.19) which admits equalities, we have the strong inequalities

$$N_1 > N_2 > N_3.$$

If $i = j$, then, since $p^{\alpha\cdot}_{\cdot i} = l^{i\cdot}_{\cdot\alpha}$, we obtain from formula (4.18)

$$N^{i\cdot}_{\cdot i} = N_1 (l^{i\cdot}_{\cdot 1})^2 + N_2 (l^{i\cdot}_{\cdot 2})^2 + N_3 (l^{i\cdot}_{\cdot 3})^2,$$

and the relations (4.17) yield only one relationship between the three quantities $l^{i\cdot}_{\cdot k}$:

$$(l^{i\cdot}_{\cdot 1})^2 + (l^{i\cdot}_{\cdot 2})^2 + (l^{i\cdot}_{\cdot 3})^2 = 1.$$

The Lagrange equations for determining the extrema have the form

$$(N_k - \lambda)\, l^{i\cdot}_{\cdot k} = 0 \qquad (k = 1, 2, 3),$$

where λ is the Lagrange multiplier. Because $N_1 > N_2 > N_3$, we have $l^{i\cdot}_{\cdot k} = \delta^i_k$ and $\lambda = N_k = N_i$. Consequently, for $i = j$, the stationary values of $N^{i\cdot}_{\cdot j}$ correspond to N_i and are attained in the rectangular coordinate system Y for which the i axis coincides with the corresponding principal axis of the tensor N. Then,

$$\max N^{i\cdot}_{\cdot i} = N_1, \qquad \min N^{i\cdot}_{\cdot i} = N_3. \tag{4.20}$$

Consider the case for $i \neq j$. For fixed indices i and j, the six quantities $l^{i\cdot}_{\cdot k}$ and $l^{j\cdot}_{\cdot k} = p^{k\cdot}_{\cdot j}$ appearing in (4.18) are related by the equations

$$l^{i\cdot}_{\cdot 1} l^{j\cdot}_{\cdot 1} + l^{i\cdot}_{\cdot 2} l^{j\cdot}_{\cdot 2} + l^{i\cdot}_{\cdot 3} l^{j\cdot}_{\cdot 3} = 0,$$
$$(l^{i\cdot}_{\cdot 1})^2 + (l^{i\cdot}_{\cdot 2})^2 + (l^{i\cdot}_{\cdot 3})^2 = 1,$$
$$(l^{j\cdot}_{\cdot 1})^2 + (l^{j\cdot}_{\cdot 2})^2 + (l^{j\cdot}_{\cdot 3})^2 = 1.$$

In this case, the equations for determining the extremum by making use of Lagrange multipliers λ, μ, δ take the form

$$(N_k - \lambda)\, l^{j\cdot}_{\cdot k} - 2\mu l^{i\cdot}_{\cdot k} = 0, \qquad (N_k - \lambda)\, l^{i\cdot}_{\cdot k} - 2\delta l^{j\cdot}_{\cdot k} = 0 \qquad (k = 1,2,3).$$

From these equations, from the equations connecting $l^{i\cdot}_{\cdot k}$ and $l^{j\cdot}_{\cdot k}$, and from the formula for $N^{i\cdot}_{\cdot j}$, it follows that

$$\lambda = N^{i\cdot}_{\cdot i} = N^{j\cdot}_{\cdot j} \qquad \text{and} \qquad 2\mu = 2\delta = N^{i\cdot}_{\cdot j},$$
$$(N_k - \lambda + 2\mu)(l^{j\cdot}_{\cdot k} - l^{i\cdot}_{\cdot k}) = 0 \qquad (k = 1,2,3),$$

and

$$\sum_{k=1}^{3} (l^{i\cdot}_{\cdot k} - l^{j\cdot}_{\cdot k})^2 = 2.$$

From here we find that

$$N_k = \lambda - 2\mu, \qquad l^{j\cdot}_{\cdot s} = l^{i\cdot}_{\cdot s} \qquad (s \neq k),$$
$$(l^{i\cdot}_{\cdot k} - l^{j\cdot}_{\cdot k})^2 = 2 \qquad (k = 1,2,3).$$

From the equations $l^{j\cdot}_{\cdot s} = l^{i\cdot}_{\cdot s}$ with $s \neq k$, it follows that $(l^{i\cdot}_{\cdot k})^2 = (l^{j\cdot}_{\cdot k})^2$, because $l^{i\cdot}_{\cdot k}$ and $l^{j\cdot}_{\cdot k}$ are not equal to zero and can differ only in sign; therefore,

$$(l^{i\cdot}_{\cdot k})^2 = (l^{j\cdot}_{\cdot k})^2 = \tfrac{1}{2}.$$

On the basis of the equations, $l^{j\cdot}_{\cdot s} = l^{i\cdot}_{\cdot s}$, we have

$$(N_{s_\alpha} - \lambda - 2\mu)\, l^{i\cdot}_{\cdot s_\alpha} = 0 \qquad (\alpha = 1,2),$$

where s_1 and s_2 are two indices not equal to k. From these equations, and using the corresponding definitions of α_1 and α_2, it follows that

$$N_{s_1} = \lambda + 2\mu \qquad \text{and} \qquad l^{j\cdot}_{\cdot s_2} = l^{i\cdot}_{\cdot s_2} = 0,$$

and therefore,

$$(l^{i\cdot}_{\cdot s_1})^2 = (l^{j\cdot}_{\cdot s_1})^2 = \tfrac{1}{2}.$$

It thus follows that the stationary values of $N^{i\cdot}_{\cdot j}$ are attained in the coordinate system Y, in which one of the axes coincides with the principal axis of the tensor N, and the other two are oriented at 45° with the other principal axes, where

$$\lambda = \frac{N_k + N_{s_1}}{2} \qquad \text{and} \qquad 2\mu = \frac{N_{s_1} - N_k}{2}.$$

It is obvious that the maximum possible value of $N^{i\cdot}_{\cdot j}$ is attained if the i and j axes are situated in the $x^1 x^3$ plane, for which case

$$\max(N^{i\cdot}_{\cdot j}) = \frac{N_1 - N_3}{2}. \tag{4.21}$$

When the equalities in (4.19) hold, the extremals become continuous and the tensor surface becomes a surface of resolution.

For the deviator $\boldsymbol{D}$, we have

$$\mathscr{D}_1 = N_1 - \tfrac{1}{3}\mathscr{J}_1, \qquad \mathscr{D}_2 = N_2 - \tfrac{1}{3}\mathscr{J}_1, \qquad \mathscr{D}_3 = N_3 - \tfrac{1}{3}\mathscr{J}_1.$$

When the inequalities hold in (4.19), the following inequalities also hold:

$$\mathscr{D}_1 \geq \mathscr{D}_2 \geq \mathscr{D}_3. \tag{4.22}$$

It is also obvious that

$$\max \mathscr{D}^{i\cdot}_{\cdot j} = \frac{\mathscr{D}_1 - \mathscr{D}_3}{2} = \frac{N_1 - N_3}{2}. \tag{4.23}$$

Two tensors are said to be similar if, in arbitrary coordinate systems, the components of one of the tensors can be obtained from the components of the other by means of a simple multiplication by some number. Obviously, all spherical tensors are similar to one another.

The necessary and sufficient conditions for the similarity of two symmetrical tensors $\boldsymbol{N}$ and $\boldsymbol{N}'$ are that their principal axes coincide and that the two equalities be satisfied:

$$\frac{N_1}{N_1'} = \frac{N_2}{N_2'} = \frac{N_3}{N_3'}.$$

For deviators $\boldsymbol{D}$ and $\boldsymbol{D}'$ to be similar, besides the requirement of coincidence of the principal axes, it is necessary and sufficient that only one equality be satisfied:

$$\frac{\mathscr{D}_1}{\mathscr{D}_1'} = \frac{\mathscr{D}_2}{\mathscr{D}_2'}.$$

For the deviator $\boldsymbol{D}$, equation (4.15) takes the form

$$\lambda^3 + \mathscr{J}_2^d \lambda + \mathscr{J}_3^d = 0. \tag{4.24}$$

In this equation, the term containing λ^2 is absent because

$$\mathscr{J}_1^d = \mathscr{D}_1 + \mathscr{D}_2 + \mathscr{D}_3 = 0.$$

The invariant tensors $\boldsymbol{D}$ and $\boldsymbol{N}$ are related by the formulas

$$\begin{aligned}\mathscr{I}_2^d &= \mathscr{D}_1\mathscr{D}_2 + \mathscr{D}_1\mathscr{D}_3 + \mathscr{D}_2\mathscr{D}_3 = -\tfrac{1}{6}\{(N_1 - N_2)^2 + (N_1 - N_3)^2 \\ &\quad + (N_2 - N_3)^2\} = \mathscr{I}_2^n - \tfrac{1}{3}(\mathscr{I}_1^n)^2, \\ \mathscr{I}_3^d &= \mathscr{D}_1\mathscr{D}_2\mathscr{D}_3 = \tfrac{1}{27}(3N_1 - \mathscr{I}_1)(3N_2 - \mathscr{I}_1)(3N_3 - \mathscr{I}_1) \\ &= \mathscr{I}_3^n - \tfrac{1}{3}\mathscr{I}_1^n\mathscr{I}_2^n + \tfrac{2}{27}(\mathscr{I}_1^n)^3.\end{aligned} \tag{4.25}$$

For an arbitrary coordinate system, the expression for $\mathscr{I}_2^d$ and $\mathscr{I}_3^d$ in terms of components $N_{\cdot j}^{i\cdot}$ takes the form

$$\begin{aligned}\mathscr{I}_2^d = \mathscr{I}_2^n - \tfrac{1}{3}(\mathscr{I}_1^n)^2 &= -\tfrac{1}{6}\{(N_{\cdot 1}^{1\cdot} - N_{\cdot 2}^{2\cdot})^2 + (N_{\cdot 1}^{1\cdot} - N_{\cdot 3}^{3\cdot})^2 \\ &\quad + (N_{\cdot 2}^{2\cdot} - N_{\cdot 3}^{3\cdot})^2 + 6[(N_{\cdot 2}^{1\cdot})^2 + (N_{\cdot 3}^{1\cdot})^2 + (N_{\cdot 3}^{2\cdot})^2]\}.\end{aligned} \tag{4.26}$$

It is obvious that for two deviators with common principal axes to be similar, it is necessary and sufficient that the equality

$$\frac{\mathscr{I}_3^d}{|\mathscr{I}_2^d|^{\frac{3}{2}}} = \frac{\mathscr{I}_3^{d'}}{|\mathscr{I}_2^{d'}|^{\frac{3}{2}}}$$

be fulfilled.

It is not difficult to verify directly that the roots of the cubic equation (4.24) are given by

$$\begin{aligned}\mathscr{D}_1 &= 2\theta \sin\left(\psi + \frac{2\pi}{3}\right), \\ \mathscr{D}_2 &= 2\theta \sin\psi, \\ \mathscr{D}_3 &= 2\theta \sin\left(\psi + \frac{4\pi}{3}\right),\end{aligned} \tag{4.27}$$

where

$$\theta = \sqrt{-\frac{\mathscr{I}_2^d}{3}} = \frac{1}{\sqrt{18}}\sqrt{(\mathscr{D}_1 - \mathscr{D}_2)^2 + (\mathscr{D}_1 - \mathscr{D}_3)^2 + (\mathscr{D}_2 - \mathscr{D}_3)^2}, \tag{4.28}$$

and

$$\sqrt{3}\tan\psi = \frac{(\mathscr{D}_2 - \mathscr{D}_1) + (\mathscr{D}_2 - \mathscr{D}_3)}{\mathscr{D}_1 - \mathscr{D}_3} = \mu, \qquad \sin 3\psi = -\frac{\mathscr{I}_3^d\sqrt{27}}{2|\mathscr{I}_2^d|^{\frac{3}{2}}}, \tag{4.29}$$

with $-\pi/6 \leq \psi \leq \pi/6$; therefore, $\mathscr{D}_1 \geq \mathscr{D}_2 \geq \mathscr{D}_3$ and $\mathscr{D}_1 > 0$, but $\mathscr{D}_3 < 0$; also, if $\mathscr{I}_3^d > 0$, then $\mathscr{D}_2 < 0$, $\psi < 0$, and if $\mathscr{I}_3^d < 0$, then $\mathscr{D}_2 > 0$ and $\psi > 0$. Equations (4.27) are easily verified by substituting them into equation (4.24). In formulas (4.28) and (4.29), the differences $\mathscr{D}_i - \mathscr{D}_k$ can be replaced by the equivalent differences $N_i - N_k$. The invariants $\mathscr{I}_2^d$ and $\mathscr{I}_3^d$ can be replaced by the invariants $\mathscr{I}_1^n$, $\mathscr{I}_2^n$, and $\mathscr{I}_3^n$, by using formulas (4.25) and (4.26).

The quantity μ is called the Lode parameter. The condition for the similarity of two deviators with coincident principal axes is reduced to the condition of equality of their Lode parameters.

The quantity θ characterizes the scale of the deviator. For fixed principal axes and for values of the Lode parameter $\mu(\psi)$ but variable θ, the deviator varies similarly. For operations with similar deviators, it is necessary only to establish the connection between their respective scales defined by the corresponding values of θ.

From formulas (4.28) and (4.29) it is clear that in order to determine the values of θ and $\mu(\psi)$, it is sufficient that the components of the deviator $\boldsymbol{D}$ in any arbitrary coordinate system be known. The quantities ψ and θ can be thought of as a complete system of invariants of the deviator $\boldsymbol{D}$. The quantities $\mathscr{I}_1$, ψ, and θ can be thought of as a complete system of invariants of the tensor $\boldsymbol{N}$. The system of invariants of a spherical tensor $\boldsymbol{P}$ amounts to one scalar $\mathscr{I}_1$.

Let us now consider canonical coordinate systems and the canonical forms of the matrices of nonsymmetric tensors. Using the tensor $\boldsymbol{T}$ according to equations (4.2), one can put certain vectors $\boldsymbol{b}$ and $\boldsymbol{b}'$ in correspondence with an arbitrary vector $\boldsymbol{a}$. For the colinearity of the vectors $\boldsymbol{a}$ and $\boldsymbol{b}$ (that is, $\boldsymbol{b} = \lambda\,\boldsymbol{a}$), it is necessary and sufficient that the following equalities be fulfilled:

$$\begin{aligned} (\lambda - T^{1\cdot}_{\cdot 1})\,a^1 - T^{1\cdot}_{\cdot 2}a^2 - T^{1\cdot}_{\cdot 3}a^3 &= 0\,, \\ - T^{2\cdot}_{\cdot 1}a^1 + (\lambda - T^{2\cdot}_{\cdot 2})\,a^2 - T^{2\cdot}_{\cdot 3}a^3 &= 0\,, \\ - T^{3\cdot}_{\cdot 1}a^1 - T^{3\cdot}_{\cdot 2}a^2 + (\lambda - T^{3\cdot}_{\cdot 3})\,a^3 &= 0\,, \end{aligned} \tag{4.30}$$

that is,

$$\lambda\boldsymbol{a} - \boldsymbol{T}\cdot\boldsymbol{a} = 0\,, \qquad (\lambda\delta^{i\cdot}_{\cdot\alpha} - T^{i\cdot}_{\cdot\alpha})\,a^\alpha = 0\,.$$

The analogous condition for the colinearity of the vectors $\boldsymbol{b}'$ and $\boldsymbol{a}$ is

$$(\lambda\delta^{\cdot i}_{\alpha\cdot} - T^{\cdot i}_{\alpha\cdot})\,a^\alpha = 0\,, \qquad \boldsymbol{a}\lambda - \boldsymbol{a}\cdot\boldsymbol{T} = 0\,. \tag{4.31}$$

The systems of linear homogeneous equations (4.30) and (4.31) can have nontrivial solutions $\boldsymbol{a} \not\equiv 0$ only if the determinants of these systems vanish.

On the basis of equations (4.1) and the relationship $|g^{ik}| = |g_{ik}|^{-1}$, it follows that the determinants of these systems are always equal to one another:

$$|\lambda\delta^{i\cdot}_{\cdot j} - T^{i\cdot}_{\cdot j}| = |\lambda\delta^{\cdot i}_{j\cdot} - T^{\cdot i}_{j\cdot}| = \Delta(\lambda)\,. \tag{4.32}$$

The cubic equation

$$\Delta(\lambda) = \lambda^3 - \mathscr{I}_1\lambda^2 + \mathscr{I}_2\lambda - \mathscr{I}_3 = 0 \tag{4.33}$$

is called the characteristic equation.

It is clear from earlier considerations that the characteristic equation is invariant under coordinate transformation and always has at least one real root $\overset{*}{\lambda}$, to which there correspond, according to (4.30), a certain eigenvector $\overset{*}{\boldsymbol{a}} \neq 0$ and, according to (4.31), a certain eigenvector $\overset{*}{\boldsymbol{a}}'$. In general, the vectors $\overset{*}{\boldsymbol{a}}$ and $\overset{*}{\boldsymbol{a}}'$ are different.

Let us choose a coordinate system such that the base vector $\overset{*}{Э}_3$ will be the eigenvector of the system (4.30) or (4.31), i.e., such that it will coincide either with $\overset{*}{\boldsymbol{a}}$ or with $\overset{*}{\boldsymbol{a}}'$. It is obvious that in such coordinate systems the matrices $\| T^{i\cdot}_{\cdot j} \|$ and $\| T^{\cdot i}_{j\cdot} \|$ will have the form

$$\begin{Vmatrix} T^{1\cdot}_{\cdot 1} & T^{1\cdot}_{\cdot 2} & 0 \\ T^{2\cdot}_{\cdot 1} & T^{2\cdot}_{\cdot 2} & 0 \\ T^{3\cdot}_{\cdot 1} & T^{3\cdot}_{\cdot 2} & T^{3\cdot}_{\cdot 3} = \overset{*}{\lambda} \end{Vmatrix} \quad \text{and} \quad \begin{Vmatrix} T^{\cdot 1}_{1\cdot} & T^{\cdot 2}_{1\cdot} & T^{\cdot 3}_{1\cdot} \\ T^{\cdot 1}_{2\cdot} & T^{\cdot 2}_{2\cdot} & T^{\cdot 3}_{2\cdot} \\ 0 & 0 & T^{\cdot 3}_{3\cdot} = \overset{*}{\lambda} \end{Vmatrix}.$$

If all three roots of equation (4.33) are real and distinct, then to each root λ_i for each of the systems (4.30) and (4.31) there corresponds a certain vector $Э_i$, and it is easily seen that in each system these three vectors form a linearly independent system. In fact, if there exists a linear relationship

$$C_1 Э_1 + C_2 Э_2 + C_3 Э_3 = 0, \tag{4.34}$$

and if we apply to this equality the operation (4.38) or (4.31) twice and make use of $\boldsymbol{T}$, we get the two additional relationships

$$\begin{aligned} \lambda_1 C_1 Э_1 + \lambda_2 C_2 Э_2 + \lambda_3 C_3 Э_3 = 0, \\ \lambda_1^2 C_1 Э_1 + \lambda_2^2 C_2 Э_2 + \lambda_3^2 C_3 Э_3 = 0. \end{aligned} \tag{4.35}$$

The determinant of the homogeneous system of linear equations (4.34) and (4.35) in terms of the quantities $C_1Э_1$, $C_2Э_2$, and $C_3Э_3$ is different from zero:

$$\begin{vmatrix} 1 & 1 & 1 \\ \lambda_1 & \lambda_2 & \lambda_3 \\ \lambda_1^2 & \lambda_2^2 & \lambda_3^2 \end{vmatrix} = (\lambda_1 - \lambda_2)(\lambda_2 - \lambda_3)(\lambda_3 - \lambda_1) \neq 0;$$

therefore $C_1 = C_2 = C_3 = 0$.

If the system of vectors $Э_i$ or $Э'_i$ is chosen as the coordinate base, then the matrix of the mixed components of the tensor $\boldsymbol{T}$ assumes the canonical form

$$\begin{Vmatrix} \lambda_1 & 0 & 0 \\ 0 & \lambda_2 & 0 \\ 0 & 0 & \lambda_3 \end{Vmatrix}. \tag{4.36}$$

In the case of a symmetric tensor, such a canonical form always occurs; then, the bases $Э_i$ and $Э'_i$ coincide and form an orthogonal system of vectors directed along the principal axes of the tensor surface.

If a tensor $\boldsymbol{T}$ is nonsymmetric, then the canonical bases $Э_i$ and $Э_i'$ are formed by linearly independent vectors, which, in general, are not orthogonal.

If the characteristic equation (4.33) has a complex root λ_1, then there is also a complex conjugate root $\lambda_2 = \bar{\lambda}_1$ and a real root λ_3. Thus, in this case, all three roots are distinct.

If complex numbers are used for transformations and for the components of vectors and tensors, all the foregoing conclusions hold. Therefore, in this case, the matrix of the tensor $\boldsymbol{T}$ can also be put in the form (4.36), in which λ_1 and λ_2 will be complex conjugate quantities. Let $\lambda_1 = \lambda + i\mu$ and $\lambda_2 = \lambda - i\mu$. Then, by an additional transformation from the complex quantities y^1 and y^2 to the real ones ξ^1 and ξ^2, according to formulas

$$\begin{aligned} \xi^1 + i\xi^2 &= y^1, \\ \xi^1 - i\xi^2 &= y^2, \\ \xi^3 &= y^3, \end{aligned}$$

the matrix (4.36) is reduced to the canonical real form

$$\begin{Vmatrix} \lambda & -\mu & 0 \\ \mu & \lambda & 0 \\ 0 & 0 & \lambda_3 \end{Vmatrix}. \tag{4.37}$$

Thus, it follows that if there exist complex roots of the characteristic equation (4.33), a nonsymmetric matrix of the tensor $\boldsymbol{T}$ may be transformed by using a real transformation to the form (4.37).

In case the roots of equation (4.33) are equal (which can occur only if they are real), a transformation of the matrix to the form (4.36) is also possible if the elementary divisors of the matrix

$$\Sigma = \|\lambda\delta^{i\cdot}_{\cdot j} - T^{i\cdot}_{\cdot j}\|$$

are prime. This means that for a double root together with the determinant of the matrix Σ, all second-order minors are zero, and for a triple root, all the first-order minors are zero.

If the elementary divisors are not prime, then, if a special real basis is chosen, the matrix of the tensor $\boldsymbol{T}$ can be written in the following canonical forms [4]:*

$$\begin{Vmatrix} \lambda & 1 & 0 \\ 0 & \lambda & 0 \\ 0 & 0 & \lambda_3 \end{Vmatrix} \tag{4.38}$$

---

* Numbers in brackets are keyed to the bibliography at the end of the book.

or

$$\begin{Vmatrix} \lambda & 1 & 0 \\ 0 & \lambda & 1 \\ 0 & 0 & \lambda \end{Vmatrix}. \tag{4.39}$$

In the canonical form (4.38) of the matrix, cases in which $\lambda_3 = \lambda$ are also possible. Case (4.39) can occur if λ is a triple root of (4.33).

As was noted earlier, cases (4.37), (4.38), and (4.39) can occur only for a nonsymmetric tensor $\boldsymbol{T}$.

5. Tensor functions

The invariant quantities, scalars, vectors, and tensors, completely defined by the fundamental tensor $\boldsymbol{G}$ and some tensor $\boldsymbol{T}$, are called tensor functions of the tensor $\boldsymbol{T}$.

In general, apart from the tensor $\boldsymbol{G}$, whose components determine the properties of the coordinate system used and which serve as a reference points for the components of the tensor $\boldsymbol{T}$, the functional relation in question can also depend on a number of other tensors $\boldsymbol{A}_1, \boldsymbol{A}_2, \ldots$, and in this way we are led to the idea of a tensor function of several tensors. If the tensor $\boldsymbol{T}$ is variable, while the tensors $\boldsymbol{A}_1, \boldsymbol{A}_2, \ldots$ are held fixed, then $\boldsymbol{A}_1 \boldsymbol{A}_2$ play the role of parametric tensors.

For simplicity, and also for future applications of tensor functions to the mechanics of a continuous medium, we limit ourselves to a consideration of three-dimensional space and to the case in which $\boldsymbol{T}$ is a second-rank tensor.

We shall call a tensor function isotropic if, except for the tensors $\boldsymbol{G}$ and $\boldsymbol{T}$, all other variable or parametric quantities on which the function in question depends are scalars that can be regarded as spherical second-order tensors.

For an isotropic function, the parametric tensors $\boldsymbol{A}_1, \boldsymbol{A}_2$, etc., are spherical; these tensors are of the form $\boldsymbol{A}_s = C_s \boldsymbol{G}$, where the C_s are some scalars. Thus, the supplementary tensor parameters are reduced to the tensor $\boldsymbol{G}$ and certain scalar parameters. Below, we shall consider only isotropic functions. Non-isotropic functions will be dealt with in Section 6.

The systems of components of the tensors $\boldsymbol{G}$ and $\boldsymbol{T}$ form square matrices. Problems of tensor functions can be formulated as problems of functions of matrices [4]. We shall consider functions of this kind as relationships – principles of an invariant character in various coordinate systems.

Let us use the matrices of the components of tensors $\boldsymbol{G}$ and $\boldsymbol{T}$ with mixed indices

$$\boldsymbol{G} = \delta^i_j \boldsymbol{\partial}_i \boldsymbol{\partial}^j, \qquad \boldsymbol{T} = T^{i}_{\cdot j} \boldsymbol{\partial}_i \boldsymbol{\partial}^j = T_{i\cdot}^{\cdot j} \boldsymbol{\partial}^i \boldsymbol{\partial}_j. \tag{5.1}$$

The tensor $\boldsymbol{G}$ is spherical, and its invariants are fixed numbers $\mathcal{J}_i = 3$,

$\mathcal{J}_2 = 3$, $\mathcal{J}_3 = 1$. In general, the matrices $\|T^{i\cdot}_{\cdot j}\|$ and $\|T_{i\cdot}^{\cdot j}\|$ are different, and for these matrices we have

$$\|T_{i\cdot}^{\cdot j}\| = \|g_{i\alpha}\|\,\|T^{\alpha\cdot}_{\cdot\beta}\|\,\|g^{\beta j}\|\,. \tag{5.2}$$

Let α be some scalar function of the tensor $\boldsymbol{T}$. Obviously, α can be considered a scalar invariant of the tensors $\boldsymbol{G}$ and $\boldsymbol{T}$. In Sections 3 and 4 we have already encountered examples of such invariant scalars.

As was shown in Section 4, for a symmetric tensor, there exist only three independent invariants, for example $\mathcal{J}_1$, $\mathcal{J}_2$, $\mathcal{J}_3$ or N_1, N_2, N_3; therefore, for a symmetric tensor, the invariant function $\alpha(\mathrm{T}^{i\cdot}_{\cdot j})$ can, in the general case, be written as

$$\alpha = f(\mathcal{J}_1,\ \mathcal{J}_2,\ \mathcal{J}_3)$$

or

$$\alpha = F(N_1,\ N_2,\ N_3). \tag{5.3}$$

If the tensor $\boldsymbol{T}$ is nonsymmetric, equations of the type (5.3) containing six independent arguments are valid, because, in the general case, not more than six independent real scalar invariants exist.

As was shown in Section 2, new tensors can be formed from tensors $\boldsymbol{T}$ and $\boldsymbol{G}$ with the aid of the operations of multiplication of tensors by numbers, tensor addition, and forming of scalar tensor products. These new tensors can be regarded as functions of the tensors $\boldsymbol{T}$ and $\boldsymbol{G}$. For example,

$$\boldsymbol{H}_1 = k\boldsymbol{T} = kT^{i\cdot}_{\cdot j}\boldsymbol{\ni}_i\boldsymbol{\ni}^j, \qquad \boldsymbol{H}_2 = k_1\boldsymbol{G} + k_2\boldsymbol{T},$$
$$\boldsymbol{H}_3 = \boldsymbol{T}\cdot\boldsymbol{T} = \boldsymbol{T}^2 = T^{i\cdot}_{\cdot\alpha}T^{\alpha\cdot}_{\cdot j}\boldsymbol{\ni}_i\boldsymbol{\ni}^j,$$

and obviously,

$$\boldsymbol{T}\cdot\boldsymbol{G} = \boldsymbol{T} \qquad \text{and} \qquad \boldsymbol{G}\cdot\boldsymbol{G} = \boldsymbol{G}.$$

By repeated multiplication, one can define an arbitrary power tensor function or, in general, a polynomial

$$\boldsymbol{H} = k_0\boldsymbol{G} + k_1\boldsymbol{T} + k_2\boldsymbol{T}^2 + \cdots + k_n\boldsymbol{T}^n, \tag{5.4}$$

where k_0, $k_1,\ldots$, k_n are certain numbers, which can also be regarded as spherical tensors $k_j\boldsymbol{G}$.

The tensor $\boldsymbol{H}$, defined by (5.4), has components $H^{i\cdot}_{\cdot j}$ equal to certain polynomials of the components of $T^{i\cdot}_{\cdot j}$; the corresponding formulas are obvious from the definition of the sum and scalar product of tensors.

Formula (5.4) can be generalized, and the series on the right-hand side examined under the assumption that all nine series for the components $H^{i\cdot}_{\cdot j}$ are convergent. In this way, one can construct tensor functions beginning with ordinary analytic functions.

For example, proceeding from the function $e^z = 1 + z/1! + z^2/2! + \cdots$, we can define a function $\boldsymbol{H} = e^{\boldsymbol{T}}$ from the series

$$\boldsymbol{H} = e^{\boldsymbol{T}} = \boldsymbol{G} + \frac{\boldsymbol{T}}{1!} + \frac{\boldsymbol{T}^2}{2!} + \frac{\boldsymbol{T}^3}{3!} + \cdots,$$

which converges for all finite values of $T^{i\cdot}_{\cdot j}$.

The tensor function $e^{\boldsymbol{T}}$ has certain properties analogous to the properties of the scalar function e^z. For example, by multiplying the series in the definition with itself, we obtain directly

$$\boldsymbol{H}^2 = e^{\boldsymbol{T}} e^{\boldsymbol{T}} = e^{2\boldsymbol{T}}, \qquad \boldsymbol{H}^n = e^{n\boldsymbol{T}}.$$

If the tensor $\boldsymbol{H}^{-1}$ is defined by the formula

$$\boldsymbol{H}^{-1}\boldsymbol{H} = \boldsymbol{G}, \qquad \text{then} \qquad \boldsymbol{H}^{-1} = e^{-\boldsymbol{T}}.$$

In connection with this, it is obvious that the formula for scalar quantities

$$e^{z_1} e^{z_2} = e^{z_1 + z_2}$$

does not hold for matrix tensors if the product of the corresponding tensors does not commute, i.e., if

$$\boldsymbol{T}_1 \boldsymbol{T}_2 \neq \boldsymbol{T}_2 \boldsymbol{T}_1 .$$

In an analogous way, by starting with various analytic functions, one can construct other tensor functions and study their properties.

The general properties of tensor functions can conveniently be derived by using the characteristic equations and the canonical coordinate systems of the tensor $\boldsymbol{T}$.

Consider the matrices

$$\|\lambda\delta^i_j - T^{i\cdot}_{\cdot j}\| \qquad \text{and} \qquad \|\lambda\delta^i_j - T_{i\cdot}^{\cdot j}\|, \tag{5.5}$$

where λ is some numerical parameter.

It is evident that for these matrices, the roots of the characteristic equation $\lambda_1, \lambda_2, \lambda_3$ are invariant, and in general, complex quantities. One can consider them as functions of the real invariants $\mathscr{J}_1$, $\mathscr{J}_2$, and $\mathscr{J}_3$.

In Section 4, it was shown that if a tensor $\boldsymbol{T} = \boldsymbol{N}$ is symmetric, then all three roots λ_1, λ_2, and λ_3 are real and that there exists a real transformation A, reducing the matrices (5.5) to the canonical form

$$\begin{Vmatrix} \lambda - \lambda_1 & 0 & 0 \\ 0 & \lambda - \lambda_2 & 0 \\ 0 & 0 & \lambda - \lambda_3 \end{Vmatrix}. \tag{5.6}$$

If the tensor $\boldsymbol{T}$ is nonsymmetric, then two roots of the characteristic equation, in general, can be complex. The matrices (5.5) can, in general, also be reduced to the canonical form (5.6) by means of a complex transformation if all roots of the characteristic equation are distinct or if the elementary divisors of matrices (5.5) are primes in the case of repeated roots (see Section 4). Obviously, one can always eliminate the case of repeated roots of the matrices considered above with the aid of infinitesimal variations of their components.

Let us now consider the tensor $\boldsymbol{H}$ with matrices $\|\boldsymbol{H}^{i\cdot}_{\cdot j}\|$, which is an isotropic function of the tensor $\boldsymbol{T}$ with matrix $\boldsymbol{T}^{i\cdot}_{\cdot j}$. We have

$$\boldsymbol{H} = f(\boldsymbol{T}). \tag{5.7}$$

Above we have exhibited examples of such functions constructed from given analytic functions $f(z)$.

Let A be some coordinate transformation. From the definition of tensor functions, it follows that the matrix equation*

$$A^{-1}\|H^{i\cdot}_{\cdot j}\|\,A = f\left(A^{-1}\|T^{i\cdot}_{\cdot j}\|\,A\right) \tag{5.8}$$

holds. Let us now suppose that the transformation A reduces the matrix $\|T^{i\cdot}_{\cdot j}\|$ to the canonical form

$$A^{-1}\|T^{i\cdot}_{\cdot j}\|\,A = \begin{Vmatrix}\lambda_1 & 0 & 0\\ 0 & \lambda_2 & 0\\ 0 & 0 & \lambda_3\end{Vmatrix},$$

which is always possible provided that the roots are distinct or if the roots are repeated, but the elementary divisors of matrix (5.5) are prime. Obviously, in this case, the transformed matrix for the tensor $\boldsymbol{H}$ and associated with the analytic function $f(z)$ also acquires a canonical form; then the following holds:

$$A^{-1}\|H^{i\cdot}_{\cdot j}\|\,A = \begin{Vmatrix}f(\lambda_1) & 0 & 0\\ 0 & f(\lambda_2) & 0\\ 0 & 0 & f(\lambda_3)\end{Vmatrix}. \tag{5.9}$$

From this it follows that in an arbitrary coordinate system, the isotropic tensor relation (5.7) can be written in matrix form as

$$\|H^{i\cdot}_{\cdot j}\| = A\begin{Vmatrix}f(\lambda_1) & 0 & 0\\ 0 & f(\lambda_2) & 0\\ 0 & 0 & f(\lambda_3)\end{Vmatrix}A^{-1}, \tag{5.10}$$

where A is the matrix of the corresponding coordinate transformation.

---

* The following tensor functions $f(T)$ are determined as functions of the matrix corresponding to the scalar functions $f(z)$ from the scalar argument z.

If λ_1, λ_2, and λ_3 are the characteristic values of the tensor $\boldsymbol{T}$, then the characteristic values of the tensor $\boldsymbol{H} = f(\boldsymbol{T})$ are given by the formulas $f(\lambda_1)$, $f(\lambda_2)$, and $f(\lambda_3)$, whereupon the tensors $\boldsymbol{T}$ and $\boldsymbol{H}$ are simultaneously reduced to canonical form.

If the tensor $\boldsymbol{T}$ is symmetric, then the tensor $\boldsymbol{H}$ is also symmetric; thus the principal axes of these tensors are orthogonal and coincident.

Let $f(z)$ be some function of a complex variable represented by the series

$$f(z) = a_0 + a_1 z + a_2 z^2 + a_3 z^3 + \cdots, \tag{5.11}$$

Then, if the characteristic values lie within the circle of convergence of the power series (5.11), the nine series corresponding to the matrix function $f(\| T^{i\cdot}_{\cdot j} \|)$ converge.

In the given function $f(z)$, the coefficients a_0, a_1, a_2,... can be regarded as functions of the invariants λ_1, λ_2, λ_3, that is,

$$f(z) = f(\lambda_1, \lambda_2, \lambda_3, z).$$

Therefore, formula (5.10) can be written in a still more general form:

$$\|H^{i\cdot}_{\cdot j}\| = A \begin{Vmatrix} f(\lambda_1, \lambda_2, \lambda_3, \lambda_1) & 0 & 0 \\ 0 & f(\lambda_1, \lambda_2, \lambda_3, \lambda_2) & 0 \\ 0 & 0 & f(\lambda_1, \lambda_2, \lambda_3, \lambda_3) \end{Vmatrix} A^{-1}.$$

It is easy to see that if λ_1, λ_2, and λ_3 are distinct, then, in particular, for the functions

$$f(\lambda_1, \lambda_2, \lambda_3, \lambda) = \frac{(\lambda - \lambda_2)(\lambda - \lambda_3)}{(\lambda_1 - \lambda_2)(\lambda_1 - \lambda_3)} \phi(\lambda_1, \lambda_2, \lambda_3)$$
$$+ \frac{(\lambda - \lambda_3)(\lambda - \lambda_1)}{(\lambda_2 - \lambda_3)(\lambda_2 - \lambda_1)} \psi(\lambda_1, \lambda_2, \lambda_3) + \frac{(\lambda - \lambda_1)(\lambda - \lambda_2)}{(\lambda_3 - \lambda_1)(\lambda_3 - \lambda_2)} \chi(\lambda_1, \lambda_2, \lambda_3), \tag{5.12}$$

the relationships

$$f(\lambda_1, \lambda_2, \lambda_3, \lambda_1) = \phi(\lambda_1, \lambda_2, \lambda_3), \qquad f(\lambda_1, \lambda_2, \lambda_3, \lambda_2) = \psi(\lambda_1, \lambda_2, \lambda_3),$$

and

$$f(\lambda_1, \lambda_2, \lambda_3, \lambda_3) = \chi(\lambda_1, \lambda_2, \lambda_3)$$

hold, where the functions ϕ, ψ, and χ may be arbitrary functions of their arguments. In particular, two tensors, written in canonical form in one and the same coordinate system and having the same charcateristic values (though numbered in a different way), can be represented as functions of one another by means of a formula of the type (5.12). In such a way, tensor functions, including their transformation, are reduced to functional relations between the roots of the characteristic equation, the relationship being defined by the function $f(\lambda_1, \lambda_2, \lambda_3, z)$.

Let us examine the matrix function $\Delta(\|T^{i}_{\cdot j}\|)$, where $\Delta(\lambda) = |\lambda\delta^{i}_{j} - T^{i}_{\cdot j}|$ is a polynomia in λ. Since $\Delta(\lambda_1) = \Delta(\lambda_2) = \Delta(\lambda_3) = 0$, by using (5.9), we obtain

$$\Delta(\|T^{i}_{\cdot j}\|) \equiv 0,$$

i.e.,

$$\|T^{i}_{\cdot j}\|^3 - \mathscr{I}_1 \|T^{i}_{\cdot j}\|^2 + \mathscr{I}_2 \|T^{i}_{\cdot j}\| - \mathscr{I}_3 \|\delta^{i}_{j}\| = 0 \tag{5.13}$$

or

$$\boldsymbol{T}^3 - \mathscr{I}_1 \boldsymbol{T}^2 + \mathscr{I}_2 \boldsymbol{T} - \mathscr{I}_3 \boldsymbol{G} = 0.$$

The matrix identity (5.13), which holds for any matrix, is called the *Hamilton-Cayley identity.*

Identity (5.13) was established above for all matrices $\|T^{i}_{\cdot j}\|$; it holds provided that their characteristic values are distinct. It is easy to verify that (5.13) is always true, because, in the case of equal roots of the characteristic equation, the validity follows from the limiting process while giving infinitesimal variations to the components of the matrix of the tensor $\boldsymbol{T}$.

For matrix tensors of a particular form, in addition to relationship (5.13), equations of the following types may be satisfied:

$$\boldsymbol{T}^2 + a\boldsymbol{T} + b\boldsymbol{G} = 0 \tag{5.14}$$

or

$$\boldsymbol{T} + a\boldsymbol{G} = 0. \tag{5.15}$$

Formula (5.15) corresponds to the case in which the tensor $\boldsymbol{T}$ is spherical.

If the matrix of the tensor $\boldsymbol{T}$ is reduced to the canonical form

$$\begin{Vmatrix} \lambda & 0 & 0 \\ 0 & \lambda & 0 \\ 0 & 0 & \lambda_1 \end{Vmatrix},$$

a formula of the type (5.14) holds.

Using the Hamilton-Cayley relationship, we can write any matric function for second-order matrices as a matric polynomial of second degree. For polynomial functions of the type (5.4), this obviously follows at once, because any matrix of a degree greater than two can be represented in terms of a matric polynomial of second degree by using equations (5.13).

We can show the validity of this proposal for an arbitrary matric function $f(\|T^{i}_{\cdot j}\|)$. Consider the general case in which the roots of the characteristic equation are distinct, and consider the function $f(z)$ of the complex variable z.

We define the quadratic polynomial $k_0 + k_1 z + k_2 z^2 = P(z)$, which at points $z = \lambda_i$ $(i = 1, 2, 3)$ has values equal to $f(\lambda_i)$. If the roots λ_i are distinct, then the coefficients k_0, k_1, k_2 are uniquely defined. The difference

$$f(z) - P(z)$$

becomes identically zero at the points λ_1, λ_2, λ_3.

If at points $\lambda_1, \lambda_2, \lambda_3$, the function $f(\lambda)$ is regular, we have

$$f(\lambda) = P(\lambda) + (\lambda - \lambda_1)(\lambda - \lambda_2)(\lambda - \lambda_3)\psi(\lambda) = P(\lambda) + \Delta(\lambda)\psi(\lambda), \quad (5.16)$$

and the function $\psi(\lambda)$ has a finite value at the points $\lambda_1, \lambda_2, \lambda_3$.

If the parameter λ in (5.16) is replaced by the matrix $\|T^{i}_{\cdot j}\|$ or the tensor $\boldsymbol{T}$, on the basis of the Hamilton-Cayley identity, we have

$$\boldsymbol{H} = P(\boldsymbol{T}) = f(\boldsymbol{T})$$

or, in open form,

$$\boldsymbol{H} = k_0\boldsymbol{G} + k_1\boldsymbol{T} + k_2\boldsymbol{T}^2, \quad (5.17)$$

where k_0, k_1, and k_2 are scalar functions of the invariants of the tensor $\boldsymbol{T}$. The coefficients k_0, k_1, and k_2 and formula (5.17) can easily be written in explicit form.

In fact, if the characteristic roots $\lambda_1, \lambda_2, \lambda_3$ are distinct, then, for the polynomial $P(z)$, the formula

$$P(z) = \frac{(z-\lambda_2)(z-\lambda_3)}{(\lambda_1-\lambda_2)(\lambda_1-\lambda_3)} f(\lambda_1) + \frac{(z-\lambda_3)(z-\lambda_1)}{(\lambda_2-\lambda_3)(\lambda_2-\lambda_1)} f(\lambda_2) + \frac{(z-\lambda_1)(z-\lambda_2)}{(\lambda_3-\lambda_1)(\lambda_3-\lambda_2)} f(\lambda_3).$$

is valid. From this, it follows that

$$\boldsymbol{H} = f(\boldsymbol{T}) = \frac{(\boldsymbol{T}-\lambda_2\boldsymbol{G})(\boldsymbol{T}-\lambda_3\boldsymbol{G})}{(\lambda_1-\lambda_2)(\lambda_1-\lambda_3)} f(\lambda_1) + \frac{(\boldsymbol{T}-\lambda_3\boldsymbol{G})(\boldsymbol{T}-\lambda_1\boldsymbol{G})}{(\lambda_2-\lambda_3)(\lambda_2-\lambda_1)} f(\lambda_2) + \frac{(\boldsymbol{T}-\lambda_1\boldsymbol{G})(\boldsymbol{T}-\lambda_2\boldsymbol{G})}{(\lambda_3-\lambda_1)(\lambda_3-\lambda_2)} f(\lambda_3). \quad (5.18)$$

Formula (5.18) is called the Lagrange-Sylvester equation. According to it, a particular form of the function $f(z)$ appears in the functional relationship (5.17) or (5.18) only in the form of a linear dependence on the quantities $f(\lambda_1)$, $f(\lambda_2)$, and $f(\lambda_3)$.

Formula (5.17) can be generalized to include the case of equal roots of the characteristic equation by using the limiting process. In formula (5.18), this can easily be done if, for the corresponding two equal roots of equation $\Delta(\lambda) = 0$, the derivative $f'(\lambda_i)$ retains a finite value. To make use of the limiting process in the case of three repeated roots $\lambda_1 = \lambda_2 = \lambda_3$, for passage to the limit in formula (5.18), it is sufficient to assume that the derivatives $f'(\lambda_1)$ and $f''(\lambda_1)$ are finite.

Thus, the considered nonlinear functional relations between tensors amount to a determination of the values of the function in question at points corresponding to the roots of the characteristic equation. If the roots are repeated, then the values of the derivatives of the function in question at the point corresponding to the multiple root must be known.

From (5.17), it is immediately obvious that if the characteristic equation of the tensor $\boldsymbol{T}$ has equal roots, then the characteristic equation for the tensor $\boldsymbol{H}$ also has equal roots.

If the tensor $\boldsymbol{T}$ is spherical, the tensor $\boldsymbol{H}$ also is spherical. However, if $\boldsymbol{T}$ is skew-symmetric, $\boldsymbol{H}$, generally, is not skew-symmetric.

The foregoing theory was developed for application to tensors and matrices in three-dimensional space, but it can easily be extended to n-dimensional space.

If the space is two-dimensional, then all the considered matrices will consist of four elements; the determinant $\Delta(\lambda)$, in such case, reduces to a quadratic multinomial. In this case, the identity (5.13) also takes the form of a quadratic multinominal, and, instead, of (5.17) we have a formula of the form

$$\boldsymbol{H} = k_0 \boldsymbol{G} + k_1 \boldsymbol{T}. \tag{5.19}$$

Formula (5.13) defines a quasi-linear relation between the tensors $\boldsymbol{H}$ and $\boldsymbol{T}$.

For the general three-dimensional case, equation (5.17) yields a quasi-linear relationship if the equalities $k_2 = 0$ or

$$\frac{f(\lambda_1)}{(\lambda_1 - \lambda_2)(\lambda_1 - \lambda_3)} + \frac{f(\lambda_2)}{(\lambda_2 - \lambda_1)(\lambda_2 - \lambda_3)} + \frac{f(\lambda_3)}{(\lambda_3 - \lambda_1)(\lambda_3 - \lambda_2)} = 0 \tag{5.20}$$

are satisfied, where the coefficients k_0 and k_1 can be arbitrary functions of λ_1, λ_2, and λ_3 or $\mathscr{I}_1$, $\mathscr{I}_2$, and $\mathscr{I}_3$.

It is obvious that if $\boldsymbol{H}(\boldsymbol{T})$ is a quasi-linear function, then the reciprocal function $\boldsymbol{T}(\boldsymbol{H})$ is also quasi-linear.

With the aid of formula (5.17), one can express the invariants $\mathscr{I}_1^h$, $\mathscr{I}_2^h$, $\mathscr{I}_3^h$ of the tensor $\boldsymbol{H}$ in terms of the invariants $\mathscr{I}_1^t$, $\mathscr{I}_2^t$, and $\mathscr{I}_3^t$. In particular,

$$\mathscr{I}_1^h = 3k_0 + k_1 \mathscr{I}_1^t + k_2 [(\mathscr{I}_1^t)^2 - 2\mathscr{I}_2^t]. \tag{5.21}$$

Let us utilize the decomposition of each of the tensors $\boldsymbol{H}$ and $\boldsymbol{T}$ in accordance with (4.9) into spherical, deviator, and skew-symmetric tensors. Clearly, formula (5.17) is equivalent to the following three formulas:

$$\begin{aligned}
\boldsymbol{P}^h &= \{k_0 + \tfrac{1}{3} k_1 \mathscr{I}_1^t + \tfrac{1}{3} k_2 [(\mathscr{I}_1^t)^2 - 2\mathscr{I}_2^t)]\} \boldsymbol{G}, \\
\boldsymbol{D}^h &= k_1 \boldsymbol{D}^t + k_2 \{2\boldsymbol{P}^t \boldsymbol{D}^t + (\boldsymbol{P}^t)^2 + (\boldsymbol{D}^t)^2 + (\boldsymbol{\Omega}^t)^2 - \tfrac{1}{3}[(\mathscr{I}_1^t)^2 - 2\mathscr{I}_2^t] \boldsymbol{G}\}, \\
\boldsymbol{\Omega}^h &= k_1 \boldsymbol{\Omega}^t + k_2 [(\boldsymbol{D}^t \boldsymbol{\Omega}^t) + (\boldsymbol{\Omega}^t \boldsymbol{D}^t) + 2\boldsymbol{P}^t \boldsymbol{\Omega}^t].
\end{aligned} \tag{5.22}$$

If the components of the tensor $\boldsymbol{H}$ are linear homogeneous functions of the components of the tensor $\boldsymbol{T}$, then it is necessary and sufficient that the following equalities be fulfilled:

$$k_0 = c\mathscr{I}_1^t, \qquad c = \text{const}, \qquad k_1 = \text{const}, \qquad k_2 = 0. \tag{5.23}$$

In this case, the isotropic tensor function $\boldsymbol{H}(\boldsymbol{T})$ depends only on two constant scalars, and the deviators $\boldsymbol{D}^h$ and $\boldsymbol{D}^t$ are similar and differ only by a constant factor k_1.

If the relationship between $\boldsymbol{H}$ and $\boldsymbol{T}$ is quasi-linear, then $k_2 = 0$, and therefore, for a quasi-linear isotropic function, the deviators $\boldsymbol{D}^h$ and $\boldsymbol{D}^t$ are always similar, the similarity coefficient k_1 being in general a variable. The following effect is possible in the case of a quasi-linear relationship:

$$\boldsymbol{P}^t = 0 \qquad (\mathscr{I}_1 = 0), \qquad \text{but} \qquad \boldsymbol{P}^h \neq 0, \tag{5.24}$$

because of the nonlinear dependence of k_0 on the components of the tensor $\boldsymbol{T}$. This nonlinear effect is called the Kelvin effect. In the general case, if $k_2 \neq 0$, the similarity of the deviators is destroyed. It is possible for the diagonal elements of the matrices $\boldsymbol{T}$ and $\boldsymbol{D}^t$ to be zero, but the diagonal elements of the matrix $\boldsymbol{D}^h$ to be different from zero. This nonlinear effect, possible also for $\boldsymbol{\Omega}^t = 0$, is called the Poynting effect.

The condition of similarity of the deviators $\boldsymbol{D}^t$ and $\boldsymbol{D}^h$ is a necessary and sufficient condition for a quasi-linear isotropic relationship. Consequently, with a quasi-linear relationship, the Lode parameters or the angles ψ (see Section 4) for the tensors $\boldsymbol{D}^t$ and $\boldsymbol{D}^h$ are always equal to one another.

In case of an experimental study of the tensor dependence, the quasi-linear nature of the relationships can be established or refuted by comparing the experimentally observed values of the Lode parameters.

As an example of tensor functions, we shall consider the representation of orthogonal matrices in terms of independent quantities. Let us take any orthogonal matrix L, corresponding to a rotated transformation in changing from one rectangular cartesian coordinate system to another:

$$L = \|l_{ij}\|.$$

From the orthogonality condition,

$$\sum_\alpha l_{i\alpha} l_{k\alpha} = \begin{cases} 1, & i = k, \\ 0, & i \neq k, \end{cases}$$

it follows that

$$L^{-1} = \check{L} = \|\check{l}_{ij}\|,$$

where

$$\check{l}_{ij} = l_{ji}.$$

The matrix L can be considered as an array of the nine components of the tensor, out of which only three can be chosen as independent. As an independent quantity we can take the vector $\boldsymbol{K}$, directed along the axis of rotation and equal in magnitude to the angle of rotation. This vector completely defines the transformation of coordinates and, consequently, the matrix L. We define the vector $\boldsymbol{K}$ as an axial vector, which may be thought of as a skew-symmetric tensor with the following component matrix:

$$K = \begin{Vmatrix} 0 & -k_z & k_y \\ k_z & 0 & -k_x \\ -k_y & k_x & 0 \end{Vmatrix},$$

where k_x, k_y, k_z are the projections of the vector onto the coordinate axes.

We can show that the matrix L can be written as a function of the matrix K:

$$L = f(K). \tag{5.25}$$

This function in its components establishes an expression of the nine components of L in terms of three independent components of K. The six orthogonality conditions will be satisfied automatically.

We now show that the matrices L and K are related by

$$L = e^K. \tag{5.26}$$

The orthogonality conditions for L are fulfilled because $\check{K} = -K$ and therefore $\check{L} = e^{-K} = L^{-1}$. Thus, if the matrix K is skew-symmetric, then the matrix e^K is orthogonal. We note that the relation (5.26) is valid for all tensors whose components are defined respectively by the matrices L and K.

For a complete proof of (5.26), we note that if two tensors are equal in any one coordinate system, they are equal in all coordinate systems. It is not difficult to verify that L and e^K are coincident in a coordinate system chosen such that the z-axis is directed along the vector $\boldsymbol{K}$.

If the angle of rotation is denoted by ϕ, then in this coordinate system, the matrix K is of the form

$$K = \begin{Vmatrix} 0 & -\phi & 0 \\ \phi & 0 & 0 \\ 0 & 0 & 0 \end{Vmatrix}, \tag{5.27}$$

and the matrix L, defining a transformation of coordinates by rotation through an angle ϕ about the z-axis, is of the form

$$L = \begin{Vmatrix} \cos\phi & -\sin\phi & 0 \\ \sin\phi & \cos\phi & 0 \\ 0 & 0 & 1 \end{Vmatrix}. \tag{5.28}$$

If we substitute (5.27) into the series

$$e^K = G + \frac{K}{1!} + \frac{K^2}{2!} + \cdots,$$

after summing the series for the components, we obtain the matrix (5.28). The validity of this equation can also be shown by using the Lagrange-Sylvester equations.

For the invariants of the tensor with matrix K, we have

$$\mathcal{J}_1^k = K_{.1}^{1\cdot} + K_{.2}^{2\cdot} + K_{.3}^{3\cdot} = 0,$$
$$\mathcal{J}_2^k = K_{.1}^{1\cdot}K_{.2}^{2\cdot} + K_{.1}^{1\cdot}K_{.3}^{3\cdot} + K_{.2}^{2\cdot}K_{.3}^{3\cdot} + (K_{.1}^{2\cdot})^2 + (K_{.1}^{3\cdot})^2 + (K_{.2}^{3\cdot})^2 = \phi^2,$$
$$\mathcal{J}_3^k = |K_{.j}^{i\cdot}| = 0.$$

Consequently, the corresponding secular equation is of the form

$$\lambda^3 + \phi^2\lambda = 0,$$

from which we find that $\lambda_1 = i\phi$, $\lambda_2 = -i\phi$, $\lambda_3 = 0$. After simple transformations, formula (5.18) yields

$$e^K = G + \frac{\sin\phi}{\phi}K + \frac{2\sin^2(\phi/2)}{\phi^2}K^2, \tag{5.29}$$

whence, recalling that

$$K^2 = \begin{Vmatrix} -\phi^2 & 0 & 0 \\ 0 & -\phi^2 & 0 \\ 0 & 0 & 0 \end{Vmatrix},$$

we obtain

$$\exp K = \exp\begin{Vmatrix} 0 & -\phi & 0 \\ \phi & 0 & 0 \\ 0 & 0 & 0 \end{Vmatrix} = \begin{Vmatrix} \cos\phi & -\sin\phi & 0 \\ \sin\phi & \cos\phi & 0 \\ 0 & 0 & 1 \end{Vmatrix} = L.$$

Formulas (5.25) and (5.26) hold for any coordinate system.

It is not difficult to establish that the matrix K can be represented in terms of the matrix L by means of the series

$$K = \ln L = \ln[G + (L - G)] = \frac{L - G}{1} - \frac{(L - G)^2}{2} + \cdots. \tag{5.30}$$

Since

$$L_1 = e^{i\phi}, \qquad L_2 = e^{-i\phi}, \qquad L_3 = 1,$$

we have

$$\mathcal{J}_1^l = 1 + 2\cos\phi, \qquad \mathcal{J}_2^l = 1 + 2\cos\phi, \qquad \mathcal{J}_3^l = 1, \tag{5.31}$$

from which, in particular, it is easy to define the angle of rotation ϕ if the components of the matrix L are known.

If we use the Lagrange-Sylvester equations, then, instead of the series (5.30), we get the simple formula

$$K = \frac{\phi}{2\sin\phi}(L - G)\left[(1 + 2\cos\phi)G - L\right]. \tag{5.32}$$

This formula is useful for calculating the components of the matrix K, which defines the rotation vector $\boldsymbol{K}$ if the matrix L is known.

In order to establish the tensor dependence of two tensors it is necessary to study especially the question of the existence of an isotropic relationship.

As an example, let us consider an arbitrary tensor $\boldsymbol{T}$:

$$\boldsymbol{T} = T_{\alpha\beta}\mathfrak{Э}^{\alpha}\mathfrak{Э}^{\beta},$$

and let us examine the tensor

$$\overset{*}{\boldsymbol{T}} = \overset{*}{T}_{\alpha\beta}\mathfrak{Э}^{\alpha}\mathfrak{Э}^{\beta}.$$

Here, we assume that

$$\overset{*}{T}_{\alpha\beta} = T_{\beta\alpha}.$$

It is obvious that $\overset{*}{\boldsymbol{T}}$ is determined by $\boldsymbol{T}$. The tensors $\boldsymbol{T}$ and $\overset{*}{\boldsymbol{T}}$ and their matrices are said to be conjugate. Let us now examine the cases in which the tensor dependence between $\overset{*}{\boldsymbol{T}}$ and $\boldsymbol{T}$ can be considered as isotropic.

If the tensor $\boldsymbol{T}$ is symmetric, that is, $T_{\alpha\beta} = T_{\beta\alpha}$, then

$$\overset{*}{\boldsymbol{T}} = \boldsymbol{T}.$$

If the tensor $\boldsymbol{T}$ is skew-symmetric, that is, $T_{\alpha\beta} = -T_{\beta\alpha}$, then

$$\overset{*}{\boldsymbol{T}} = -\boldsymbol{T}.$$

If the coordinate system is cartesian and if the matrix of the tensor $\overset{*}{\boldsymbol{T}}$ is orthogonal but in general neither symmetric nor skew-symmetric, then, from the orthogonality conditions it follows that

$$\overset{*}{\boldsymbol{T}} = \boldsymbol{T}^{-1}.$$

Consequently, in the three cases indicated, the tensor $\overset{*}{\boldsymbol{T}}$ is a simple isotropic function of the tensor $\boldsymbol{T}$, but in these different particular cases, this function is different.

Let us consider the general case, in which $\boldsymbol{T}$ is neither a symmetric nor skew-symmetric tensor and its matrix in a cartesian coordinate system is, in general, not orthogonal. For simplicity, we suppose that the original coordinate system in which we examine the components of $\boldsymbol{T}$ is orthogonal and cartesian. Clearly, all the conclusions derived with the aid of tensor equations will hold independently of the choice of the coordinate system.

Let us find the condition of representability of the tensor $\overset{*}{T}$ as an isotropic function of T:

$$\overset{*}{T} = f(T). \tag{5.33}$$

If a formula of the form (5.33) is true, then clearly the matrix and tensor identity

$$\overset{*}{T}T = T\overset{*}{T} \tag{5.34}$$

must be satisfied; i.e., the matrices of the tensors T and $\overset{*}{T}$ commute. A matrix satisfying condition (5.34) is said to be normal. If the matrix of the tensor T is arbitrary, condition (5.34) will not be satisfied. Below we shall establish a necessary and sufficient condition for the normality of matrices. It is obvious that symmetric, skew-symmetric, and orthogonal matrices are all normal.

If we decompose the tensor T into a symmetric and a skew-symmetric part, we can write

$$T = N + \Omega \quad \text{and} \quad \overset{*}{T} = N - \Omega.$$

It is obvious that equation (5.34) is equivalent to the identity

$$\Omega N = N\Omega. \tag{5.35}$$

Consequently, a symmetric matrix of the tensor N must commute with the skew-symmetric matrix of the tensor Ω.

We have considered the cases $\Omega = 0$ and $N \neq 0$ or N $= 0$ and $\Omega \neq 0$. Now, let us consider the case in which $N \not\equiv 0$, $\Omega \not\equiv 0$.

The condition of normality of the matrix of the tensor T (5.34) or the condition (5.35) is necessary for the existence of functional relation (5.33). Let us examine the sufficiency of this condition for the functional relationship (5.33). Indeed, by definition, the coordinate system is orthogonal and cartesian. It is clear that there is always an orthogonal coordinate transformation L that reduces the symmetric matrix of the tensor N to canonical form. This means that there exist equations

$$N' = LNL^{-1}, \quad \|N'^{i\cdot}_{\cdot j}\| = \|N_i \delta^{i\cdot}_{\cdot j}\|.$$

If we apply the transformation L to the matrix of the tensor Ω, we obtain

$$\Omega' = L\Omega L^{-1}.$$

In view of the fact that the original coordinate system is orthogonal and that the transformation L is equivalent to a rotation of coordinates, it follows that the matrices of the tensors N' and Ω' may be regarded as matrices of the tensors N and Ω in the new coordinate system; therefore, $\Omega' \not\equiv 0$, $\Omega'_{ij} = -\Omega'_{ji}$, and $\Omega'_{ii} = 0$, because the arrangement of the upper and lower indices is not important in a cartesian system, and the property of skew-symmetry is invariant under tensor transformations.

Multiplying (5.35) on the right by L^{-1} and on the left by L, we obtain the equality

$$L\mathbf{\Omega}L^{-1}LNL^{-1} = LNL^{-1}L\mathbf{\Omega}L^{-1}$$

or

$$\mathbf{\Omega}'\mathbf{N}' = \mathbf{N}'\mathbf{\Omega}',$$

which in terms of components may be written as

$$\Omega'_{ij}N_j = N_i\Omega'_{ij} \qquad \text{or} \qquad \Omega'_{ij}(N_j - N_i) = 0. \tag{5.36}$$

From (5.36), it follows that N_1, N_2, N_3 cannot all be different because, if $N_1 \neq N_2 \neq N_3 \neq N_1$, it follows from (5.36) that all the $\Omega'_{ij} = 0$, which is excluded by the assumption that $\mathbf{\Omega} \not\equiv 0$. Thus, if $N_1 \neq N_2 \neq N_3 \neq N_1$ and some of the $\Omega_{ij} \neq 0$, then the matrix for $\boldsymbol{T}$ is not normal, because in this case, condition (5.34) cannot be satisfied.

For a normal matrix of the tensor $\boldsymbol{T}$, with corresponding numbering of the components N_i, two cases are possible:

(1) $$N_1 = N_2 = N_3$$

and

(2) $$N_1 = N_2 \neq N_3.$$

In case (1), the tensor $\boldsymbol{N}$ is spherical and therefore

$$\boldsymbol{T} = N_1\boldsymbol{G} + \mathbf{\Omega}, \qquad \overset{*}{\boldsymbol{T}} = N_1\boldsymbol{G} - \mathbf{\Omega},$$

and consequently,

$$\overset{*}{\boldsymbol{T}} = -\boldsymbol{T} + 2N_1\boldsymbol{G}. \tag{5.37}$$

This establishes a relationship of the form (5.33); here, N_1 is an invariant of the tensor $\boldsymbol{T}$.

In case (2), equations (5.36) have the solution

$$\Omega'_{12} = -\Omega'_{21} = \omega, \qquad \Omega'_{13} = \Omega'_{23} = 0,$$

where $\omega^2 = \Omega_{12}^2 + \Omega_{13}^2 + \Omega_{23}^2$ is an invariant of the matrix of the tensor $\mathbf{\Omega}$.

Consequently, using the transformation L, the matrix of $\overset{*}{\boldsymbol{T}}$ reduces to the form

$$\left\|\begin{matrix} N_1 & -\omega & 0 \\ \omega & N_1 & 0 \\ 0 & 0 & N_3 \end{matrix}\right\|, \tag{5.38a}$$

and the matrix of $\boldsymbol{T}$ to the form

$$\left\|\begin{matrix} N_1 & \omega & 0 \\ -\omega & N_1 & 0 \\ 0 & 0 & N_3 \end{matrix}\right\|. \tag{5.38b}$$

The matrix (5.38b) for the tensor $\boldsymbol{T}$ is generally not orthogonal. If $N_1 = \cos\phi$, $\omega = -\sin\phi$, and $N_3 = 1$, where ϕ is arbitrary, then the matrix of $\boldsymbol{T}$ is orthogonal.

On the basis of the canonical representations (5.38a) and (5.38b) of the matrices of the tensors $\boldsymbol{T}$ and $\overset{\dagger}{\boldsymbol{T}}$, it is easy to verify the functional relation

$$\overset{\dagger}{\boldsymbol{T}} = \frac{1}{(N_1 - N_3)^2 + \omega^2}\{2N_3[\omega^2 + N_1(N_3 - N_1)]\boldsymbol{G} + [4N_1^2 - \omega^2 - (N_1 + N_3)^2]\boldsymbol{T} + 2(N_3 - N_1)\boldsymbol{T}^2\}. \tag{5.39}$$

In formulas (5.37) and (5.39), the coefficients are invariants of the tensor $\boldsymbol{T}$.

If $N_1 = N_3$, then (5.39) becomes formula (5.37). The establishment of the relation (5.39) between $\overset{\dagger}{\boldsymbol{T}}$ and $\boldsymbol{T}$ demonstrates the sufficiency of the condition (5.35).

We have already used the decomposition of an arbitrary tensor into the sum of a symmetric and a skew-symmetric tensor. We now show that any second-rank tensor can be written in the form of the products

$$\boldsymbol{T} = \boldsymbol{O}\boldsymbol{H} = \boldsymbol{H}_1\boldsymbol{O}_1, \qquad \boldsymbol{O} = e^{\boldsymbol{K}}, \qquad \boldsymbol{O}_1 = e^{\boldsymbol{K}_1}, \tag{5.40}$$

where $\boldsymbol{H}$ and $\boldsymbol{H}_1$ are symmetric tensors with positive principal components (positive roots of the characteristic equation) and $\boldsymbol{K}$ and $\boldsymbol{K}_1$ are skew-symmetric tensors. From (5.26), it follows that the matrices of tensors $\boldsymbol{O}$ and $\boldsymbol{O}_1$ are orthogonal.

We shall show the validity of (5.40) from the definition of the matrices of the tensors $\boldsymbol{H}$, $\boldsymbol{K}$, $\boldsymbol{H}_1$, and $\boldsymbol{K}_1$. It is evident that in addition to (5.40), the formulas

$$\overset{\dagger}{\boldsymbol{T}} = \boldsymbol{H}\overset{\dagger}{\boldsymbol{O}} = \overset{\dagger}{\boldsymbol{O}}_1\boldsymbol{H}_1 \tag{5.41}$$

must also be fulfilled.

On the basis of (5.40) and (5.41), or, for that matter, independently, we can write

$$\boldsymbol{T}\overset{\dagger}{\boldsymbol{T}} = \boldsymbol{H}_1^2 \qquad \text{and} \qquad \overset{\dagger}{\boldsymbol{T}}\boldsymbol{T} = \boldsymbol{H}^2, \tag{5.42}$$

where the matrices corresponding to $\boldsymbol{H}_1^2$ and $\boldsymbol{H}^2$ are symmetric but generally different.

In cartesian coordinates, for the components of $\boldsymbol{T}\overset{\dagger}{\boldsymbol{T}}$ and $\overset{\dagger}{\boldsymbol{T}}\boldsymbol{T}$, we have

$$T_{i\alpha}\overset{\dagger}{T}_{\alpha k} = T_{i\alpha}T_{k\alpha}, \qquad \overset{\dagger}{T}_{i\alpha}T_{\alpha k} = T_{\alpha i}T_{\alpha k};$$

from this it is immediately apparent that these are symmetric but generally unequal tensors. They are equal to one another only when the matrix $\|T_{ik}\|$ is normal.

We further limit ourselves to the case in which the determinant $|T_{ik}| \neq 0$;

therefore, the roots of the characteristic equations

$$|G\lambda - \boldsymbol{T}\dot{\boldsymbol{T}}| = 0, \qquad |G\lambda - \dot{\boldsymbol{T}}\boldsymbol{T}| = 0 \tag{5.43}$$

are nonzero and positive, because the quadratic forms corresponding to the matrices of the tensors $\boldsymbol{T}\dot{\boldsymbol{T}}$ and $\dot{\boldsymbol{T}}\boldsymbol{T}$

$$T_{i\alpha}T_{k\alpha}x^i x^k = \sum_{\alpha=1}^{3} (T_{i\alpha}x^i)^2 \qquad \text{and} \qquad T_{\alpha i}T_{\alpha k}x^i x^k = \sum_{\alpha=1}^{3} (T_{\alpha i}x^i)^2$$

are positive-definite.

Both the equations (5.43) coincide because the invariants $\mathcal{J}_1$, $\mathcal{J}_2$, and $\mathcal{J}_3$ of both the tensors $\boldsymbol{T}\dot{\boldsymbol{T}}$ and $\dot{\boldsymbol{T}}\boldsymbol{T}$ are equal to one another; therefore the characteristic values of the matrices corresponding to tensors $\boldsymbol{T}\dot{\boldsymbol{T}}$ and $\dot{\boldsymbol{T}}\boldsymbol{T}$ are equal.

If the matrix of the tensor $\boldsymbol{T}$ is normal, the principal axes of the tensors $\boldsymbol{T}\dot{\boldsymbol{T}}$ and $\dot{\boldsymbol{T}}\boldsymbol{T}$ coincide; if it is not normal, the axes of these symmetric tensors are rotated with respect to one another.

By use of equations (5.42), symmetric tensors $\boldsymbol{H}$ and $\boldsymbol{H}_1$ with positive principal components can be defined by

$$\boldsymbol{H} = \sqrt{\dot{\boldsymbol{T}}\boldsymbol{T}} = aG + b\dot{\boldsymbol{T}}\boldsymbol{T} + c\dot{\boldsymbol{T}}\boldsymbol{T}\dot{\boldsymbol{T}}\boldsymbol{T},$$
$$\boldsymbol{H}_1 = \sqrt{\boldsymbol{T}\dot{\boldsymbol{T}}} = aG + b\boldsymbol{T}\dot{\boldsymbol{T}} + c\,\boldsymbol{T}\dot{\boldsymbol{T}}\boldsymbol{T}\dot{\boldsymbol{T}},$$

where a, b, and c are known functions of the roots of the characteristic equation (5.43). It is obvious that if $\boldsymbol{T}\dot{\boldsymbol{T}} = \dot{\boldsymbol{T}}\boldsymbol{T}$, that is, if the matrix of $\boldsymbol{T}$ is normal, then $\boldsymbol{H} = \boldsymbol{H}_1$.

If $\boldsymbol{H}$ and $\boldsymbol{H}_1$ are defined, then, since $|T_{ik}| \neq 0$, the matrices of the tensors $\boldsymbol{O}$ and $\boldsymbol{O}_1$ are uniquely determined by the formulas

$$\boldsymbol{O} = \boldsymbol{T}\boldsymbol{H}^{-1} \qquad \text{and} \qquad \boldsymbol{O}_1 = \boldsymbol{H}_1^{-1}\boldsymbol{T}.$$

Since

$$\dot{\boldsymbol{O}} = \boldsymbol{H}^{-1}\dot{\boldsymbol{T}} \qquad \text{and} \qquad \dot{\boldsymbol{O}}_1 = \dot{\boldsymbol{T}}\boldsymbol{H}_1^{-1},$$

we have

$$\dot{\boldsymbol{O}}\boldsymbol{O} = \boldsymbol{H}^{-1}\dot{\boldsymbol{T}}\boldsymbol{T}\boldsymbol{H}^{-1} = \boldsymbol{H}^{-1}\boldsymbol{H}^2\boldsymbol{H}^{-1} = \boldsymbol{G},$$

and analogously

$$\boldsymbol{O}_1\boldsymbol{O}_1 = \boldsymbol{G}.$$

Consequently, the matrices of $\boldsymbol{O}$ and $\boldsymbol{O}_1$ are orthogonal, and, therefore, the matrices of $\boldsymbol{K}$ and $\boldsymbol{K}_1$ are skew-symmetric.

Thus, this proves that the representation (5.40) is admissible. From the formulas defining $\boldsymbol{H}$ and $\boldsymbol{K}$, it is obvious that this representation is unique. It is evident that if $\boldsymbol{T}\dot{\boldsymbol{T}} = \dot{\boldsymbol{T}}\boldsymbol{T}$ and therefore $\boldsymbol{H} = \boldsymbol{H}_1$, then $\boldsymbol{K} = \boldsymbol{K}_1$ and consequently the matrices of $e^{\boldsymbol{K}}$ and $\boldsymbol{H}$ are commutative.

6. Functions of certain tensors

Any four vectors $\boldsymbol{a}$, $\boldsymbol{a}_1$, $\boldsymbol{a}_2$, $\boldsymbol{a}_3$ are linearly dependent in a three-dimensional space. This means that a linear relationship of the form

$$k\boldsymbol{a} + k_1\boldsymbol{a}_1 + k_2\boldsymbol{a}_2 + k_3\boldsymbol{a}_3 = 0 \tag{6.1}$$

always exists in which the scalar quantities k, k_1, k_2, k_3 are not all equal to zero and are invariant quantities under coordinate transformation. These scalars, k, k_1, k_2, k_3, can be changed by multiplication by some number. If the vectors $\boldsymbol{a}_1$, $\boldsymbol{a}_2$, $\boldsymbol{a}_3$ are linearly independent, then $k \neq 0$; we can take $k = -1$ and write (6.1) in the form

$$\boldsymbol{a} = k_1\boldsymbol{a}_1 + k_2\boldsymbol{a}_2 + k_3\boldsymbol{a}_3 . \tag{6.2}$$

For arbitrary $\boldsymbol{a}$, $\boldsymbol{a}_1$, $\boldsymbol{a}_2$, and $\boldsymbol{a}_3$, the scalars k_1, k_2, k_3 can be expressed in terms of the invariant products

$$\omega_i = (\boldsymbol{a}, \boldsymbol{a}_i) \qquad \text{and} \qquad \omega_{ik} = (\boldsymbol{a}_i, \boldsymbol{a}_k) \qquad (i, k = 1, 2, 3).$$

If the vector $\boldsymbol{a}$ is a function of the vectors $\boldsymbol{a}_1$, $\boldsymbol{a}_2$, $\boldsymbol{a}_3$, then the scalars ω_i can be regarded as functions of ω_{ik}. In such a case, functional relationships of the type

$$k_i = f_i(\omega_{kj}) \qquad (i, k, j = 1, 2, 3) \tag{6.3}$$

will exist.

Analogous relationships can be shown for tensors [52]. For example, ten arbitrary, generally nonsymmetric second-rank tensors (ten matrices) in three-dimensional space are always connected by the linear relationship

$$kH + \sum_{i=1}^{9} k_i T_i = 0, \tag{6.4}$$

in which the scalars k, k_i $(i = 1, 2, 3)$ are not all equal to zero and are invariant under coordinate transformation. It is clear that if the tensor equation (6.4) is true in any particular coordinate system, it will be satisfied by the same values of k and k_i in any other coordinate system.

The tensor relationships (6.4) can be written in terms of components as

$$kH^{p\cdot}_{\cdot q} + \sum_{i=1}^{9} k_i T_{(i)\cdot q}^{\ \ p\cdot} = 0 \qquad (p, q = 1, 2, 3). \tag{6.5}$$

Let us examine a matrix of order nine $\|\Omega\| = \|T_{(i)\cdot q}^{\ \ p\cdot}\|$ in which the index $i = 1, 2, \ldots, 9$ determines the number of the row, and a fixed combination of the indices p and q determines the number of the column.

If the tensors T_i $(i = 1,2,...,9)$ are linearly independent, then the determinant of the matrix $\|\Omega\| = \|T_{(i)\cdot q}^{\;p\cdot}\|$ is not zero, and consequently $k \neq 0$.

Without any loss in generality, one may put $k = -1$. Equation (6.4) can be written in this case in the form

$$H = \sum_{i=1}^{9} k_i T_i . \tag{6.6}$$

If the tensors H and T_i are symmetric, the number of possible linearly independent tensors is reduced from nine to six.

In (6.6), the scalars k_i are expressed in terms of the invariant scalars $\omega_k = H^{\alpha\cdot}_{\cdot\beta} T_{(k)\cdot\alpha}^{\;\beta\cdot}$ and $\omega_{ik} = T_{(i)\cdot\beta}^{\;\alpha\cdot} T_{(k)\cdot\alpha}^{\;\beta\cdot}$, which are examples of joint invariants. The quantities ω_{ik} can be considered as the elements of a matrix of order nine, obtained by taking the product of the two matrices $\|\Omega\|$ and $\|\Omega^*\|$, where $\|\Omega^*\|$ is obtained in turn from $\|\Omega\|$ by intercharging the rows and columns:

$$\|\omega_{ik}\| = \|\Omega\| \, \|\Omega^*\| .$$

If the determinant of the matrix $\|\Omega\|$ is not zero, then the determinant $\Delta = | \omega_{ik} |$ is also nonzero.

If the tensor H is a tensor function of the tensors T_i, then the invariant scalars ω_k are functions of the scalar invariants of the system of tensors T_i.

All the above conclusions remain valid if a relation of the form (6.6), in which the tensors T_i have fewer than nine independent components in every matrix or in different matrices, that is, $i < 9$, is given in advance. In particular, if the tensors T_i and H are symmetric, the number of independent components and indices i is equal to six.

As another example, if

$$T_1 = G, \qquad T_2 = T , \qquad \text{and} \qquad T_3 = TT$$

and

$$H = f(T),$$

then we have the linear relationship

$$H = k_1 G + k_2 T + k_3 T^2 ,$$

which coincides with (5.17).

In this case, $i = 3$ and the number of independent components of the tensors G, T, T^2 is also three. It follows that any six deviators are linearly dependent. The corresponding formula for representing a deviator in terms of linearly independent deviators will have five terms.

Let a symmetric tensor H be a function of three symmetric tensors G, P_1, and P_2, where P_1 and P_2 are not reduced simultaneously to canonical form [40].

Let us examine the six symmetric tensors

$$\begin{aligned} &\boldsymbol{T}_1 = \boldsymbol{G}, \quad \boldsymbol{T}_2 = \boldsymbol{P}_1, \quad \boldsymbol{T}_3 = \boldsymbol{P}_1^2, \quad \boldsymbol{T}_4 = \boldsymbol{P}_2, \\ &\boldsymbol{T}_5 = \boldsymbol{P}_1\boldsymbol{P}_2 + \boldsymbol{P}_2\boldsymbol{P}_1, \quad \boldsymbol{T}_6 = \boldsymbol{P}_1^2\boldsymbol{P}_2 + \boldsymbol{P}_2\boldsymbol{P}_1^2, \end{aligned} \tag{6.7}$$

together with the conditions for their linear independence. We take a cartesian system whose axes coincide with the principal axes of $\boldsymbol{P}_1$ and consider the linear forms

$$\sum_{i=1}^{6} k_i T_{pq}^{(i)} \qquad (p, q = 1, 2, 3). \tag{6.8}$$

Let λ_1, λ_2, and λ_3 be the characteristic values of the tensor $\boldsymbol{P}_1$ and let P_{ik} be the components of the tensor $\boldsymbol{P}_2$. In the chosen coordinate system, the determinant of the system of linear forms (6.8) is given by

$$\Delta = \begin{vmatrix} 1 & 1 & 1 & 0 & 0 & 0 \\ \lambda_1 & \lambda_2 & \lambda_3 & 0 & 0 & 0 \\ \lambda_1^2 & \lambda_2^2 & \lambda_3^2 & 0 & 0 & 0 \\ P_{11} & P_{22} & P_{33} & P_{12} & P_{13} & P_{23} \\ 2P_{11}\lambda_1 & 2P_{22}\lambda_2 & 2P_{33}\lambda_3 & P_{12}(\lambda_1+\lambda_2) & P_{13}(\lambda_1+\lambda_3) & P_{23}(\lambda_2+\lambda_3) \\ 2P_{11}\lambda_1^2 & 2P_{22}\lambda_2^2 & 2P_{33}\lambda_3^2 & P_{12}(\lambda_1^2+\lambda_2^2) & P_{13}(\lambda_1^2+\lambda_3^2) & P_{23}(\lambda_2^2+\lambda_3^2) \end{vmatrix}$$

$$= \begin{vmatrix} 1 & 1 & 1 \\ \lambda_1 & \lambda_2 & \lambda_3 \\ \lambda_1^2 & \lambda_2^2 & \lambda_3^2 \end{vmatrix} \begin{vmatrix} 1 & 1 & 1 \\ \lambda_1+\lambda_2 & \lambda_1+\lambda_3 & \lambda_2+\lambda_3 \\ \lambda_1^2+\lambda_2^2 & \lambda_1^2+\lambda_3^2 & \lambda_2^2+\lambda_3^2 \end{vmatrix} P_{12}P_{13}P_{23}$$

$$= -(\lambda_1-\lambda_2)^2(\lambda_2-\lambda_3)^2(\lambda_3-\lambda_1)^2 P_{12}P_{13}P_{23},$$

from which it is clear that the system of tensors (6.7) is linearly independent provided that the roots λ_1, λ_2, λ_3 are distinct and provided that $P_{12} \neq 0$, $P_{13} \neq 0, P_{23} \neq 0$.

If one of the components P_{12}, P_{13}, P_{23} vanishes, this can be interpreted geometrically as a case in which one of the principal axes of the tensor $\boldsymbol{P}_2$ lies in a plane passing through the principal axes of the tensor $\boldsymbol{P}_1$. Obviously, this is a reciprocal case; i.e., one of the principal axes of $\boldsymbol{P}_1$ lies in a plane passing through the principal axes of the tensor $\boldsymbol{P}_2$. If two components P_{ik} with different indices vanish, then one of the principal axes of the tensor $\boldsymbol{P}_2$ coincides with a principal axis of the tensor $\boldsymbol{P}_1$. If simultaneously $P_{12} = P_{13} = P_{23} = 0$, then the principal axes of the tensors $\boldsymbol{P}_1$ and $\boldsymbol{P}_2$ coincide.

If $\Delta \neq 0$, then one can write for the tensor $\boldsymbol{H}$,

$$\begin{aligned} \boldsymbol{H} = {} & k_1\boldsymbol{G} + k_2\boldsymbol{P}_1 + k_3\boldsymbol{P}_1^2 + k_4\boldsymbol{P}_2 \\ & + k_5(\boldsymbol{P}_1\boldsymbol{P}_2 + \boldsymbol{P}_2\boldsymbol{P}_1) + k_6(\boldsymbol{P}_1^2\boldsymbol{P}_2 + \boldsymbol{P}_2\boldsymbol{P}_1^2), \end{aligned} \tag{6.9}$$

where k_1, k_2, ..., k_6 are functions of the invariants of the system of tensors

$\boldsymbol{P}_1$ and $\boldsymbol{P}_2$. Formula (6.9) can be viewed as a generalization of (5.17) for the case in which the tensor $\boldsymbol{H}$ depends on two tensors $\boldsymbol{P}_1$ and $\boldsymbol{P}_2$. Let us suppose that a symmetric tensor $\boldsymbol{H}$ depends on several symmetric tensors $\boldsymbol{P}_1, \boldsymbol{P}_2, \ldots, \boldsymbol{P}_m$. Then, if $\boldsymbol{P}_1$ and $\boldsymbol{P}_2$ are two tensors satisfying the condition $\Delta \neq 0$, we find that (6.9) holds even in this more general case. Here, however, the scalars $k_1, k_2, \ldots, k_6$ are more general functions of the invariants of the system of tensors $\boldsymbol{P}_1, \boldsymbol{P}_2, \ldots, \boldsymbol{P}_m$. If two tensors $\boldsymbol{P}_1$ and $\boldsymbol{P}_2$ are constant and satisfy the condition $\Delta \neq 0$, then formula (6.9) is valid; here, the other variable tensors appear only as scalar invariants of the system $\boldsymbol{P}_1, \boldsymbol{P}_2, \ldots, \boldsymbol{P}_m$, on which the scalars $k_1, k_2, \ldots, k_6$ depend.

Let us also consider certain special cases, in which, for an arbitrary pair of tensors $\boldsymbol{P}_i$ and $\boldsymbol{P}_k$, the determinant $\Delta = 0$.

1. If all the tensors $\boldsymbol{P}_1, \boldsymbol{P}_2, \ldots, \boldsymbol{P}_m$ are spherical, then $\boldsymbol{H}$ is also spherical, because the components of the tensors $\boldsymbol{P}_1, \boldsymbol{P}_2, \ldots, \boldsymbol{P}_m$ are invariant with respect to an arbitrary orthogonal coordinate transformation, and therefore, $\boldsymbol{H}$ also possesses this property. In this case, instead of (6.9), one may write the simpler formula

$$\boldsymbol{H} = k\boldsymbol{G}, \tag{6.10}$$

where k is a scalar function of the m invariants of the tensors $\boldsymbol{P}_1, \boldsymbol{P}_2, \ldots, \boldsymbol{P}_m$.

2. If all the tensors $\boldsymbol{P}_1, \boldsymbol{P}_2, \ldots, \boldsymbol{P}_m$ have a common principal axis, then this axis is also a principal one for the tensor $\boldsymbol{H}$. Indeed, we can take a cartesian coordinate system, so that a common principal axis of the tensors $\boldsymbol{P}_1, \ldots, \boldsymbol{P}_m$ coincides with the x_1 axis. In this coordinate system, we have

$$P^i_{12} = P^i_{13} = 0.$$

Let H_{12} and H_{13} be the corresponding components of the tensor $\boldsymbol{H}$, and let us carry out the coordinate transformation

$$x'_1 = -x_1, \qquad x'_2 = x_2, \qquad x'_3 = x_3.$$

In this transformation, all the components of the tensors $\boldsymbol{P}_1, \boldsymbol{P}_2, \ldots, \boldsymbol{P}_m$ remain unchanged. For the tensor $\boldsymbol{H}$, we have

$$H'_{12} = -H_{12} \qquad \text{and} \qquad H'_{13} = -H_{13},$$

and all the rest of the components remain unchanged. Since $\boldsymbol{H} = f(\boldsymbol{P}_1, \ldots, \boldsymbol{P}_m)$ and all the $\boldsymbol{P}_i$ are unchanged, $\boldsymbol{H}$ must remain unchanged; therefore,

$$H_{12} = H_{13} = 0,$$

and consequently, the x_1 axis is also the principal one for the tensor $\boldsymbol{H}$.

3. It is obvious that if the tensors $\boldsymbol{P}_1, \boldsymbol{P}_2, \ldots, \boldsymbol{P}_m$ have coincident principal axes, the tensor $\boldsymbol{H}$ also has the same principal axes.

4. If each of the tensors $\boldsymbol{P}_1, \boldsymbol{P}_2, \ldots, \boldsymbol{P}_m$ with common principal axes has a pair of equal roots of the characteristic equation corresponding to the principal axes x_1 and x_2, then $\boldsymbol{H}$ also has equal roots corresponding to the x_1 and x_2 axes.

Tensor functions of several tensors are sometimes considered as anisotropic functions of one tensor $\boldsymbol{P}_1$; in such cases, other tensors assume the role of parametric quantities characterizing the anisotropy.

It is possible to have tensors with rank greater than two as parametric tensors characterizing the anisotropy. Such a tensor can produce an effect on a second-rank tensor $\boldsymbol{H}$ only through the invariants which are joint with the other tensors or through scalar products of this tensor with the spherical tensor $\boldsymbol{G}$ or any other second-rank tensor.

7. Potential tensor functions

Consider a given function

$$\boldsymbol{H} = f(\boldsymbol{G}, \boldsymbol{T}, \boldsymbol{A}_1, \boldsymbol{A}_2, \ldots), \tag{7.1}$$

where

$$\boldsymbol{T} = T^{i\cdot}_{\cdot j}\mathfrak{Э}_i\mathfrak{Э}^j = T_{j\cdot}^{\cdot i}\mathfrak{Э}^j\mathfrak{Э}_i = T_{ij}\mathfrak{Э}^i\mathfrak{Э}^j = T^{ij}\mathfrak{Э}_i\mathfrak{Э}_j$$

is a fundamental and generally nonsymmetric variable tensor. The tensors $\boldsymbol{A}_1, \boldsymbol{A}_2, \ldots$ are not in general spherical, constant, parametric tensors which can be viewed as characteristics of anisotropy. If $\boldsymbol{A}_1, \boldsymbol{A}_2, \ldots$ are spherical, then the function (7.1) is isotropic and can, by formula (5.17), be written as

$$\boldsymbol{H} = k\boldsymbol{G} + k_1\boldsymbol{T} + k_2\boldsymbol{T}^2. \tag{7.2}$$

For a tensor $\boldsymbol{H}$, we have the representations

$$\boldsymbol{H} = H^{i\cdot}_{\cdot j}\mathfrak{Э}_i\mathfrak{Э}^j = H_{j\cdot}^{\cdot i}\mathfrak{Э}^j\mathfrak{Э}_i = H_{ij}\mathfrak{Э}^i\mathfrak{Э}^j = H^{ij}\mathfrak{Э}_i\mathfrak{Э}_j.$$

The tensor function (7.1) is called a potential function if, for the tensor components $H^{i\cdot}_{\cdot j}$, formulas of the type

$$H^{i\cdot}_{\cdot j} = \frac{\partial W}{\partial T_{i\cdot}^{\cdot j}} \tag{7.3}$$

hold. Here, the potential W is some scalar function of the system of invariants of the tensors $\boldsymbol{G}, \boldsymbol{T}, \boldsymbol{A}_1, \boldsymbol{A}_2, \ldots$.

It is not difficult to show that if (7.3) is true in one coordinate system, it is true in any other. Indeed, let x^i and y^i be two coordinate systems:

$$y^i = y^i(x^j).$$

From equations (3.3), we have

$$T_{\beta\cdot}^{\cdot\alpha} = T_{i\cdot}^{\prime\cdot j} \frac{\partial x^\alpha}{\partial y^j} \frac{\partial y^i}{\partial x^\beta}$$

and

$$\frac{\partial W}{\partial T_{i\cdot}^{\prime\cdot j}} = \frac{\partial W}{\partial T_{\beta\cdot}^{\cdot\alpha}} \frac{\partial T_{\beta\cdot}^{\cdot\alpha}}{\partial T_{i\cdot}^{\prime\cdot j}} = H_{\cdot\alpha}^{\beta\cdot} \frac{\partial x^\alpha}{\partial y^j} \frac{\partial y^i}{\partial x^\beta} = H_{\cdot j}^{\prime i\cdot},$$

which was to be shown.

Let us now introduce formulas for the purely covariant and contravariant components of $\boldsymbol{H}$.

We have

$$T_{i\cdot}^{\cdot j} = T_{i\alpha} g^{\alpha j}, \qquad \frac{\partial W}{\partial T_{i\alpha}} = \frac{\partial W}{\partial T_{i\cdot}^{\cdot j}} g^{\alpha j} = H_{\cdot j}^{i\cdot} g^{\alpha j}.$$

In these equations, the summation is carried out only over α or j, the index i remaining fixed. We thus obtain

$$H^{i\alpha} = \frac{\partial W}{\partial T_{i\alpha}}. \tag{7.4}$$

In a similar fashion we obtain the formulas

$$H_{i\alpha} = \frac{\partial W}{\partial T^{i\alpha}} \quad \text{and} \quad H_{j\cdot}^{\cdot i} = \frac{\partial W}{\partial T_{\cdot i}^{j\cdot}}. \tag{7.5}$$

In deriving formulas (7.4) and (7.5), we consider the tensors $\boldsymbol{G}$ and $\boldsymbol{T}$ as independent quantities, and on differentiation with respect to the components of $\boldsymbol{T}$, the components of the tensor $\boldsymbol{G}$ are taken as constant. Formulas (7.3), (7.4), and (7.5) are valid in the general anisotropic case, in which the scalar W actually depends on a system of joint invariants of $\boldsymbol{T}$ and the parametric tensors $\boldsymbol{A}_1, \boldsymbol{A}_2, \ldots$.

Consider the case in which the tensor $\boldsymbol{T}$ is symmetric and the potential W depends on the components of $\boldsymbol{T}$ only in terms of the invariants of $\boldsymbol{T}$ and, moreover, can depend arbitrarily on a system of the invariants of the tensors $\boldsymbol{A}_1, \boldsymbol{A}_2, \ldots$.

This case corresponds to potential tensor functions of a rather more general type than the potential isotropic functions defined above, which may be considered as a fundamental special subcase. In the function (7.1), the tensors $\boldsymbol{A}_1, \boldsymbol{A}_2, \ldots$ are represented only by their joint invariant scalars.

In considering a complete system of invariants of a symmetric tensor $\boldsymbol{T}$, one may take its principal components T_1, T_2, and T_3 or the invariants $\mathscr{I}_1$, $\mathscr{I}_2^*$, and $\mathscr{I}_3^*$ defined in terms of the components $T_{\cdot j}^{i\cdot}$ in formula (3.9).

On the basis of (3.9) and (7.5) for the case under consideration, we have

$$H_{j\cdot}^{\cdot i} = \frac{\partial W}{\partial T_{\cdot i}^{j\cdot}} = \frac{\partial W}{\partial \mathscr{I}_1}\delta_{j\cdot}^{\cdot i} + 2\frac{\partial W}{\partial \mathscr{I}_2^*}T_{\cdot j}^{i\cdot} + 3\frac{\partial W}{\partial \mathscr{I}_3^*}T_{\cdot\alpha}^{i\cdot}T_{\cdot j}^{\alpha\cdot}. \tag{7.6}$$

If, for a given point, the directions of the coordinate lines coincide with the directions of the principal axes of the tensor $\boldsymbol{T}$, then $T_{\cdot i}^{i\cdot} = T_i$ and $T_{\cdot j}^{i\cdot} = 0$ for $i \neq j$; therefore, from (7.6), we obtain

$$H_{i\cdot}^{\cdot i} = H_i = \frac{\partial W}{\partial \mathscr{I}_1} + 2\frac{\partial W}{\partial \mathscr{I}_2^*}T_i + 3\frac{\partial W}{\partial \mathscr{I}_3^*}T_i^2 \tag{7.7}$$

and

$$H_{j\cdot}^{\cdot i} = 0 \qquad (i \neq j).$$

Consequently, from (7.6) we see that the principal axes of the tensors $\boldsymbol{H}$ and $\boldsymbol{T}$ coincide at every point.† For the principal axes, formulas (3.9) take the form

$$\begin{aligned} \mathscr{I}_1 &= T_1 + T_2 + T_3, \\ \mathscr{I}_2^* &= T_1^2 + T_2^2 + T_3^2, \\ \mathscr{I}_3^* &= T_1^3 + T_2^3 + T_3^3. \end{aligned} \tag{7.8}$$

From (7.8) and (7.7), it is obvious that

$$H_i = \frac{\partial W}{\partial T_i} \qquad (i = 1, 2, 3). \tag{7.9}$$

It is also obvious that the reverse proposition is true: if, independently of the choice of coordinate system, the potential W depends on the components of $\boldsymbol{T}$ only through the principal components T_1, T_2, T_3, then (7.6) follows from (7.9). Formulas (7.6) and (7.9) are equivalent when W depends only on T_1, T_2, and T_3.

If the potential W is given as a function of the principal components T_1, T_2, T_3, then, from (7.6) after replacing in (7.8) the derivatives of W with respect to $\mathscr{I}_1$, $\mathscr{I}_2^*$, $\mathscr{I}_3^*$ with the derivatives of W with respect to T_1, T_2, T_3,

† If the potential W is of a more general nature and depends, for example, on the invariant $\mathrm{II} = A_{\cdot\beta}^{\alpha\cdot}T_{\cdot\alpha}^{\beta\cdot}$, then on the right-hand side of (7.6) there must be added the term

$$\frac{\partial W}{\partial \mathrm{II}} A_{\cdot j}^{i\cdot} \left(\frac{\partial W}{\partial \mathrm{II}} \neq 0\right).$$

If $A_{\cdot j}^{i\cdot} \neq 0$ for $i \neq j$, then the principal axes of $\boldsymbol{H}$ and $\boldsymbol{T}$ do not coincide.

we obtain

$$H_{j\cdot}^{\cdot i} = \frac{1}{(T_1 - T_2)(T_2 - T_3)(T_3 - T_1)} \left\{ \begin{vmatrix} \frac{\partial W}{\partial T_1} & \frac{\partial W}{\partial T_2} & \frac{\partial W}{\partial T_3} \\ T_1 & T_2 & T_3 \\ T_1^2 & T_2^2 & T_3^2 \end{vmatrix} \delta_{j\cdot}^{\cdot i} \right.$$

$$\left. + \begin{vmatrix} 1 & 1 & 1 \\ \frac{\partial W}{\partial T_1} & \frac{\partial W}{\partial T_2} & \frac{\partial W}{\partial T_3} \\ T_1^2 & T_2^2 & T_3^2 \end{vmatrix} T_{\cdot j}^{i\cdot} + \begin{vmatrix} 1 & 1 & 1 \\ T_1 & T_2 & T_3 \\ \frac{\partial W}{\partial T_1} & \frac{\partial W}{\partial T_2} & \frac{\partial W}{\partial T_3} \end{vmatrix} T_{\cdot\alpha}^{i\cdot} T_{\cdot j}^{\alpha\cdot} \right\}. \tag{7.10}$$

For tensor functions possessing potentials, formulas (7.6) and (7.10) specify the form of the coefficients k_0, k_1, k_2 in (7.2).

If the function $W(\mathscr{I}_1, \overset{*}{\mathscr{I}}_2, \overset{*}{\mathscr{I}}_3)$ or $W(T_1, T_2, T_3)$ is given, then the dependence of the scalars k_0, k_1, k_3 on $\mathscr{I}_1, \overset{*}{\mathscr{I}}_2, \overset{*}{\mathscr{I}}_3$ is defined by formula (7.6) and that on (T_1, T_2, T_3) by formula (7.10).

From (7.6) and (7.10), it follows that for a potential dependence between two tensors $\boldsymbol{H}$ and $\boldsymbol{T}$, the quasi-linearity condition can be written in the form

$$\left(\frac{\partial W}{\partial \overset{*}{\mathscr{I}}_3}\right)_{\mathscr{I}_1, \overset{*}{\mathscr{I}}_2} = 0 \tag{7.11}$$

or

$$\left(\frac{\partial W}{\partial T_1}\right)_{T_2,T_3}(T_3 - T_2) + \left(\frac{\partial W}{\partial T_2}\right)_{T_1,T_3}(T_1 - T_3) + \left(\frac{\partial W}{\partial T_3}\right)_{T_1,T_2}(T_2 - T_1) = 0.$$

If to the tensor function

$$\boldsymbol{H} = f(\boldsymbol{T})$$

there corresponds a scalar function $f(T_1, T_2, T_3, z)$, then on the basis of the formulas of Section 5, we have

$$H_1 = f(T_1, T_2, T_3, T_1) = \phi(T_1, T_2, T_3),$$
$$H_2 = f(T_1, T_2, T_3, T_2) = \psi(T_1, T_2, T_3),$$
$$H_3 = f(T_1, T_2, T_3, T_3) = \chi(T_1, T_2, T_3),$$

where ϕ, ψ, and χ are arbitrary functions of their arguments.

It is obvious that for the existence of a potential it is necessary and sufficient that the following conditions be fulfilled:

$$\frac{\partial \phi}{\partial T_2} - \frac{\partial \psi}{\partial T_1} = 0,$$
$$\frac{\partial \psi}{\partial T_3} - \frac{\partial \chi}{\partial T_2} = 0, \tag{7.12}$$
$$\frac{\partial \chi}{\partial T_1} - \frac{\partial \phi}{\partial T_3} = 0.$$

Obviously, for an arbitrary function $f(T_1, T_2, T_3, T)$, these conditions are not fulfilled.

In particular, if the corresponding function $f(z)$ depends only on z and does not otherwise depend on the invariant scalars of the tensor $\boldsymbol{T}$, then the conditions (7.12) will be satisfied; in this case, the potential W is determined by a simple relation,

$$W = \mathscr{F}(T_1) + \mathscr{F}(T_2) + \mathscr{F}(T_3), \tag{7.13}$$

in which functions $\mathscr{F}(z)$ and $f(z)$ are connected by the direct relationship

$$\mathscr{F}'(z) = f(z).$$

In this case, the condition of quasi-linear dependence of $\boldsymbol{H}$ and $\boldsymbol{T}$ takes the form

$$f(T) = aT + b,$$

where a and b are certain constants; then, the potential W is determined by

$$W = \frac{a}{2}(T_1^2 + T_2^2 + T_3^2) + b(T_1 + T_2 + T_3).$$

Let us consider an isotropic tensor function $\boldsymbol{H} = f(\boldsymbol{G}, P_1, P_2, P_3, \boldsymbol{P})$. For this function, the following equations in terms of its principal components are satisfied:

$$H_i = \frac{1}{\phi_i'(P_i)} \frac{\partial W(P_1, P_2, P_3)}{\partial P_i} \qquad (i = 1, 2, 3), \tag{7.14}$$

where $\phi_i'(P_i)$ is the derivative of $\phi_i(P_i)$ with respect to P_i.

According to the general theory developed in Section 5 and from formula (5.12), the function $f(\boldsymbol{G}, P_1, P_2, P_3, \boldsymbol{P})$ can be expressed in terms of the functions $\phi_1'(P_1), \phi_2'(P_2), \phi_3'(P_3)$, and $W(P_1, P_2, P_3)$.

If a tensor $\boldsymbol{T}$, defined by the formula

$$\boldsymbol{T} = \boldsymbol{\Phi}(\boldsymbol{G}, P_1, P_2, P_3, \boldsymbol{P})$$

is introduced, where

$$\boldsymbol{\Phi}(\boldsymbol{G}, P_1, P_2, P_3, \lambda) = \frac{(\lambda - P_2\boldsymbol{G})(\lambda - P_3\boldsymbol{G})}{(P_1 - P_2)(P_1 - P_3)} \phi_1(P_1) + \frac{(\lambda - P_3\boldsymbol{G})(\lambda - P_1\boldsymbol{G})}{(P_2 - P_3)(P_2 - P_1)} \phi_2(P_2) + \frac{(\lambda - P_1\boldsymbol{G})(\lambda - P_2\boldsymbol{G})}{(P_3 - P_1)(P_3 - P_2)} \phi_3(P_3), \tag{7.15}$$

then $\boldsymbol{H}$ can be considered as a potential function of the tensor $\boldsymbol{T}$, because the relationship between H_i and T_i is defined by formula (7.9).

In particular, if $\phi_1'(x) = \phi_2'(x) = \phi_3'(x) = \phi(x)$, then, instead of (7.12), one may use the matric tensor formula

$$T = \phi(P).$$

For example, if the formulas

$$\sigma_{j\cdot}^{\cdot i} = (\delta_{\cdot\mu}^{i\cdot} - 2\varepsilon_{\cdot\mu}^{i\cdot})\frac{\partial W}{\partial \varepsilon_{\cdot\mu}^{j\cdot}}, \tag{7.16}$$

in which the potential W depends only on the invariants of the symmetric tensor $\mathscr{E} = \varepsilon_{\cdot j}^{i\cdot}\boldsymbol{\vartheta}_i\boldsymbol{\vartheta}^j$ hold, then, from (7.16), it follows that

$$\sigma_i = (1 - 2\varepsilon_i)\frac{\partial W}{\partial \varepsilon_i} \qquad \text{and} \qquad \sigma_{j\cdot}^{\cdot i} = \frac{\partial W}{\partial h_{j\cdot}^{\cdot i}}; \tag{7.17}$$

here, the tensor $\boldsymbol{H} = h_{j\cdot}^{\cdot i}\boldsymbol{\vartheta}^j\boldsymbol{\vartheta}^i$ is defined as an isotropic tensor function of the tensor $\mathscr{E}$ by the formula

$$\boldsymbol{H} = -\ln\sqrt{\boldsymbol{G} - 2\mathscr{E}} \qquad (H_i = -\ln\sqrt{1 - 2\varepsilon_i}), \tag{7.18}$$

where $\boldsymbol{G}$ is the fundamental tensor $\boldsymbol{G} = g_{ij}\boldsymbol{\vartheta}^i\boldsymbol{\vartheta}^j$.

8. Differentiation of a tensor with respect to the space coordinates

Many tensors are encountered in applications to mechanics. In particular, there exist certain tensors which are obtained from other tensors as a result of the use of differential operators.

Suppose that a curvilinear coordinate system x^1, x^2, x^3 is given for the region under consideration. Let $f(x^1, x^2, x^3)$ be a scalar function of the coordinates with values independent of the choice of coordinate system.

The system of derivatives

$$\frac{\partial f}{\partial x^1}, \quad \frac{\partial f}{\partial x^2}, \quad \frac{\partial f}{\partial x^3}$$

can be considered as the components of a covariant vector $\boldsymbol{a}$. In fact, it is easy to see that the quantity

$$\boldsymbol{a} = \frac{\partial f}{\partial x^1}\boldsymbol{\vartheta}^1 + \frac{\partial f}{\partial x^2}\boldsymbol{\vartheta}^2 + \frac{\partial f}{\partial x^3}\boldsymbol{\vartheta}^3 \tag{8.1}$$

is invariant, and that under any coordinate transformation, the right-hand side will preserve its form.

Instead of the scalar f, let us now take some vector $\boldsymbol{a}$, defined by the formula

$$\boldsymbol{a} = a_1\boldsymbol{\vartheta}^1 + a_2\boldsymbol{\vartheta}^2 + a_3\boldsymbol{\vartheta}^3,$$

where a_1, a_2, a_3 are the components of the vector and are some functions of the coordinates x^1, x^2, x^3. The vectors of the base $\mathfrak{Э}^1$, $\mathfrak{Э}^2$, $\mathfrak{Э}^3$ in the curvilinear coordinate system also depend on the coordinates of the points in space.

In Section 1, formulas (1.16) and (1.20) serve to define the derivatives with respect to the coordinates of the vector basis; using these formulas and the general rules for differentiating the product of a numerical function and a vector, we obtain a definition of the derivative of an arbitrary vector $\boldsymbol{a}$ with respect to the coordinates. We set

$$\boldsymbol{T} = \frac{\partial \boldsymbol{a}}{\partial x^1}\mathfrak{Э}^1 + \frac{\partial \boldsymbol{a}}{\partial x^2}\mathfrak{Э}^2 + \frac{\partial \boldsymbol{a}}{\partial x^3}\mathfrak{Э}^3 = \left(\frac{\partial a_\alpha}{\partial x^j} - a_\beta \Gamma^\beta_{\alpha j}\right)\mathfrak{Э}^\alpha \mathfrak{Э}^j = \nabla_j a_\alpha \mathfrak{Э}^\alpha \mathfrak{Э}^j. \tag{8.2}$$

It is obvious that the quantity $\boldsymbol{T}$ is invariant and is a second-rank tensor. In cartesian coordinates (or more generally, at points at which $\Gamma^i_{\alpha j} = 0$), the components $\nabla_j a_\alpha$ of the tensor $\boldsymbol{T}$ coincide with the ordinary derivatives of the vector components with respect to the coordinates. In the general case, the system of derivatives

$$\frac{\partial a_\alpha}{\partial x^j}$$

cannot be regarded as a system of components of a tensor. For an arbitrary coordinate transformation, the derivatives $\partial a_\alpha / \partial x^j$ do not transform according to the rules of transformation of tensor components.

If we use the formula

$$\boldsymbol{a} = a^1 \mathfrak{Э}_1 + a^2 \mathfrak{Э}_2 + a^3 \mathfrak{Э}_3,$$

we obtain, by analogy, the tensor $\boldsymbol{T}_1$:

$$\boldsymbol{T}_1 = \left(\frac{\partial a^\alpha}{\partial x^j} + a^\beta \Gamma^\alpha_{\beta j}\right)\mathfrak{Э}_\alpha \mathfrak{Э}^j = \nabla_j a^\alpha \mathfrak{Э}_\alpha \mathfrak{Э}^j. \tag{8.3}$$

It is obvious that the equality

$$\boldsymbol{T}_1 = \boldsymbol{T}$$

is fulfilled, because these are tensors with identical components in a cartesian coordinate system. Hence, it follows that the equations

$$\nabla_j a_\alpha = g_{\alpha\beta} \nabla_j a^\beta = \nabla_j g_{\alpha\beta} a^\beta \tag{8.4}$$

must be satisfied, which we shall later verify directly.

For the tensor $\boldsymbol{T}$, it is easy to form the contravariant components with respect to the index j.

From the general rules, we have

$$\nabla^j a_\alpha \mathfrak{I}^\alpha \mathfrak{I}_j = g^{j\beta}\nabla_\beta a_\alpha \mathfrak{I}^\alpha \mathfrak{I}_j = \left(g^{j\beta}\frac{\partial a_\alpha}{\partial x^\beta} - g^{j\beta} a_\omega \Gamma^\omega_{\alpha\beta} \right) \mathfrak{I}^\alpha \mathfrak{I}_j .$$

The relationship between the covariant (dx_i) and the contravariant (dx^i) components of the vector $d\boldsymbol{r}$ and the derivatives $\partial \mathfrak{I}^i / \partial x_j$, is given by equations (1.12), (1.14), and (1.21):

$$dx^\beta = g^{\beta\omega} dx_\omega , \qquad \frac{\partial \mathfrak{I}^\omega}{\partial x_j} = - \Gamma^\omega_{\alpha\beta} \mathfrak{I}^\alpha g^{\beta j} .$$

Hence,

$$\frac{\partial a_\alpha}{\partial x_j} = \frac{\partial a_\alpha}{\partial x^\beta} g^{\beta j} ,$$

and, consequently,

$$\boldsymbol{T} = \nabla^j a_\alpha \mathfrak{I}^\alpha \mathfrak{I}_j = \frac{\partial \boldsymbol{a}}{\partial x_j} \mathfrak{I}_j . \tag{8.5}$$

In a similar fashion, we can establish one more relation:

$$\boldsymbol{T} = \nabla^j a^\alpha \mathfrak{I}_\alpha \mathfrak{I}_j = \frac{\partial \boldsymbol{a}}{\partial x_j} \mathfrak{I}_j . \tag{8.6}$$

Thus, differentiation of a vector with respect to the space coordinates results in a second-rank tensor whose components can be written in one of the forms

$$\nabla_j a^\alpha , \qquad \nabla_j a_\alpha , \qquad \nabla^j a^\alpha , \qquad \nabla^j a_\alpha ,$$

which are related to one another by the tensor rules of raising or lowering indices by means of the fundamental tensor $\boldsymbol{G}$.

The above-described method for obtaining vectors and second-rank tensors by differentiation of scalars and vectors is easily generalized to the case of tensors of arbitrary rank.

For example, consider a third-rank tensor $\boldsymbol{T}$:

$$\boldsymbol{T} = T^{\alpha\beta\cdot}_{\cdot\cdot\gamma} \mathfrak{I}_\alpha \mathfrak{I}_\beta \mathfrak{I}^\gamma .$$

The quantity

$$\boldsymbol{\Omega} = \frac{\partial \boldsymbol{T}}{\partial x^j} \mathfrak{I}^j$$

is invariant and is a fourth-rank tensor. Differentiating the components $T^{\alpha\beta\cdot}_{\cdot\cdot\gamma}$ and the basis vectors $\mathfrak{I}_\alpha$, $\mathfrak{I}_\beta$, $\mathfrak{I}^\gamma$, we obtain

$$\begin{aligned} \boldsymbol{\Omega} &= \nabla_j T^{\alpha\beta\cdot}_{\cdot\cdot\gamma} \mathfrak{I}_\alpha \mathfrak{I}_\beta \mathfrak{I}^\gamma \mathfrak{I}^j \\ &= \left(\frac{\partial T^{\alpha\beta\cdot}_{\cdot\cdot\gamma}}{\partial x^j} + T^{\mu\beta\cdot}_{\cdot\cdot\gamma} \Gamma^\alpha_{\mu j} + T^{\alpha\mu\cdot}_{\cdot\cdot\gamma} \Gamma^\beta_{\mu j} - T^{\alpha\beta\cdot}_{\cdot\cdot\mu} \Gamma^\mu_{\gamma j} \right) \mathfrak{I}_\alpha \mathfrak{I}_\beta \mathfrak{I}^\gamma \mathfrak{I}^j . \end{aligned} \tag{8.7}$$

In direct analogy with the vector case, we can obtain an expression for the components of an arbitrary tensor

$$\nabla^j T^{\alpha\beta\cdot}_{\cdot\cdot\gamma} = g^{j\omega}\nabla_\omega T^{\alpha\beta\cdot}_{\cdot\cdot\gamma}\,.$$

We shall now consider certain properties of the invariant differentiation of tensors.

Take two tensors $\boldsymbol{A}$ and $\boldsymbol{B}$ with components A^α and $B^{\beta\cdot}_{\cdot\gamma}$ and form their product $\boldsymbol{T}$ as a tensor with components $A^\alpha_\cdot B^{\beta\cdot}_{\cdot\gamma}$.

It is easy to verify directly that for the covariant components of the invariant derivative of $\boldsymbol{T}$, the following holds true:

$$\nabla_j(A^\alpha_\cdot B^{\beta\cdot}_{\cdot\gamma}) = (\nabla_j A^\alpha_\cdot)\,B^{\beta\cdot}_{\cdot\gamma} + A^\alpha_\cdot(\nabla_j B^{\beta\cdot}_{\cdot\gamma})\,. \tag{8.8}$$

Thus, the differentiation of tensor products follows the general rule for differentiating products of scalar functions.

Consider tensor $\boldsymbol{T}$ with components $T^{\alpha\beta\cdot}_{\cdot\cdot\gamma}$ and tensor $\boldsymbol{D}$ with components $\mathscr{D}^\alpha$, which is obtained from $\boldsymbol{T}$ by means of convolution of indices β and γ, where $\beta = \gamma$.

From formula (8.7), it is evident that the operations of convolution and differentiation are commutative. If the convolution, i.e., the transition, to tensor $\boldsymbol{D}$ is carried out first, followed by the process of invariant differentiation, we obtain the same result as if we had differentiated $\boldsymbol{T}$ and then applied the process of convolution with respect to the same indices.

In particular, let the scalar product of two vectors $\boldsymbol{a}$ and $\boldsymbol{b}$ be given. In this case we have

$$(\boldsymbol{a}, \boldsymbol{b}) = a_\alpha b^\alpha$$

and

$$\nabla_j(\boldsymbol{a}, \boldsymbol{b}) = (\nabla_j a_\alpha)\,b^\alpha + a_\alpha(\nabla_j b^\alpha) = \frac{\partial a_\alpha}{\partial x^j}\,b^\alpha + a_\alpha\frac{\partial b^\alpha}{\partial x^j}\,.$$

Let the given vector be $\boldsymbol{a} = a_\alpha\,\mathbf{Э}^\alpha$. We define the tensor

$$\boldsymbol{\Omega} = (\nabla_j a_\alpha - \nabla_\alpha a_j)\,\mathbf{Э}^j\mathbf{Э}^\alpha\,.$$

It is obvious that $\boldsymbol{\Omega}$ is skew-symmetric. The components $\Omega_{j\alpha}$ will be expressed as

$$\Omega_{j\alpha} = \nabla_j a_\alpha - \nabla_\alpha a_j = \frac{\partial a_\alpha}{\partial x^j} - \Gamma^\mu_{\alpha j}a_\mu - \frac{\partial a_j}{\partial x^\alpha} + \Gamma^\mu_{j\alpha}a_\mu = \frac{\partial a_\alpha}{\partial x^j} - \frac{\partial a_j}{\partial x^\alpha} \tag{8.9}$$

in any coordinate system.

The skew-symmetric tensor $\boldsymbol{\Omega}$ has only three independent components which, according to (3.14) after multiplying by $\sqrt{g_1}$ ($g_1 = 1/g = |g^{ik}|$), can be regarded as components of the vector $\boldsymbol{\omega}$ [$\omega^\beta = \sqrt{g_1}\,(\delta a_\alpha/\delta x^j - \delta a_j/\delta x^\alpha)$].

The index β is a supplementary index to α and j, and the sequence of β, j, and α can be obtained from the sequence 1, 2, 3 by means of a cyclic permutation of letters. The vector $\boldsymbol{\omega}$ is called the curl of vector $\boldsymbol{a}$:

$$\boldsymbol{\omega} = \text{curl}\, \boldsymbol{a}\,.$$

We now show that the fundamental tensor $\boldsymbol{G}$ can be thought of as a constant tensor for invariant differentiation. Indeed, we have

$$\nabla_j g_{ik} = \frac{\partial g_{ik}}{\partial x^j} - g_{\mu k}\Gamma^{\mu}_{ij} - g_{i\mu}\Gamma^{\mu}_{kj}\,. \tag{8.10}$$

On the basis of equation (1.18), we obtain $\nabla_j g_{ik} = 0$. The validity of the form $\nabla_j g^{ik} = 0$ is also easy to show in a similar fashion. In applying the process of invariant differentiation, the components of the tensor $\boldsymbol{G}$ can be treated as constants, i.e., they can be taken outside the differentiation signs. This property was already established by means of rules governing the differentiation of vectors in deriving equation (8.4).

9. The Riemann-Christoffel tensor

The Christoffel symbols Γ^k_{ij} in three-dimensional space form an array of twenty-seven components. According to (1.19), we have

$$\Gamma^k_{ij} = \tfrac{1}{2} g^{ks}\left(\frac{\partial g_{is}}{\partial x^j} + \frac{\partial g_{js}}{\partial x^i} - \frac{\partial g_{ij}}{\partial x^s}\right). \tag{9.1}$$

It is obvious that if all the derivatives $\partial g_{ik}/\partial x^j = 0$ $(i,j,k = 1,2,3)$, then $\Gamma^k_{ij} = 0$, and, conversely, from (8.10) and the equation $\nabla_j g_{ik} = 0$, it follows immediately that if all $\Gamma^k_{ij} \equiv 0$, then all $g_{ij} = \text{const}$.

In Euclidean space, it is permissible to introduce a cartesian coordinate system for the entire region. In the cartesian system, $g_{ik} = \text{const}$, and therefore all the Γ^k_{ij} become zero identically. In the cartesian system, the invariant derivatives coincide with the ordinary derivatives.

On the other hand, in Euclidean space for a curvilinear coordinate system, g_{ik} depend on the points in space and on the Christoffel symbols Γ^k_{ij}, which are, in general, different from zero.

For the reasons indicated, it follows that the array Γ^k_{ij} cannot be regarded as an array of the components of a tensor. Therefore, the formulas for the transformation of the symbols Γ^k_{ij} from one coordinate system to another must be different from the transformation formulas for tensor components.

Let Γ'^k_{ij} be the Christoffel symbols in the coordinate system y^i and Γ^k_{ij} in x^i. The transformation formulas for the Christoffel symbols can be easily obtained from

$$\mathbf{Э}'_i = \mathbf{Э}_\alpha \frac{\partial x^\alpha}{\partial y^i}.$$

Differentiating with respect to y^i, and noting that

$$\frac{\partial \mathbf{Э}'_i}{\partial y^j} = \Gamma'^{\alpha}_{ij} \mathbf{Э}'_\alpha$$

and

$$\frac{\partial \mathbf{Э}_\alpha}{\partial x^\beta} = \Gamma^{\omega}_{\alpha\beta} \mathbf{Э}_\omega = \Gamma^{\omega}_{\alpha\beta} \frac{\partial y^\gamma}{\partial x^\omega} \mathbf{Э}'_\gamma,$$

because

$$\mathbf{Э}_\omega = \frac{\partial y^\gamma}{\partial x^\omega} \mathbf{Э}'_\gamma,$$

we obtain

$$\Gamma'^{\alpha}_{ij} \mathbf{Э}'_\alpha = \left[\Gamma^{\omega}_{\alpha\beta} \frac{\partial y^\gamma}{\partial x^\omega} \frac{\partial x^\alpha}{\partial y^i} \frac{\partial x^\beta}{\partial y^j} + \frac{\partial^2 x^\omega}{\partial y^i \partial y^j} \frac{\partial y^\gamma}{\partial x^\omega}\right] \mathbf{Э}'_\gamma.$$

Whence, forming the scalar product with $\mathbf{Э}'$ on both sides, we obtain the relation we sought:

$$\Gamma'^{\gamma}_{ij} = \left(\Gamma^{\omega}_{\alpha\beta} \frac{\partial x^\alpha}{\partial y^i} \frac{\partial x^\beta}{\partial y^j} + \frac{\partial^2 x^\omega}{\partial y^i \partial y^j}\right) \frac{\partial y^\gamma}{\partial x^\omega}. \tag{9.2}$$

Formulas (9.2) become identical with the tensor transformation formulas only in the case when the relationship between x^i and y^i is linear.

In the general case of Riemannian space, the coordinates in which the $\Gamma^{\gamma}_{\alpha\beta}$ are zero at a given point are called *geodesic* at that point.

If $\Gamma'^{\gamma}_{ij} = 0$, then, since the determinant $|\partial y^\gamma / \partial x^\alpha| \neq 0$, the following equations must be satisfied:

$$\Gamma^{\omega}_{\alpha\beta} \frac{\partial x^\alpha}{\partial y^i} \frac{\partial x^\beta}{\partial y^j} + \frac{\partial^2 x^\omega}{\partial y^i \partial y^j} = 0 \qquad (\omega, i, j = 1, 2, 3). \tag{9.3}$$

It is always possible to introduce new coordinates y^i so that at a given point in space, $\overset{1}{x_0}$, $\overset{2}{x_0}$, $\overset{3}{x_0}$, corresponding to $\overset{1}{y_0}$, $\overset{2}{y_0}$, $\overset{3}{y_0}$, all the Γ'^{γ}_{ij} become zero identically. To obtain this, it is sufficient to put

$$x^\omega - x^\omega_0 = \delta^\omega_s (y^s - \overset{s}{y_0}) - \tfrac{1}{2} \Gamma^{\omega}_{0\alpha\beta} (y^\alpha - \overset{\alpha}{y_0})(y^\beta - \overset{\beta}{y_0}) + \cdots, \tag{9.4}$$

where all terms of order higher than two have not been dropped.

If equation (9.3) is satisfied in the entire region, one obtains a differential equation which determines the transformation from the given coordinate system x^i to a cartesian one y^i.

For an arbitrary fundamental tensor g_{ik} and the corresponding $\Gamma^{\omega}_{\alpha\beta}$, equations (9.3) are not integrable.

The necessary conditions for the space to be Euclidean are identical with the conditions of integrability of the system (9.3).

Let us differentiate equation (9.3) with respect to y^k. After eliminating second derivatives and making use of (9.3), we obtain

$$\left(\frac{\partial \Gamma^{\omega}_{\alpha\beta}}{\partial x^s} - \Gamma^{\omega}_{\lambda\beta}\Gamma^{\lambda}_{\alpha s} - \Gamma^{\omega}_{\alpha\lambda}\Gamma^{\lambda}_{\beta s}\right)\frac{\partial x^s}{\partial y^k}\frac{\partial x^\alpha}{\partial y^i}\frac{\partial x^\beta}{\partial y^j} + \frac{\partial^3 x^\omega}{\partial y^i \partial y^k \partial y^j} = 0 .$$

By rearranging the indices of summation s_z and β and the indices k, j, we have, together with the above, a second equation

$$\left(\frac{\partial \Gamma^{\omega}_{\alpha s}}{\partial x^\beta} - \Gamma^{\omega}_{\lambda s}\Gamma^{\lambda}_{\alpha\beta} - \Gamma^{\omega}_{\alpha\lambda}\Gamma^{\lambda}_{\beta s}\right)\frac{\partial x^s}{\partial y^k}\frac{\partial x^\alpha}{\partial y^i}\frac{\partial x^\beta}{\partial y^j} + \frac{\partial^3 x^\omega}{\partial y^i \partial y^k \partial y^j} = 0 .$$

After eliminating the third-order derivatives by subtracting the above two equations and noting that a Jacobian of the transformation with respect to x^i and y^i is nonsingular, we obtain necessary and sufficient conditions for the integrability of the system (9.37) in the form

$$R_{\beta s\alpha\cdot}^{\cdot\cdot\cdot\omega} = \frac{\partial \Gamma^{\omega}_{\alpha\beta}}{\partial x^s} - \frac{\partial \Gamma^{\omega}_{\alpha s}}{\partial x^\beta} + \Gamma^{\omega}_{\lambda s}\Gamma^{\lambda}_{\alpha\beta} - \Gamma^{\omega}_{\lambda\beta}\Gamma^{\lambda}_{\alpha s} = 0 . \tag{9.5}$$

Equations (9.5) must be satisfied in any coordinate system if the space is Euclidean.

We shall show below that for the general case of Riemannian space, the quantities $R_{\beta s\mu\cdot}^{\cdot\cdot\cdot\alpha}$ may be viewed as the components of a fourth-rank tensor. If equations (9.5) are not satisfied, then it is impossible to introduce a cartesian coordinate system for the entire region. In this case, the space would not be Euclidean, but would, in fact, be a curvilinear Riemannian space.

In order to prove the tensor character of the quantities $R_{\beta s\mu\cdot}^{\cdot\cdot\cdot\alpha}$, and also in connection with the striking properties of this tensor, we shall examine in greater detail the properties of the invariant derivatives defined in the previous section.

Given an arbitrary variable vector $\boldsymbol{a}$. Let us examine tensors of the following form that are obtained by differentiation:

$$\boldsymbol{T}_1 = \frac{\partial \boldsymbol{a}}{\partial x^i}\boldsymbol{\vartheta}^i = \nabla_i a^\alpha \boldsymbol{\vartheta}_\alpha \boldsymbol{\vartheta}^i \quad \text{and} \quad \boldsymbol{T}_2 = \frac{\partial \boldsymbol{T}_1}{\partial x^j}\boldsymbol{\vartheta}^j = \nabla_j \nabla_i a^\alpha \boldsymbol{\vartheta}_\alpha \boldsymbol{\vartheta}^i \boldsymbol{\vartheta}^j .$$

Along with the tensor $\boldsymbol{T}_2$, we examine the tensor $\mathring{\boldsymbol{T}}_2$, obtained by interchanging the indices i and j of the components of $\boldsymbol{T}_2$, while maintaining the order of i and j of the indices of the base vectors

$$\overset{*}{\boldsymbol{T}}_2 = \nabla_i \nabla_j a^\alpha \text{Э}_\alpha \text{Э}^i \text{Э}^j .$$

It is obvious that, in general, $\overset{*}{\boldsymbol{T}}_2 \neq \boldsymbol{T}_2$. The equality $\overset{*}{\boldsymbol{T}}_2 = \boldsymbol{T}_2$ is true only when the tensor $\boldsymbol{T}_2$ is symmetric with respect to indices i and j.

A simple direct calculation yields

$$\boldsymbol{T}_2 - \overset{*}{\boldsymbol{T}}_2 = R_{ij\mu\cdot}^{\cdot\cdot\cdot\alpha} a^\mu \text{Э}_\alpha \text{Э}^i \text{Э}^j . \tag{9.6}$$

From this, it follows that the quantities $R_{ij\mu\cdot}^{\cdot\cdot\cdot\alpha}$ form a tensor. This tensor is called the Riemann-Christoffel tensor. Obviously, for Euclidean space the Riemann-Christoffel tensor is identically equal to zero. The tensor $\boldsymbol{T}_2$, in Euclidean space, is always symmetric with respect to i and j; that is, $\overset{*}{\boldsymbol{T}}_2 = \boldsymbol{T}_2$.

The foregoing considerations, examined for a vector $\boldsymbol{a}$, can be generalized for a tensor of any rank. For any tensor, it is easy to obtain the formula

$$\nabla_j \nabla_i T^{\alpha\beta\cdot}_{\cdot\cdot\gamma} - \nabla_i \nabla_j T^{\alpha\beta\cdot}_{\cdot\cdot\gamma} = R_{ij\mu\cdot}^{\cdot\cdot\cdot\alpha} T^{\mu\beta\cdot}_{\cdot\cdot\gamma} + R_{ij\mu\cdot}^{\cdot\cdot\cdot\beta} T^{\alpha\mu\cdot}_{\cdot\cdot\gamma} + R_{ij\gamma\cdot}^{\cdot\cdot\cdot\mu} T^{\alpha\beta\cdot}_{\cdot\cdot\mu} . \tag{9.7}$$

In the general case of Riemann space, the tensor $R_{ij\mu\cdot}^{\cdot\cdot\cdot\mu}$ is different from zero. Lowering the index α, one may write

$$R_{ij\mu\nu} = g_{\alpha\nu} R_{ij\mu\cdot}^{\cdot\cdot\cdot\alpha} = \frac{\partial \Gamma_{\nu\mu i}}{\partial x^j} - \frac{\partial \Gamma_{\nu\mu j}}{\partial x^i} + g^{\alpha\omega}\left[\Gamma_{\omega\mu j}\Gamma_{\alpha\nu i} - \Gamma_{\omega\mu i}\Gamma_{\alpha\nu j}\right], \tag{9.8}$$

where

$$\Gamma_{\nu\alpha j} = \frac{1}{2}\left[\frac{\partial g_{\alpha\nu}}{\partial x^j} + \frac{\partial g_{j\nu}}{\partial x^\alpha} - \frac{\partial g_{\alpha j}}{\partial x^\nu}\right]. \tag{9.9}$$

For an arbitrary given point in the geodesic coordinates, $\Gamma_{\nu\alpha j} = 0$, and, therefore,

$$R_{ij\mu\nu} = \frac{1}{2}\left[\frac{\partial^2 g_{\nu i}}{\partial x^j \partial x^\mu} + \frac{\partial^2 g_{\mu j}}{\partial x^i \partial x^\nu} - \frac{\partial^2 g_{\mu i}}{\partial x^j \partial x^\nu} - \frac{\partial^2 g_{\nu j}}{\partial x^i \partial x^\mu}\right]. \tag{9.10}$$

The following symmetry properties, which, according to the properties of tensor transformations, can be used in any coordinate system, follow immediately from equation (9.10):

$$\begin{aligned} &R_{ij\mu\nu} = -R_{ji\mu\nu}, \qquad R_{ii\mu\nu} = 0, \\ &R_{ij\mu\nu} = -R_{ij\nu\mu}, \qquad R_{ij\mu\mu} = 0, \\ &R_{ij\mu\nu} = R_{\mu\nu ij}, \\ &R_{ij\mu\nu} + R_{\mu ij\nu} + R_{j\mu i\nu} = 0 . \end{aligned} \tag{9.11}$$

In a three-dimensional space with $n = 3$, the tensor $R_{ij\mu\nu}$ has only six independent components whose values may be other than zero. These are the components

$$\begin{array}{lll} R_{1212}, & R_{1313}, & R_{2323}, \\ R_{1213}, & R_{2123}, & R_{3132}. \end{array} \tag{9.12}$$

In order to determine the independent components whose values may differ from zero, we can use the following considerations.

Obviously, if all four indices are identical, the component R_{iiii} is zero for any i.

In one-dimensional space, when the metric is given on a curve, there is only one index equal to unity; therefore, in a one-dimensional space $R_{ij\mu\nu} \equiv 0$.

If there are only two unequal indices, then, for two given indices, only one component is independent.

Thus, for $n = 3$, with two different indices, there are only the three independent components

$$R_{1212}, \qquad R_{1313}, \qquad R_{2323}. \tag{9.12a}$$

In two-dimensional space, i.e., a plane surface with $n = 2$, it is obvious that the Riemannian tensor has only one independent component which can differ from zero: R_{1212}.

If there are three different indices, then among the four indices of the Riemannian components, two will always be identical; these equal indices for nonzero components must be associated with the first and the second pairs of independent components. These indices can always be taken as located in the first and third positions. After fixing the identical indices, it is easy to see that only one component will be independent. It thus follows that for $n = 3$, only the following three components of the Riemannian tensor, having unequal indices, are independent:

$$R_{1213}, \qquad R_{2123}, \qquad R_{3132}. \tag{9.12b}$$

The condition for the vanishing of the tensor $R_{ij\mu\nu}$ is equivalent to six equations obtained by equating the six components shown in (9.12) to zero.

10. Differentiation of tensors with respect to a parameter

In the present section, we shall establish rules and formulas for differentiating tensors with respect to a parameter t. Time can serve as an example of a variable scalar parameter.

Later, we shall examine tensors that are dependent on t and shall study the case where the basis in which the components of the tensor are given also depends on the same parameter t. In such a case, the dependence of the variable basis on t can be prescribed arbitrarily. In certain cases, the ways in which the basis and the given tensor depend on t can be related.

The variation of a single tensor can be examined by using various bases that depend in different ways on the same parameter.

The formulas and tensor derivatives of different senses with respect to the parameter t which follow can be thought of as a generalization of the familiar rules of differentiation of vectors with respect to time for moving or stationary coordinate axes.

In the particular region considered, we take the following two coordinate systems: a stationary one with the covariant basis $\mathring{Э}_1, \mathring{Э}_2, \mathring{Э}_3$ and a moving one with a covariant basis $\hat{Э}_1, \hat{Э}_2, \hat{Э}_3$. The moving system is chosen in such manner that for fixed moving points of the continuum, the coordinates ξ^1, ξ^2, ξ^3 remain constant. Further, we can assume that the coordinate system moving together with the continuum in motion will coincide with the stationary system; when this happens, the individual fixed points in both coordinate systems will be defined by a single set of coordinates, ξ^1, ξ^2, ξ^3.

The coordinates of moving points ξ^1, ξ^2, ξ^3 defined in this context are Lagrangian coordinates. In Lagrangian coordinates introduced in this manner, the motion of the continuum will amount to a displacement and a deformation of the moving coordinate system. In the stationary system with basis $\mathring{Э}_i$, fixed stationary points correspond to the individual points moving in space.

We further introduce a stationary coordinate system $x^1 x^2 x^3$ with covariant basis $Э_1, Э_2, Э_3$. In this system, the coordinates of moving points vary. The functions

$$x^i = x^i(\xi^1, \xi^2, \xi^3, t) \tag{10.1}$$

define the law of motion for the particles of a continuum. The system with basis $Э_i$ is introduced to serve as a reference system with respect to which we examine the motion of the continuum. The stationary system with basis $\mathring{Э}_i$ and the moving one with basis $\hat{Э}_i$ should be thought of as complementary coordinate systems in which it is possible to determine the scalar and tensor characteristics of the motion.

The basis $Э_i$ and the coordinates x^1, x^2, x^3 may be thought of as a coordinate system corresponding to Euler's point of view. We further assume that at a given instant of time all three coordinate systems coincide; therefore, the tensor components corresponding to the various bases coincide at a given instant of time, t.

The coordinate systems described above enable us to determine the time derivatives, in various senses, of the tensor quantities.

Let $\boldsymbol{r}$ be the radius vector of a point in space. The differential $d\boldsymbol{r}$ may be defined by

$$d\boldsymbol{r} = dx^\alpha \boldsymbol{\vartheta}_\alpha, \qquad d\boldsymbol{r} = d\xi^\alpha \mathring{\boldsymbol{\vartheta}}_\alpha, \qquad d\boldsymbol{r} = d\xi^\alpha \hat{\boldsymbol{\vartheta}}_\alpha. \tag{10.2}$$

The first of these formulas may correspond to a displacement $d\boldsymbol{r}$ of a fixed point with $\xi^i = \text{const}$; the other two define the differentials $d\boldsymbol{r}$ for a fixed value of t.

The velocity vector of points in the moving volume is defined by

$$\mathbf{v} = \frac{d\boldsymbol{r}}{dt} = \frac{\partial \boldsymbol{r}(\xi^1, \xi^2, \xi^3, t)}{\partial t} = \frac{\partial x^\alpha}{\partial t}\boldsymbol{\vartheta}_\alpha = v^\alpha \boldsymbol{\vartheta}_\alpha.$$

Consider, first of all, the time derivatives of the basis vectors for the different coordinate systems introduced above.

The vectors $\mathring{\boldsymbol{\vartheta}}_i$ and $\hat{\boldsymbol{\vartheta}}^i$ can be introduced for every instant of time t from the condition $\mathring{\boldsymbol{\vartheta}}_i = \hat{\boldsymbol{\vartheta}}_i$, but the basis vectors $\mathring{\boldsymbol{\vartheta}}_i$ are independent of variation in time and can depend only on the Lagrangian coordinates ξ^i.

Thus, it follows that for the individual fixed points of a moving continuum with constant ξ^1, ξ^2, ξ^3 we have

$$\frac{d\mathring{\boldsymbol{\vartheta}}_i}{dt} = 0, \qquad \frac{d\mathring{\boldsymbol{\vartheta}}^i}{dt} = 0. \tag{10.3}$$

In the space occupied by the continuum, on the basis of equations (10.2), it follows that

$$\hat{\boldsymbol{\vartheta}}_i = \frac{\partial \boldsymbol{r}}{\partial \xi^i} \qquad \text{and} \qquad \hat{\boldsymbol{\vartheta}}_i = \frac{\partial \boldsymbol{r}}{\partial x^\alpha}\frac{\partial x^\alpha}{\partial \xi^i} = \boldsymbol{\vartheta}_\alpha \frac{\partial x^\alpha}{\partial \xi^i}.$$

From this, after differentiating with respect to time t, while holding ξ constant, we have

$$\frac{d\hat{\boldsymbol{\vartheta}}_i}{dt} = \frac{\partial \mathbf{v}}{\partial \xi^i} = \nabla_i v^\omega \hat{\boldsymbol{\vartheta}}_\omega$$

and (10.4)

$$\frac{d\hat{\boldsymbol{\vartheta}}_i}{dt} = \frac{d\boldsymbol{\vartheta}_\alpha}{dt}\frac{\partial x^\alpha}{\partial \xi^i} + \boldsymbol{\vartheta}_\alpha \frac{\partial^2 x^\alpha}{\partial \xi^i \partial t}.$$

Moreover, since at the instant in question $\partial x^\alpha / \partial \xi^i = \delta_i^\alpha$ and $\partial x^\alpha / \partial t = v^\alpha$, we have

$$\frac{d\boldsymbol{\vartheta}_\alpha}{dt} = v^\lambda \Gamma_{\lambda\alpha}^\omega \boldsymbol{\vartheta}_\omega \qquad (\xi^1, \xi^2, \xi^3 = \text{const}). \tag{10.5}$$

The derivatives of the contravariant basis vectors are easily found after differentiating the scalar products

$$(\hat{\mathbf{Э}}^i, \hat{\mathbf{Э}}_j) = \delta^i_j \qquad \text{and} \qquad (\mathbf{Э}^i, \mathbf{Э}_j) = \delta^i_j .$$

On the basis of (10.4), we obtain

$$\left(\frac{d\hat{\mathbf{Э}}^i}{dt}, \hat{\mathbf{Э}}_j\right) = -\left(\hat{\mathbf{Э}}^i, \frac{d\hat{\mathbf{Э}}_j}{dt}\right) = -\nabla_j v^i ,$$

and therefore,

$$\frac{d\hat{\mathbf{Э}}^i}{dt} = -\nabla_\omega v^i \hat{\mathbf{Э}}^\omega . \tag{10.6}$$

In an analogous manner, we find

$$\frac{d\mathbf{Э}^i}{dt} = -v^\lambda \Gamma^i_{\lambda\omega} \mathbf{Э}^\omega . \tag{10.7}$$

The above formulas, established for the differentiation of the basis vectors, make it easy to derive formulas for the differentiation of a tensor of any value with respect to the parameter t.

Let us take a tensor $\boldsymbol{T}$ which may be referred to either in terms of the moving basis of a Lagrangian coordinate system or in terms of the stationary basis of an Eulerian coordinate system. We have

$$\boldsymbol{T} = \hat{T}^{\alpha\beta\cdot}_{\cdot\cdot\gamma} \hat{\mathbf{Э}}_\alpha \hat{\mathbf{Э}}_\beta \hat{\mathbf{Э}}^\gamma = T^{\alpha\beta\cdot}_{\cdot\cdot\gamma} \mathbf{Э}_\alpha \mathbf{Э}_\beta \mathbf{Э}^\gamma . \tag{10.8}$$

The components $\hat{T}^{\alpha\beta\cdot}_{\cdot\cdot\gamma}$ and $T^{\alpha\beta\cdot}_{\cdot\cdot\gamma}$ coincide at the instant t, and for instants $t' > t$, these components and the corresponding bases become different. However, by definition, $\hat{T}^{\alpha\beta\cdot}_{\cdot\cdot\gamma}$ and $T^{\alpha\beta\cdot}_{\cdot\cdot\gamma}$ are the components of a single tensor $\boldsymbol{T}$.

Together with the tensor $\boldsymbol{T}$, we consider a tensor $\mathring{\boldsymbol{T}}$, defined by

$$\mathring{\boldsymbol{T}} = \mathring{T}^{\alpha\beta\cdot}_{\cdot\cdot\gamma} \mathring{\mathbf{Э}}_\alpha \mathring{\mathbf{Э}}_\beta \mathring{\mathbf{Э}}^\gamma . \tag{10.9}$$

At the instant t in question, $\boldsymbol{T}$ and $\mathring{\boldsymbol{T}}$ coincide and, by definition, at subsequent instants of time, the components or these tensors are identical, but $\boldsymbol{T}$ and $\mathring{\boldsymbol{T}}$ themselves are different, because their respective reference bases are different. Consequently, for each instant of time $t' > t$, the components $\mathring{T}^{\alpha\beta\cdot}_{\cdot\cdot\gamma} = \hat{T}^{\alpha\beta\cdot}_{\cdot\cdot\gamma}$ can be regarded as the components of two different tensors $\boldsymbol{T}$ and $\mathring{\boldsymbol{T}}$.

For the tensors, $\boldsymbol{T}$ and $\mathring{\boldsymbol{T}}$, we can write

$$\boldsymbol{T} = \hat{T}^{\alpha\beta\cdot}_{\cdot\cdot\gamma} \hat{\mathbf{Э}}_\alpha \hat{\mathbf{Э}}_\beta \hat{\mathbf{Э}}^\gamma = \hat{T}^{\cdot\beta\cdot}_{\alpha\cdot\gamma} \hat{\mathbf{Э}}^\alpha \hat{\mathbf{Э}}_\beta \hat{\mathbf{Э}}^\gamma = \hat{T}_{\alpha\beta\gamma} \hat{\mathbf{Э}}^\alpha \hat{\mathbf{Э}}^\beta \hat{\mathbf{Э}}^\gamma = \cdots ,$$

$$\mathring{\boldsymbol{T}} = \hat{T}^{\alpha\beta\cdot}_{\cdot\cdot\gamma} \mathring{\mathbf{Э}}_\alpha \mathring{\mathbf{Э}}_\beta \mathring{\mathbf{Э}}^\gamma = \mathring{T}^{\cdot\beta\cdot}_{\alpha\cdot\gamma} \mathring{\mathbf{Э}}^\alpha \mathring{\mathbf{Э}}_\beta \mathring{\mathbf{Э}}^\gamma = \mathring{T}_{\alpha\beta\gamma} \mathring{\mathbf{Э}}^\alpha \mathring{\mathbf{Э}}^\beta \mathring{\mathbf{Э}}^\gamma = \cdots .$$

The coordinates ξ^i of the individual points in both systems, but in different spaces, are the same. The transformation of the coordinates ξ^i in both systems leads to identical transformations of the components with an arbitrary structure of indices.

Since at a given instant t, $\mathring{Э}_i = \hat{Э}_i$, it is obvious that

$$\hat{T}^{\cdot\beta\cdot}_{\alpha\cdot\gamma} = \mathring{T}^{\cdot\beta\cdot}_{\alpha\cdot\gamma}, \qquad \hat{T}_{\alpha\beta\gamma} = \mathring{T}_{\alpha\beta\gamma}, \ldots .$$

However, for $t' > t$, $\mathring{Э}_i \neq \hat{Э}_i$, and therefore these equalities will be violated because

$$\hat{T}^{\cdot\beta\cdot}_{\alpha\cdot\gamma} = \hat{g}_{\alpha\omega}\hat{T}^{\omega\beta\cdot}_{\cdot\cdot\gamma} \neq \mathring{T}^{\cdot\beta\cdot}_{\alpha\cdot\gamma} = \mathring{g}_{\alpha\omega}\hat{T}^{\omega\beta\cdot}_{\cdot\cdot\gamma},$$

where

$$g_{\alpha\omega} = (\hat{Э}_\alpha, \hat{Э}_\omega) \qquad \text{and} \qquad \mathring{g}_{\alpha\omega} = (\mathring{Э}_\alpha, \mathring{Э}_\omega).$$

For a given tensor $\boldsymbol{T}$, in addition to the tensor $\mathring{\boldsymbol{T}}$ contained in the basis $\mathring{Э}_i$, one can introduce other tensors, whose components with a different arrangement of indices will, by definition, coincide with the components of the tensor $\boldsymbol{T}$ for arbitrary $t' \geq t$.

In particular, for a second-order tensor, we have

$$\boldsymbol{H} = \hat{h}^{\alpha\beta}\hat{Э}_\alpha\hat{Э}_\beta = \hat{h}^{\alpha\cdot}_{\cdot\beta}\hat{Э}_\alpha\hat{Э}^\beta = \hat{h}^{\cdot\beta}_{\alpha\cdot}\hat{Э}^\alpha\hat{Э}_\beta = \hat{h}_{\alpha\beta}\hat{Э}^\alpha\hat{Э}^\beta. \tag{10.10a}$$

In the basis $\mathring{Э}_i$ there are four, generally different, tensors corresponding to this tensor:

$$\boldsymbol{H}_1 = \hat{h}^{\alpha\beta}\mathring{Э}_\alpha\mathring{Э}_\beta, \qquad \boldsymbol{H}_2 = \hat{h}^{\alpha\cdot}_{\cdot\beta}\mathring{Э}_\alpha\mathring{Э}^\beta, \qquad \boldsymbol{H}_3 = \hat{h}^{\cdot\beta}_{\alpha\cdot}\mathring{Э}^\alpha\mathring{Э}_\beta, \qquad \boldsymbol{H}_4 = \hat{h}_{\alpha\beta}\mathring{Э}^\alpha\mathring{Э}^\beta. \tag{10.10b}$$

It is obvious that to each of the tensors $\boldsymbol{H}_j$ in the basis $\hat{Э}_i$ there correspond four tensors of their own. The properties of the collection of tensors that is obtained in this way and of their invariants are discussed in the work of V. D. Bondar [1].

Differentiating (10.8) with respect to the parameter t, and using (10.5), (10.6), (10.7), and (10.4), we obtain

$$\begin{aligned}\frac{d\boldsymbol{T}}{dt} &= \left[\left(\frac{\partial \hat{T}^{\alpha\beta\cdot}_{\cdot\cdot\gamma}}{\partial t}\right)_{\xi^i=\text{const}} + \hat{T}^{\mu\beta\cdot}_{\cdot\cdot\gamma}\nabla_\mu v^\alpha + \hat{T}^{\alpha\mu\cdot}_{\cdot\cdot\gamma}\nabla_\mu v^\beta - \hat{T}^{\alpha\beta\cdot}_{\cdot\cdot\mu}\nabla_\gamma v^\mu\right]\hat{Э}_\alpha\hat{Э}_\beta\hat{Э}^\gamma \\ &= \left[\left(\frac{\partial T^{\alpha\beta\cdot}_{\cdot\cdot\gamma}}{\partial t}\right)_{\xi^i=\text{const}} + T^{\mu\beta\cdot}_{\cdot\cdot\gamma}v^\lambda\Gamma^\alpha_{\lambda\mu} + T^{\alpha\mu\cdot}_{\cdot\cdot\gamma}v^\lambda\Gamma^\beta_{\lambda\mu} - T^{\alpha\beta\cdot}_{\cdot\cdot\mu}v^\lambda\Gamma^\mu_{\lambda\gamma}\right]Э_\alpha Э_\beta Э^\gamma.\end{aligned} \tag{10.11}$$

For $\hat{T}^{\alpha\beta\cdot}_{\cdot\cdot\gamma} = \text{const}$, the differential dT/dt is generally nonzero.

Differentiating (10.9) and using (10.3), we have

$$\frac{d\mathring{\boldsymbol{T}}}{dt} = \left(\frac{\partial \mathring{T}^{\alpha\beta\cdot}_{\cdot\cdot\gamma}}{\partial t}\right)_{\xi^i=\text{const}} \mathring{Э}_\alpha\mathring{Э}_\beta\mathring{Э}^\gamma. \tag{10.12}$$

It follows from this and directly from (10.11) that the derivatives $(\partial \mathring{T}^{\alpha\beta\cdot}_{\cdot\cdot\gamma}/\partial t)_{\xi^i=\text{const}}$ can be regarded as the components of a tensor.

On the other hand, from (10.11) it follows that the inequality

$$\left(\frac{\partial T^{\alpha\beta\cdot}_{\cdot\cdot\gamma}}{\partial t}\right)_{\xi^i=\text{const}} \neq \left(\frac{\partial \hat{T}^{\alpha\beta\cdot}_{\cdot\cdot\gamma}}{\partial t}\right)_{\xi^i=\text{const}} \tag{10.13}$$

holds. The system of derivatives $(\partial T^{\alpha\beta\cdot}_{\cdot\cdot\gamma}/\partial t)_{\xi^i}$ does not form a tensor, because the additional parts in the parentheses, containing the Christoffel symbols, are not tensor components.

In this way, for a given tensor $\boldsymbol{T}$, we can examine the individual time derivatives (for constant ξ^i), $d\boldsymbol{T}/dt$ and $d\mathring{\boldsymbol{T}}/dt$. In formula (10.11), various expressions are given for the derivative, $d\boldsymbol{T}/dt$, depending on the use of Lagrangian or Eulerian coordinate systems. To the tensor $d\mathring{\boldsymbol{T}}/dt$ in the basis $\mathring{\boldsymbol{\partial}}_i$ there corresponds a tensor $d\boldsymbol{T}_1/dt$ in the basis $\hat{\boldsymbol{\partial}}_i$ having identical components for a given index structure. Also, at the instant t, when $\mathring{\boldsymbol{\partial}}_i = \hat{\boldsymbol{\partial}}_i$, we have

$$\frac{d\mathring{\boldsymbol{T}}}{dt} = \frac{d\boldsymbol{T}_1}{dt}$$

and

$$\frac{d\boldsymbol{T}}{dt} = \frac{d\boldsymbol{T}_1}{dt} + [\hat{T}^{\mu\beta\cdot}_{\cdot\cdot\gamma}\nabla_\mu v^\alpha + \hat{T}^{\alpha\mu\cdot}_{\cdot\cdot\gamma}\nabla_\mu v^\beta - \hat{T}^{\alpha\beta\cdot}_{\cdot\cdot\mu}\nabla_\gamma v^\mu]\,\hat{\boldsymbol{\partial}}_\alpha\hat{\boldsymbol{\partial}}_\beta\hat{\boldsymbol{\partial}}^\gamma. \tag{10.14}$$

For $t' > t$, the tensors $d\mathring{\boldsymbol{T}}/dt$ and $d\boldsymbol{T}_1/dt$ are unequal and are defined in different bases.

Formula (10.14), equivalent to the first of the formulas (10.11), can be viewed as a generalization of the well-known rule for differentiation of vectors in moving coordinate systems to the case of motion of a deformable continuum.

Indeed, for vector $\boldsymbol{A} = a^\alpha\hat{\boldsymbol{\partial}}_\alpha$, formula (10.14) can be written in the form

$$\frac{d\boldsymbol{A}}{dt} = \frac{da^\alpha}{dt}\hat{\boldsymbol{\partial}}_\alpha + a^\alpha\frac{\partial\hat{\boldsymbol{\partial}}_\alpha}{dt} = \frac{d\boldsymbol{A}_1}{dt} + a^\alpha\nabla_\mu v^\alpha\hat{\boldsymbol{\partial}}_\alpha. \tag{10.15}$$

If the medium moves as a rigid body, then

$$\mathbf{v} = [\boldsymbol{\Omega}, \boldsymbol{r}] \quad\text{and}\quad \frac{d\boldsymbol{A}}{dt} = \frac{\widetilde{d\boldsymbol{A}}}{dt} + [\boldsymbol{\Omega}, \boldsymbol{A}], \tag{10.16}$$

where $\boldsymbol{\Omega}$ is the instantaneous angular velocity, and $\widetilde{d\boldsymbol{A}}/dt$ is the derivative of the vector with respect to the moving but otherwise constant system.

Furthermore, because

$$\frac{\partial\mathbf{v}}{\partial\xi^\mu} = [\boldsymbol{\Omega}, \hat{\boldsymbol{\partial}}_\mu],$$

one can write

$$[\boldsymbol{\Omega}, A] = a^{\mu}[\boldsymbol{\Omega}, \hat{\mathbf{э}}_{\mu}] = a^{\mu}\frac{\partial \mathbf{v}}{\partial \xi^{\mu}} = a^{\mu}\nabla_{\mu}v^{\alpha}\hat{\mathbf{э}}_{\alpha} \qquad \text{and} \qquad \frac{\tilde{d}A}{dt} = \frac{dA_1}{dt}.$$

Thus, it is clear that equation (10.15), which becomes identical with equation (10.16) in the case of a rigid body, furnishes a relationship between the total derivative dA/dt, and the derivative of the vector dA_1/dt which characterizes the variation of the vector A relative to the moving basis $\hat{\mathbf{э}}_i$ in the case of a deformable medium.

In addition to formula (10.15), we may also write

$$\frac{dA}{dt} = \frac{da_{\alpha}}{dt}\hat{\mathbf{э}}^{\alpha} + a_{\alpha}\frac{\partial \mathbf{э}^{\alpha}}{dt} = \frac{dA_2}{dt} - a_{\mu}\nabla_{\alpha}v^{\mu}\hat{\mathbf{э}}^{\alpha}. \tag{10.17}$$

It is easy to see that the relativistic derivatives $dA_1/dt = (da^{\alpha}/dt)\,\hat{\mathbf{э}}_{\alpha}$ and $dA_2/dt = (da_{\alpha}/dt)\,\hat{\mathbf{э}}^{\alpha}$ are generally not equal to one another, because

$$a^{\alpha}\frac{\partial \hat{\mathbf{э}}_{\alpha}}{dt} = a^{\alpha}\hat{g}_{\alpha\omega}\hat{g}^{\omega s}\frac{dg_{s\beta}\hat{\mathbf{э}}^{\beta}}{dt} = a_{\alpha}\frac{d\hat{\mathbf{э}}^{\alpha}}{dt} + a^{\alpha}\hat{\mathbf{э}}^{\beta}\frac{d\hat{g}_{\alpha\beta}}{dt}.$$

In general, $\hat{g}_{\alpha\beta}(\xi^i, t)$ is a time-dependent quantity; consequently, $d\hat{g}_{\alpha\beta}/dt \neq 0$ and, therefore, $dA_1/dt \neq dA_2/dt$.

If the medium moves as a rigid body, we have $g_{\alpha\beta} = (\hat{\mathbf{э}}_{\alpha}, \hat{\mathbf{э}}_{\beta}) = \text{const.}$ Consequently, we have the following equation for the relativistic derivatives dA_1/dt and dA_2/dt in the case of rigid-body motion:

$$\frac{dA_1}{dt} = \frac{dA_2}{dt}.$$

In examining the derivatives dA_1/dt, and dA_2/dt, it is necessary to consider the coordinate lines ξ^i and the basis vectors $\hat{\mathbf{э}}_i$ as being frozen into the deformable medium, since the quantities $d\xi_i = \hat{g}_{i\alpha}(\xi^i, t)\,d\xi^{\alpha}$ and the basis vectors $\hat{\mathbf{э}}^i$ are moving with respect to the medium. Therefore, the derivative dA_2/dt characterizes the variation of the vector with respect to the basis $\hat{\mathbf{э}}^i$ which moves relative to the deformable medium whose points, in turn, are defined by the Lagrangian coordinates ξ^i.

On the other hand, when we consider the time variation of a scalar having the form

$$dW = a^{\alpha}d\xi_{\alpha} = a_{\alpha}d\xi^{\alpha} = (A, d\mathbf{r})$$

it is clear that the individual time derivative of dW is given by

$$\frac{d\,dW}{dt} = \frac{da^{\alpha}}{dt}d\xi_{\alpha} + a^{\alpha}\frac{d\,d\xi_{\alpha}}{dt} = \frac{da_{\alpha}}{dt}d\xi^{\alpha} = \left(\frac{dA_2}{dt}, d\mathbf{r}\right).$$

Consequently, it follows that it is convenient and natural to use the relativistic derivative dA_2/dt for the definition of the derivative $d\,dW/dt$.

The second of equations (10.11) can be rewritten in the form

$$\frac{dT}{dt} = \left\{\left(\frac{\partial T^{\alpha\beta\cdot}_{\cdot\cdot\gamma}}{\partial t}\right)_{x^i=\text{const}} + v^\lambda\left[\frac{\partial T^{\alpha\beta\cdot}_{\cdot\cdot\gamma}}{\partial x^\lambda} + T^{\mu\beta\cdot}_{\cdot\cdot\gamma}\Gamma^\alpha_{\lambda\mu} + T^{\alpha\mu\cdot}_{\cdot\cdot\gamma}\Gamma^\beta_{\lambda\mu} - T^{\alpha\beta\cdot}_{\cdot\cdot\mu}\Gamma^\mu_{\lambda\gamma}\right]\right\}\mathfrak{Э}_\alpha\mathfrak{Э}_\beta\mathfrak{Э}^\gamma$$

$$= \left[\left(\frac{\partial T^{\alpha\beta\cdot}_{\cdot\cdot\gamma}}{\partial t}\right)_{x^i=\text{const}} + v^\lambda\nabla_\lambda T^{\alpha\beta\cdot}_{\cdot\cdot\gamma}\right]\mathfrak{Э}_\alpha\mathfrak{Э}_\beta\mathfrak{Э}^\gamma = \left(\frac{dT^{\alpha\beta\cdot}_{\cdot\cdot\gamma}}{dt}\right)_{\text{total}}\mathfrak{Э}_\alpha\mathfrak{Э}_\beta\mathfrak{Э}^\gamma, \qquad (10.18)$$

where $(dT^{\alpha\beta\cdot}_{\cdot\cdot\gamma}/dt)_{\text{total}}$ denotes the total time derivative with respect to a stationary Eulerian coordinate system.

Obviously, this formula is a generalization of the familiar rules for obtaining the total time derivatives of vectors by means of Eulerian variables x^i for tensors and arbitrary curvilinear coordinate systems.

Clearly, the quantities $(\partial T^{\alpha\beta\cdot}_{\cdot\cdot\gamma}/\partial t)_{x^i=\text{const}}$ form a tensor which characterizes the local variation of the tensor $\boldsymbol{T}$ at stationary points of the space. The components of the tensor $v^\lambda\nabla_\lambda T^{\alpha\beta\cdot}_{\cdot\cdot\gamma}$ characterize the convective effects of the variation of $\boldsymbol{T}$.

From (10.11) we have the following equations:

$$\left(\frac{\partial \hat{T}^{\alpha\beta\cdot}_{\cdot\cdot\gamma}}{\partial t}\right)_{\xi^i=\text{const}} = \left(\frac{\partial T^{\alpha\beta\cdot}_{\cdot\cdot\gamma}}{\partial t}\right)_{\xi^i=\text{const}} - T^{\mu\beta\cdot}_{\cdot\cdot\gamma}\frac{\partial v^\alpha}{\partial \xi^\mu} - T^{\alpha\mu\cdot}_{\cdot\cdot\gamma}\frac{\partial v^\beta}{\partial \xi^\mu} + T^{\alpha\beta\cdot}_{\cdot\cdot\mu}\frac{\partial v^\mu}{\partial \xi^\gamma}, \qquad (10.19)$$

$$\left(\frac{\partial \hat{T}^{\alpha\beta\cdot}_{\cdot\cdot\gamma}}{\partial t}\right)_{\xi^i=\text{const}} = \left(\frac{\partial T^{\alpha\beta\cdot}_{\cdot\cdot\gamma}}{\partial t}\right)_{x^i=\text{const}} + v^\lambda\nabla_\lambda T^{\alpha\beta\cdot}_{\cdot\cdot\gamma} - T^{\lambda\beta\cdot}_{\cdot\cdot\gamma}\nabla_\lambda v^\alpha - T^{\alpha\lambda\cdot}_{\cdot\cdot\gamma}\nabla_\lambda v^\beta \qquad (10.20)$$
$$+ T^{\alpha\beta\cdot}_{\cdot\cdot\lambda}\nabla_\gamma v^\lambda.$$

Formula (10.19) was derived by Oldroyd in 1950 [75].

In linear theories, when the components of the tensor $\boldsymbol{T}$ and the velocity $\mathbf{v}$ are small quantities, all the terms containing derivatives of the components of $\boldsymbol{T}$ and $\mathbf{v}$ drop out. Therefore, all the foregoing effects associated with distinction of the coordinate systems are not reflected in the values of the derivatives.

The above formulas were established for first-order derivatives with respect to the parameter t. By applying analogous operations to the first derivatives, we can find derivatives of second-order, etc.

If equations (10.11) and (10.12) are multiplied by dt, we obtain formulas for small variations, i.e., the differentials $d\boldsymbol{T}$, $d\boldsymbol{T}_1$, and $d\hat{\boldsymbol{T}}$, which can be introduced in examining the tensor $\boldsymbol{T}$.

Let us consider other relative derivatives, *viz.*, the velocities of variation for second-rank tensors [25;30].

The components of the tensor $\boldsymbol{H}$ in a moving system in accordance with formula (10.10) are denoted by italic letters with the circumflex above them. The analogous components in the reference system are designated by the same letters, but without the circumflex. All the components will be considered as functions of the Lagrangian coordinates ξ^i and the time t.

We shall differentiate with respect to time the various tensors $\boldsymbol{H}_i$ defined by formulas (10.10b). After this, we shall perform a transition to the corresponding tensors in the moving basis. As a result, we shall obtain four different relative derivatives of the tensor

$$V_1 = \frac{d\hat{h}^{\alpha\beta}}{dt}\hat{\mathfrak{Z}}_\alpha\hat{\mathfrak{Z}}_\beta, \qquad V_2 = \frac{d\hat{h}^{\alpha\cdot}_{\cdot\beta}}{dt}\hat{\mathfrak{Z}}_\alpha\hat{\mathfrak{Z}}^\beta,$$
$$V_3 = \frac{d\hat{h}^{\cdot\beta}_{\alpha\cdot}}{dt}\hat{\mathfrak{Z}}^\alpha\hat{\mathfrak{Z}}_\beta, \qquad V_4 = \frac{d\hat{h}_{\alpha\beta}}{dt}\hat{\mathfrak{Z}}^\alpha\hat{\mathfrak{Z}}^\beta, \tag{10.21}$$

which are defined in the deformable space coinciding with the space of the reference system.

The components of the tensors for the relative velocities of the tensors $\boldsymbol{V}_i$, having the index structure in formulas (10.21) in terms of the components of $\boldsymbol{H}$, and connected with the reference system by formula (10.19), are given by the following:

$$\frac{d\hat{h}^{\alpha\beta}}{dt} = \left.\frac{dh^{\alpha\beta}}{dt}\right|_{\xi^i=\text{const}} - h^{\omega\beta}\frac{\partial v^\alpha}{\partial x^\omega} - h^{\alpha\omega}\frac{\partial v^\beta}{\partial x^\omega}, \tag{10.22}$$

$$\frac{d\hat{h}^{\alpha\cdot}_{\cdot\beta}}{dt} = \left.\frac{dh^{\alpha\cdot}_{\cdot\beta}}{dt}\right|_{\xi^i=\text{const}} - h^{\omega\cdot}_{\cdot\beta}\frac{\partial v^\alpha}{\partial x^\omega} + h^{\alpha\cdot}_{\cdot\omega}\frac{\partial v^\omega}{\partial x^\beta}, \tag{10.23}$$

$$\frac{d\hat{h}^{\cdot\beta}_{\alpha\cdot}}{dt} = \left.\frac{dh^{\cdot\beta}_{\alpha\cdot}}{dt}\right|_{\xi^i=\text{const}} + h^{\cdot\beta}_{\omega\cdot}\frac{\partial v^\omega}{\partial x^\alpha} - h^{\cdot\omega}_{\alpha\cdot}\frac{\partial v^\beta}{\partial x^\omega}, \tag{10.24}$$

$$\frac{d\hat{h}_{\alpha\beta}}{dt} = \left.\frac{dh_{\alpha\beta}}{dt}\right|_{\xi^i=\text{const}} + h_{\omega\beta}\frac{\partial v^\omega}{\partial x^\alpha} + h_{\alpha\omega}\frac{\partial v^\omega}{\partial x^\beta}. \tag{10.25}$$

Using equation (10.20), we obtain formulas for these components that are convenient for applying Euler's approach:

$$\frac{d\hat{h}^{\alpha\beta}}{dt} = \left(\frac{dh^{\alpha\beta}}{dt}\right)_{\text{total}} - h^{\omega\beta}\nabla_\omega v^\alpha - h^{\alpha\omega}\nabla_\omega v^\beta, \tag{10.26}$$

$$\frac{d\hat{h}^{\alpha\cdot}_{\cdot\beta}}{dt} = \left(\frac{dh^{\alpha\cdot}_{\cdot\beta}}{dt}\right)_{\text{total}} - h^{\omega\cdot}_{\cdot\beta}\nabla_\omega v^\alpha + h^{\alpha\cdot}_{\cdot\omega}\nabla_\beta v^\omega, \tag{10.27}$$

$$\frac{d\hat{h}^{\cdot\beta}_{\alpha\cdot}}{dt} = \left(\frac{dh^{\cdot\beta}_{\alpha\cdot}}{dt}\right)_{\text{total}} + h^{\cdot\beta}_{\omega\cdot}\nabla_\alpha v^\omega - h^{\cdot\omega}_{\alpha\cdot}\nabla_\omega v^\beta, \tag{10.28}$$

$$\frac{d\hat{h}_{\alpha\beta}}{dt} = \left(\frac{dh_{\alpha\beta}}{dt}\right)_{\text{total}} + h_{\omega\beta}\nabla_\alpha v^\omega + h_{\alpha\omega}\nabla_\beta v^\omega, \tag{10.29}$$

where

$$\left(\frac{dh^{\alpha\beta}}{dt}\right)_{\text{total}} = \left(\frac{\partial h^{\alpha\beta}}{\partial t}\right)_{x^i=\text{const}} + v^\lambda \nabla_\lambda h^{\alpha\beta}, \text{etc.}$$

It is obvious that quantities of the type $(dh^{\alpha\beta}/dt)_{\xi^i=\text{const}}$ are not tensor components in curvilinear systems; however, they can be considered as tensors in cartesian systems. On the other hand, quantities of the type $(\partial h^{\alpha\beta}/\partial t)_{x^i=\text{const}}$ and $(dh^{\alpha\beta}/dt)_{\text{total}}$ are tensor components in any coordinate system.

Formulas (10.22) to (10.29) yield tensor components for the corresponding tensor velocities V_i, characterizing the variation of the tensor $\boldsymbol{H}$. These formulas will be true in any curvilinear coordinate system.

We considered above various concepts having to do with the individual derivatives of tensors with respect to the parameter t. All the above formulas were derived on the assumption that the Lagrangian basis $\hat{Э}_i$ is connected with an associated coordinate system ξ^1, ξ^2, ξ^3, frozen into the medium and that the basis $Э_i$ and the coordinates x^1, x^2, x^3 correspond to a reference system, relative to which the moving medium is examined.

The laws of motion and the velocities of points in a medium are given by the formulas

$$x^i = x^i(\xi^1, \xi^2, \xi^3, t) \qquad \text{and} \qquad \mathbf{v} = \left(\frac{\partial x^i}{\partial t}\right)_{\xi^i=\text{const}} Э_i = v^i Э_i.$$

Any desired coordinate system may be taken as the reference system. Let us consider together with the system x^1, x^2, x^3 with basis $Э_i$, another generally deformable moving system y^1, y^2, y^3 with basis $\mathring{Э}_i$. We note that the essential difference between the bases $\mathring{Э}_i$ and $Э_i$ consists in the fact that $(Э_i, Э_k) = g_{ik}(x^i)$ and $(\mathring{Э}_i, \mathring{Э}_k) = \mathring{g}_{ik}(y^i, t)$; i.e., in the first case the components of the fundamental tensor depend only on the coordinates, but in the second case they depend, generally speaking, both on the coordinates and on time.

For the study and definition of tensor derivatives, it can be assumed, without any loss in generality, that at a given instant of time all three bases $\hat{Э}_i$, $Э_i$, $\mathring{Э}_i$ coincide, and at successive instants they all become distinct.

The law of the translation motion of a moving basis $\mathring{Э}_i$ for constant y^i and the velocity of the translational motion are defined by the formulas

$$x^i = x^i(y^1, y^2, y^3, t), \qquad \mathbf{v}_{\text{trans}} = \left(\frac{\partial x^i}{\partial t}\right)_{y^j} Э_i = -\left(\frac{\partial y^i}{\partial t}\right)_{x^j} \mathring{Э}_i = v^i_{\text{trans}} \mathring{Э}_i,$$

since

$$\left(\frac{\partial x^i}{\partial t}\right)_{x^j=\text{const}} = \left(\frac{\partial x^i}{\partial t}\right)_{y^j} + \frac{\partial x^i}{\partial y^\omega}\left(\frac{\partial y^\omega}{\partial t}\right)_{x^j} = 0,$$

whence

$$\left(\frac{\partial x^i}{\partial t}\right)_{y^j} = -\left(\frac{\partial y^i}{\partial t}\right)_{x^j},$$

because at a given instant $\mathbf{Э}_i = \hat{\mathbf{Э}}_i$ and $(\partial x^i/\partial y^\omega) = \delta^{i\cdot}_{\cdot\omega}$. It thus follows that the velocities of points of the continuum connected with the coordinates ξ^1, ξ^2, ξ^3, with respect to the system $\mathbf{Э}_i$ are defined by the formulas

$$\mathring{\mathbf{v}} = \mathring{v}^i\hat{\mathbf{Э}}_i = \left(\frac{\partial y^i}{\partial t}\right)_{\xi^i}\hat{\mathbf{Э}}_i = \frac{\partial y^i}{\partial x^\omega}\left(\frac{\partial x^\omega}{\partial t}\right)_{\xi^j}\hat{\mathbf{Э}}_i + \left(\frac{\partial y^i}{\partial t}\right)_{x^j}\hat{\mathbf{Э}}_i = \mathbf{v} - \mathbf{v}_{\text{trans}}. \tag{10.30}$$

This equation is simply the well-known law of addition of velocities (applicable, obviously, to any deformable reference system), in which $\mathring{\mathbf{v}}$ is to be thought of as the relative velocity and $\mathbf{v}$ as the absolute velocity.

Clearly, the components of the different velocities are related by the equation

$$\mathring{v}^i = v^i - v^i_{\text{trans}}.$$

All the above formulas may be considered as applicable for the motion of fixed points of the medium having coordinates ξ^i relative to the reference system $\mathbf{Э}_i$ (with coordinates x^i), or relative to the reference system $\hat{\mathbf{Э}}_i$ with coordinates y^i. In the first case, the velocity $\mathbf{v}$ with components v^i should be used in all equations, and in the second case, $\mathring{\mathbf{v}}$ with components $\mathring{v}^i$.

If, in a given reference system, the continuous medium is stationary, that is, if $\hat{\mathbf{Э}}_i = \mathbf{Э}_i$ at every instant of time $\mathbf{v} = 0$, $\hat{g}_{ik} = (\hat{\mathbf{Э}}_i\hat{\mathbf{Э}}_k) = \text{const}$ in a particle, then

$$\left(\frac{\partial \hat{T}^{\alpha\beta\cdot}_{\cdot\cdot\gamma}}{\partial t}\right)_{\xi^i=\text{const}} = \left(\frac{\partial T^{\alpha\beta\cdot}_{\cdot\cdot\gamma}}{\partial t}\right)_{\xi^i=\text{const}} = \left(\frac{\partial T^{\alpha\beta\cdot}_{\cdot\cdot\gamma}}{\partial t}\right)_{x^i=\text{const}};$$

also the derivatives of the components with a different arrangement of indices correspond respectively to one and the same differentiated tensor with unequal indices. This differentiated tensor is nonzero if the components of the tensor are time-dependent.

It is obvious that the above-defined derivative of the type

$$\left(\frac{\partial \hat{T}^{\alpha\beta\cdot}_{\cdot\cdot\gamma}}{\partial t}\right)_{\xi^i}\hat{\mathbf{Э}}_\alpha\hat{\mathbf{Э}}_\beta\hat{\mathbf{Э}}^\gamma$$

and, in particular, the tensors V_1, V_2, V_3, V_4, obtained from the differentiation of the components of the initial tensor with a different arrangement of the indices, define, generally speaking, different tensors, which depend also on the choice of the reference system, $\mathfrak{Э}_i$ or $\mathring{\mathfrak{Э}}_i$, if one of the systems is moving with respect to the other.

Some of these tensors can be presented in a simple form by using at the instant of time in question a rectangular cartesian system for the coincident bases $\hat{\mathfrak{Э}}_i$, $\mathfrak{Э}_i$, $\mathring{\mathfrak{Э}}_i$.

The derivatives, defined by equations (10.26) to (10.29) for a basis regarded as frozen into the medium, $\hat{\mathfrak{Э}}_i$, characterize the variation of the components of the tensor with respect to the particles of the medium; a variation in which the effects of rotation and the effects of deformation of the movable coordinate system connected with the particles is excluded.

The individual total derivatives of the type $(dh^{\alpha\beta}/dt)_{\text{total}}$ taken in the stationary basis $\mathfrak{Э}_i$ are nonzero also in those cases in which the tensor components $h^{\alpha\beta}$ in the coordinate system accompanying the particle are constant. These derivations also characterize the variation of the components considered for a given particle, relative to the stationary basis $\mathfrak{Э}_i$, and resulting from the rotation and deformation of the particle.

G. Jaumann [61] and W. Prager [25] have examined the relative derivatives of second-rank tensors in cases when, instead of the basis $\hat{\mathfrak{Э}}_i$, frozen in the medium, there exists at every point of the medium a constant (rigid) basis $\mathfrak{Э}'_i$, which moves with an instantaneous angular velocity $\mathbf{\Omega}$ equal to the curl of the velocity field of a moving continuum.

For the derivatives defined in the context of G. Jaumann's work, all the relationships established in this paragraph remain true when the basis $\hat{\mathfrak{Э}}_i$ is replaced by $\mathfrak{Э}'_i$ and the velocity vector has the special form

$$\mathbf{v} = [\mathbf{\Omega}, \boldsymbol{r}].$$

Moreover, since $(\mathfrak{Э}'_i \mathfrak{Э}'_k) = g'_{ik} = \text{const}$ and $(\mathfrak{Э}_i \mathfrak{Э}_k) = g_{ik} = \text{const}$, it is obvious that all the derivatives of the components of a tensor with different arrangements of the indices define one and the same tensor.

In individual derivatives defined in the sense of Jaumann, the variation of the components of the tensor resulting only from the rotation of the particle is excluded.

It is obvious that in the case of a potential motion of a deformable medium, the relative Jaumann derivative and the total individual derivative of a tensor with respect to a stationary reference system are identical.

If, together with the accompanying basis $\hat{\mathfrak{Э}}_i$, instead of a stationary basis $\mathfrak{Э}_i$, we take, at every point of the medium, a moving basis $\mathring{\mathfrak{Э}}_i$ which corresponds to the velocity field that is determined by a pure deformation of the particles, it is obvious that also in this case the velocity $\mathring{\mathbf{v}}$ is defined by

$$\mathring{\mathbf{v}} = [\boldsymbol{\Omega}, \boldsymbol{r}],$$

where $\boldsymbol{\Omega}$ is the rotation vector.

Thus, a system of formulas similar in form to the formulas defining derivatives in the sense of G. Jaumann in the bases $\text{Э}'_i$ and Э_i is obtained.

However, the meaning of the derivatives so defined is different; also, in this case, the derivatives of the components of tensors with a different arrangement of indices generally define different tensors both in the basis $\hat{\text{Э}}_i$, where the components of the fundamental tensor $\hat{g}_{ik} \neq \text{const}$, and also in $\mathring{\text{Э}}_i$, where $\mathring{g}_{ik} \neq \text{const}$.

In cartesian coordinates, the tensor of the relative variation, defined by equations (10.22) and (10.26), was examined by Oldroyd [75], and the tensors of the velocities, defined by (10.25) and (10.29), were treated by Cotter and Rivlin [47].

The systems of invariants defined by formulas (3.9) for the tensors $\boldsymbol{H}$, $\boldsymbol{H}_2$, and $\boldsymbol{H}_3$ are identical, but they generally differ from the invariants of $\boldsymbol{H}_1$ and $\boldsymbol{H}_4$. For example, for the second invariants of the tensors $\boldsymbol{H}_1$ and $\boldsymbol{H}$, we can write

$$\mathring{\mathscr{I}}_2 = \mathring{h}^{\alpha\cdot}_{\cdot\beta}\mathring{h}^{\beta\cdot}_{\cdot\alpha} = \mathring{g}_{\alpha\lambda}\mathring{g}_{\beta\mu}\hat{h}^{\lambda\beta}\hat{h}^{\mu\alpha},$$

$$\hat{\mathscr{I}}_2 = \hat{h}^{\alpha\cdot}_{\cdot\beta}\hat{h}^{\beta\cdot}_{\cdot\alpha} = \hat{g}_{\alpha\lambda}\hat{g}_{\beta\mu}\hat{h}^{\lambda\beta}\hat{h}^{\mu\alpha}.$$

If the derivatives $d\hat{h}^{\alpha\beta}/dt$ defined by equations (10.22) are zero, then $d\mathring{\mathscr{I}}_2/dt = 0$, and $d\hat{\mathscr{I}}_2/dt$ is generally nonzero.

It is obvious that the derivatives of $\mathring{\mathscr{I}}_1$ and $\mathring{\mathscr{I}}_3$ of the tensor $\boldsymbol{H}_1$ are zero if $d\hat{h}^{\alpha\beta}/dt = 0$ and that the derivatives of $\mathring{\mathscr{I}}_1$, $\mathring{\mathscr{I}}_2$, $\mathring{\mathscr{I}}_3$ of the tensor $\boldsymbol{H}_4$ are zero if $d\hat{h}_{\alpha\beta}/dt = 0$.

The derivatives of the corresponding invariants of $\boldsymbol{H}$ and $\boldsymbol{H}_2$ become zero if $d\hat{h}^{\alpha\cdot}_{\cdot\beta}/dt = 0$.

CHAPTER II

THE KINEMATICS OF A DEFORMED MEDIUM

1. General properties of continuous deformations

We consider a displacement and motion of a continuum as a set of points filling some three-dimensional volume of space continuously. In kinematics, various types of geometric figures, phase spaces, material bodies, and other objects can be regarded as a movable continuum.

The position, motion, and deformation of a continuum can be studied as the motion of the whole object, but it is most important to consider the motion of a continuum as the aggregate of the motions of all its individual points.

By way of definition, we assume that if the motion of the constituent points is known, the motion of the continuum as a whole can be found. In taking this approach, we suppose that rules exist for the individualization of the points in a moving medium; i.e., rules exist for the separation and identification of the points at any given instant of time.

In some cases such an individualization, is not always obvious beforehand, for example, if the moving continuum is a shadow of some moving object cast by a system of light sources.

For a material continuum, the individualization can be theoretically carried out using a closed system of physical equations of motion which define unambiguously the laws of motion of the fixed-point particles of the points in the medium.

Let $Ox^1\ x^2\ x^3$ be a coordinate system with respect to which the various points of the continuum move.

The assumption as to the possibility of individualizing the points of the medium is equivalent, from the mathematical point of view, to admitting the possibility of introducing Lagrangian coordinates ξ^1, ξ^2, ξ^3; the fixing of these coordinates determines the individual point for whose motion the corresponding coordinates x^1, x^2, x^3 are time-dependent.

The law of motion of the investigated object in a continuous medium is given by the following functions:

$$\begin{aligned} x\ &= f_1(\xi^1, \xi^2, \xi^3, t), \\ x^2 &= f_2(\xi^1, \xi^2, \xi^3, t), \\ x^3 &= f_3(\xi^1, \xi^2, \xi^3, t), \end{aligned} \tag{1.1}$$

where t is the time.

The systems of coordinate lines $O\xi^1$, $O\xi^2$, and $O\xi^3$ form moving sets of coordinates in which the coordinates of the individual points are constant. The points of the continuum are at rest with respect to the coordinate system $O\xi^1\ \xi^2\ \xi^3$, and therefore the motion of the continuum can be reduced to the motion of the coordinate system $O\xi^1\ \xi^2\ \xi^3$.

For Lagrangian coordinates ξ^i, we can take values of the coordinates x_0^i at some instant of time t_0 or certain arbitrary continuous fixed functions of these coordinates.

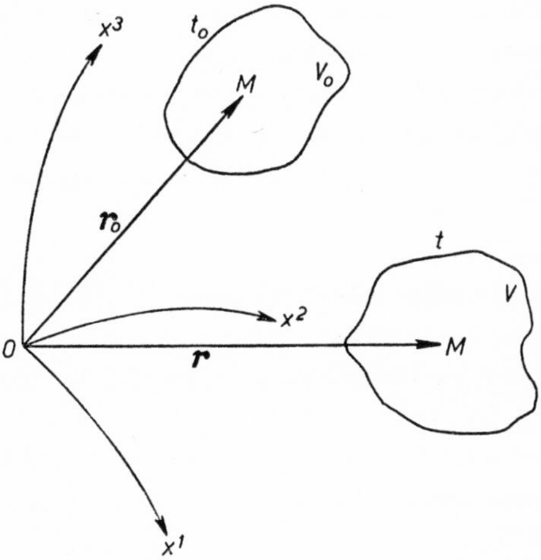

Figure 2

The functional relationships (1.1) indicate that it is possible to follow with the course of time the course of the different individual points which have various values of Lagrangian coordinates ξ^i.

The coordinates x_0^i and $x^i(x_0^i, t)$ can be thought of respectively as the components of the radius vectors $\boldsymbol{r}_0$ and $\boldsymbol{r}$ of a moving point M at times t_0 and t (Fig. 2).

For fixed t_0 and t, the functional relationships

$$x^i = x^i(x_0^1, x_0^2, x_0^3, t) \qquad \text{and} \qquad \boldsymbol{r} = G(\boldsymbol{r}_0, t) \tag{1.2}$$

will be considered, in accordance with the assumption, as a mutually univalued continuous representation of a certain volume V_0 with coordinates of points x_0^i, by a corresponding displaced and deformed volume V with coordinates of points x^i.

We shall further assume that the functions (1.2) are piecewise-smooth, i.e., differentiable with respect to all the arguments, though the derivatives can have discontinuities at certain points, or along certain generally isolated moving surfaces, which can be separated and considered individually. The determinant of the transformation is

$$\Delta = \left| \frac{\partial x^i}{\partial x_0^j} \right| \neq 0 . \qquad (1.3)$$

A continuous mutually univalued transformation of the type (1.2) corresponds to a displacement and a deformation in which points are mapped into points, lines into lines, volumes into volumes, while closed lines correspond to closed lines, and closed surfaces to closed surfaces.

If the x^i are the cartesian coordinates, then in the general case, the scalar equations for the functions $x^i(x_0^1, x_0^2, x_0^3)$ corresponding to the operator

$$\boldsymbol{r} = G(\boldsymbol{r}_0)$$

are nonlinear. When a continuum as a solid body is displaced, these are special linear operators which are the same as the operators used in the transformation of cartesian axes. Let us consider two displacements corresponding to operators G_1 and G_2. Let

$$\boldsymbol{r}_1 = G_1(\boldsymbol{r}_0) \qquad \text{and} \qquad \boldsymbol{r}_2 = G_2(\boldsymbol{r}_1) .$$

Then, the transformation from $\boldsymbol{r}_0$ to $\boldsymbol{r}_2$ can be performed using the operator $G_2 G_1$ in accordance with the equation

$$\boldsymbol{r}_2 = G_2(G_1(\boldsymbol{r}_0)) = G_2 G_1(\boldsymbol{r}_0) .$$

It is not difficult to show that in general

$$\boldsymbol{r}_2' = G_1 G_2(\boldsymbol{r}_0) \neq \boldsymbol{r}_2 ,$$

i.e., that the result of successive displacements corresponding to operators G_1 and G_2 will depend on the order; continuum displacements in general are not commutative.

The noncommutative effect is easy to show, as a simple example, for the case of a finite rotation of a solid.

In fact we shall consider the displacements of a flat plate initially placed in the x^1Ox^2 plane as shown in Fig. 3(a). Let a displacement G_1 correspond to a

90° rotation about the Ox^1-axis and G_2 to a 90° rotation about the Ox^3-axis, the directions of rotation being indicated by the arrows.

Figure 3(b) shows the result of the rotation G_1 followed by the rotation G_2; the result of the rotation G_2 followed by the rotation G_1 is shown in Fig. 3(c); the final position of the plate is different in these cases.

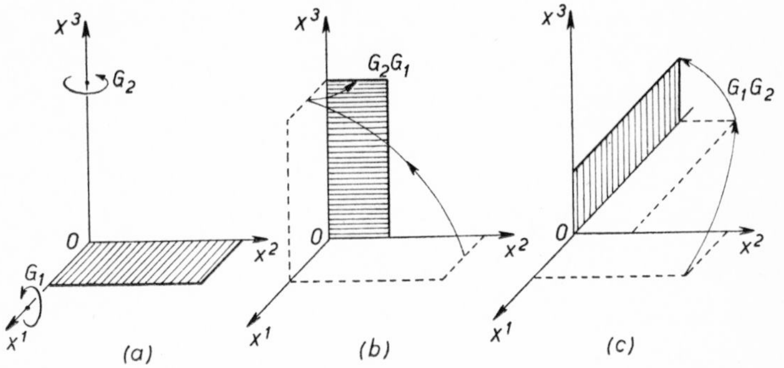

Figure 3

2. Affine deformations

Let x^1, x^2, x^3 be the coordinates of points in space in some rectilinear but generally oblique (nonorthogonal) coordinate system.

Let us examine displacements of a deformable continuum. Let the coordinates of a given point M in the initial position be x_0^i, and in the displaced position x^i (see Fig. 2). The coordinates x_0^i and x^i can be thought of as the components of the vectors $\boldsymbol{r}_0$ and $\boldsymbol{r}$, respectively:

$$\boldsymbol{r}_0 = x_0^\alpha \boldsymbol{\mathfrak{Э}}_\alpha, \qquad \boldsymbol{r} = x^\alpha \boldsymbol{\mathfrak{Э}}_\alpha, \tag{2.1}$$

where the $\boldsymbol{\mathfrak{Э}}_i$ are the basis vectors directed along the coordinate axes.

The deformation of a continuum in some moving volume V_0 is called homogeneous or affine if, for every point M within the volume V_0, linear equations of the following type hold:

$$x^i = C^{i\cdot}_{\cdot\alpha} x_0^\alpha \qquad (i, \alpha = 1, 2, 3), \tag{2.2}$$

where the coefficients $C^{i\cdot}_{\cdot\alpha}$ are constants forming a system of components of a second-rank tensor $\boldsymbol{C}$:

$$\boldsymbol{C} = C^{\beta\cdot}_{\cdot\alpha} \boldsymbol{\mathfrak{Э}}_\beta \boldsymbol{\mathfrak{Э}}^\alpha. \tag{2.3}$$

The tensor $\boldsymbol{C}$ can be an arbitrary second-rank tensor. From formulas (2.2), it follows that for the displacement in question, the origin of the coordinate system does not move. The general case in which the origin of the coordinates is displaced reduces to the case that we just examined if the vectors $\boldsymbol{r}_0$ and $\boldsymbol{r}$ and the corresponding coordinates x_0^i and x^i are considered in two different coordinate systems that are progressively displaced with respect to one another by an amount equal to the displacement of the origin of the coordinates OO' (Fig. 4).

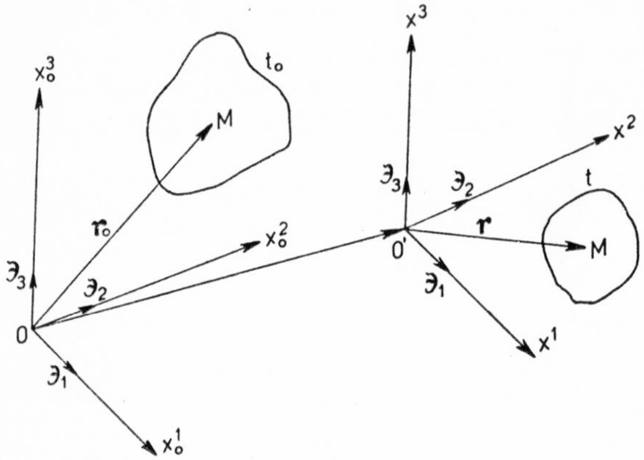

Figure 4

Thus, in the general case, formulas (2.2) define the displacements and, correspondingly, the deformations with respect to a moving point O, which is chosen as the origin of the coordinate system.

With an affine deformation, the relative displacements and deformations are identical for all points having the same relative coordinates with respect to any point B in the volume V.

Indeed, let x_{0B}^i and x_B^i be the coordinates of a point B in the original and displaced positions, respectively. From (2.2), we have

$$x_B^i = C_{\cdot\alpha}^{i\cdot} x_{0B}^\alpha .$$

Subtracting these equations from (2.2), we have

$$y^i = C_{\cdot\alpha}^{i\cdot} y_0^\alpha , \tag{2.4}$$

where $y^i = x^i - x_B^i$ and $y_0^i = x_0^i - x_{0B}^i$ are the coordinates of the progressively displaced systems in which the point B is taken as the origin. Formulas (2.2) and (2.4) differ only in the notations for the coordinates of the various points which are identically situated with respect to the coordinate system with origin O or origin B.

This feature manifests the property of homogeneity of an affine deformation, which consists in the fact that the relative displacements and deformations do not depend on the choice of the point in the volume V_0.

From the mutual single-valued nature and the continuity, it follows that the determinant $|C^{i}_{\cdot j}| = \Delta$ is nonsingular and positive. Hence, if $\Delta \neq 0$, the affine transformation is called nonsingular.

If the volume V_0 is displaced as a rigid body, an arbitrary relative displacement will, according to D'Alembert's principle, correspond to a simple rotation. In this case, the tensor $\boldsymbol{C}$ is denoted by $\boldsymbol{L}$. The tensor $\boldsymbol{L}$ and its matrix $\|l^{i}_{\cdot j}\|$ have a special form. The rigidity condition may be written in the form

$$(\boldsymbol{r}, \boldsymbol{r}) = (\boldsymbol{r}_0, \boldsymbol{r}_0) \qquad \text{or} \qquad g_{\lambda\mu}x^{\lambda}x^{\mu} = g_{\chi\beta}l^{\chi\cdot}_{\cdot\lambda}l^{\beta\cdot}_{\cdot\mu}x_0^{\lambda}x_0^{\mu} = g_{\lambda\mu}x_0^{\lambda}x_0^{\mu},$$

from which, because of the arbitrariness of x_0^i, it follows that

$$g_{\alpha\beta}l^{\alpha\cdot}_{\cdot\lambda}l^{\beta\cdot}_{\cdot\mu} = g_{\lambda\mu}$$

or

$$l_{\beta\lambda}l^{\beta\nu} = \delta_{\lambda\cdot}^{\cdot\nu},$$

which means that matrices

$$\|l_{\lambda\beta}\| \qquad \text{and} \qquad \|\mathring{l}^{\beta\nu}\|,$$

where

$$\mathring{l}^{\beta\nu} = l^{\nu\beta},$$

are reversible. In the matrix elements, the first index specifies the number of the row and the second that of the column.

The matrix $\|l_{\lambda\beta}\|$ is formed from the covariant components of the tensor $\boldsymbol{L}$, and the matrix $\|\mathring{l}^{\beta\nu}\|$ from the contravariant components of the tensor $\mathring{\boldsymbol{L}}$, the conjugate of $\boldsymbol{L}$. The tensor $\mathring{\boldsymbol{L}}$ is obtained from the tensor $\boldsymbol{L}$ by changing the order of the indices of the covariant or contravariant components of the tensor $\boldsymbol{L}$.

If the coordinate system is orthogonal, $l_{\lambda\beta} = l^{\lambda\beta}$, and therefore the matrix $\|\mathring{l}^{\beta\nu}\|$ will be obtained from $\|l_{\lambda\beta}\|$ by a simple interchange of rows and columns.

If the matrix $\|l_{\lambda\beta}\|$ is symmetric, for rectangular coordinates $\|\mathring{l}^{\beta\nu}\| = \|l_{\lambda\beta}\|$; therefore, in this case, the matrix equality

$$\|l_{\lambda\beta}\|^2 = \begin{vmatrix} 1 & 0 & 0 \\ 0 & 1 & 0 \\ 0 & 0 & 1 \end{vmatrix} \tag{2.5}$$

holds.

Because the transformation $\boldsymbol{L}$ always corresponds to a pure rotation and equation (2.5) holds in any orthogonal coordinate system, then, if we choose our coordinate system such that the axis of rotation coincides with the z-axis, we obtain, in accordance with formula (5.28) of Chapter I,

$$\|l_{\lambda\beta}\|^2 = \begin{vmatrix} \cos 2\phi & -\sin 2\phi & 0 \\ \sin 2\phi & \cos 2\phi & 0 \\ 0 & 0 & 1 \end{vmatrix}. \tag{2.6}$$

If the matrix $\|l_{\lambda\beta}\|$ is symmetric by equating (2.5) to (2.6), we find that the angle of rotation is

$$\phi = k\pi ,$$

where k is an integer.

Thus, a symmetric matrix $\|l_{\lambda\beta}\|$ in the general case corresponds to a rotation about any axis through an angle that is a multiple of π. As a special case, this transformation can be the identity transformation, i.e., a transformation in which no displacement occurs.

In accordance with formulas (5.31) and (5.32) of Chapter I, for a general angle of rotation ϕ and a matrix defining a rotation vector $\boldsymbol{K}$ in any coordinate system, we have

$$\mathscr{I}_1^l = l^{\alpha\cdot}_{\cdot\alpha} = 1 + 2\cos\phi , \tag{2.7}$$

$$\boldsymbol{K} = \frac{\phi}{2\sin\phi}(\boldsymbol{L} - \boldsymbol{G})\big[(1 + 2\cos\phi)\boldsymbol{G} - \boldsymbol{L}\big]. \tag{2.8}$$

Consider the particular case of affine deformation when the relation (2.2) takes the form

$$\begin{aligned} x^1 &= C^{1\cdot}_{\cdot 1} x_0^1 , \\ x^2 &= x_0^2 , \\ x^3 &= x_0^3 . \end{aligned} \tag{2.9}$$

Such a deformation corresponds to a pure extension along the direction of the Ox^i-axis. If $C^{1\cdot}_{\cdot 1} > 1$, then $x^i > x_0^i$; consequently, we will have an increase in the lengths in the direction of the Ox^1-axis. This increase is characterized by the coefficients $C^{1\cdot}_{\cdot 1}$. If $0 < C^{1\cdot}_{\cdot 1} < 1$, the lengths along Ox^1 in the deformed state are decreased, and we have a compression which can be thought of as a negative extension. In the case in question, the matrix of the tensor $\boldsymbol{C}$ has the special form

$$\begin{Vmatrix} C^{1\cdot}_{\cdot 1} & 0 & 0 \\ 0 & 1 & 0 \\ 0 & 0 & 1 \end{Vmatrix}.$$

In the general case when the matrix of the tensor $\boldsymbol{C}$ is diagonal, we have

$$\begin{aligned} x^1 &= C^{1\cdot}_{\cdot 1} x^1_0 , \\ x^2 &= C^{2\cdot}_{\cdot 2} x^2_0 , \\ x^3 &= C^{3\cdot}_{\cdot 3} x^3_0 . \end{aligned} \tag{2.10}$$

This deformation corresponds to the set of simple elongations along the coordinate axes, and these elongations can be regarded as the result of the successive elongations of the type (2.9) along the corresponding coordinate axes. It is obvious that the components of the elongations along the coordinate axes can be taken in any order; i.e., the three deformations shown are commutative.

If for a deformation (2.10), the equalities

$$C^{1\cdot}_{\cdot 1} = C^{2\cdot}_{\cdot 2} = C^{3\cdot}_{\cdot 3}$$

are true; i.e., if the tensor $\boldsymbol{C}$ is spherical, the deformations obviously reduce to an analogous elongation or a compression which is the same at all points in the volume.

Consider two affine transformations C_1 and C_2, and let their matrix components be denoted by $\|C^{i\cdot}_{\cdot j}\|$ and $\|\tilde{C}^{i\cdot}_{\cdot j}\|$:

$$\|C^{i\cdot}_{\cdot j}\| = \|\delta^{i\cdot}_{\cdot j} + a^{i\cdot}_{\cdot j}\| \qquad \text{and} \qquad \|\tilde{C}^{i\cdot}_{\cdot j}\| = \|\delta^{i\cdot}_{\cdot j} + b^{i\cdot}_{\cdot j}\| .$$

It is obvious that the results of these two successive deformations are also affine deformations, which can be represented by the following formulas.

If the deformation C_1 is performed first and C_2 afterwards, formulas (2.2) become

$$x^i = (\delta^{i\cdot}_{\cdot\alpha} + a^{i\cdot}_{\cdot\alpha} + b^{i\cdot}_{\cdot\alpha} + b^{i\cdot}_{\cdot\beta} a^{\beta\cdot}_{\cdot\alpha}) x^\alpha_0 ;$$

however, if C_2 is performed first and followed by C_1, we get

$$x'^i = (\delta^{i\cdot}_{\cdot\alpha} + b^{i\cdot}_{\cdot\alpha} + a^{i\cdot}_{\cdot\alpha} + a^{i\cdot}_{\cdot\beta} b^{\beta\cdot}_{\cdot\alpha}) x^\alpha_0 .$$

The noncommutative nature of the deformations corresponding to the transformations C_1 and C_2 is due to the inequalities

$$b^{i\cdot}_{\cdot\beta} a^{\beta\cdot}_{\cdot\alpha} \neq a^{i\cdot}_{\cdot\beta} b^{\beta\cdot}_{\cdot\alpha} .$$

The validity of these inequalities, even for rigid-body displacements, was demonstrated in § 1.

The transformations C_1 and C_2 and the deformations corresponding to them are said to be infinitesimal if $a^{i\cdot}_{\cdot j}$ and $b^{i\cdot}_{\cdot j}$ are infinitesimal. Clearly, for infinitesimal transformations, the following equation is valid with an accuracy up to first order, inclusively:

$$x^i = x'^i .$$

Consequently, arbitrary infinitesimal affine deformations can be considered commutative. The noncommutative nature appears as a nonlinear effect for successive deformations.

Let us now note the general properties of arbitrary nonsingular ($\Delta \neq 0$) affine deformations.

On the basis of formulas (2.2), defining affine deformations, the following assumptions are obvious.

1. Every plane transforms to a plane.
2. Every straight line transforms to a straight line.
3. A system of parallel planes transforms to a system of parallel planes.
4. A system of parallel lines transforms to a system of parallel lines.
5. Every parallelogram transforms to a parallelogram.
6. Any rectilinear segment transforms to a rectilinear segment, and the ratio of the length after deformation to the original length depends only on the orientation of the segment and not on the original undeformed length.
7. In the case of a similarity transformation, for an arbitrary segment, the ratio of the final to the original length is the same independently of the orientation.
8. Let three points a, b, c be given, initially located on a single straight line, and suppose that on deformation these points transform to a' b' c' also lying on a straight line. The ratios of the corresponding lengths are clearly given by

$$ab/bc = a'b'/b'c'.$$

9. Any sphere S and its interior in the original state transforms in the deformed state to an ellipsoid Э and its interior.
10. Any three mutually perpendicular diameters of the sphere S transform to three conjugate diameters of the ellipsoid Э.
11. An orthogonal trihedral of the principal axes of the ellipsoid corresponds to an orthogonal trihedral of the axes of the sphere S. In general, an ellipsoid has three axes and therefore only one trihedral can exist which is displaced as a rigid body upon an affine deformation.

The axes of a nonvarying orthogonal trihedral are called the principal axes of the deformation. In the general case such a trihedral is unique.

If the ellipsoid Э is an ellipsoid of revolution or a sphere, the principal axes of deformation are not defined uniquely.

12. A plane area ω bounded by a closed curve transforms into a plane area ω' bounded by a transformed closed curve. The ratio of the areas ω'/ω does not depend on the shape of the boundary, but only on the orientation of the area ω.
13. A volume V_0 transforms into a volume V. The volume ratio V/V_0

does not depend on the size or shape of the original volume V. It is easy to see that this ratio is given by

$$V/V_0 = \Delta = |C^{i\cdot}_{\cdot j}| = \sqrt{|C^{i\cdot}_{\cdot\alpha} C^{k\cdot}_{\cdot\alpha}|}, \tag{2.11}$$

where Δ is the determinant of the affine transformation (2.2). In formula (2.11), the expression under the radical must be summed over α.

An affine transformation is called a pure deformation if the principal axes of the deformation remain stationary.

It is obvious that in the general case, with arbitrary $C^{i\cdot}_{\cdot\alpha}$, the transformation (2.10) defines a pure deformation if the coordinate system is orthogonal. For an oblique system with difference $C^{i\cdot}_{\cdot i}$, the principal axes rotate.

3. Continuous finite displacements of a continuum

Let us consider arbitrary continuous displacements of a continuum.

Let $Ox^1x^2x^3$ be a coordinate system relative to which the positions of the various points of the medium are defined. In this system, the coordinates of fixed points of the medium are variable. Further, let ξ^1, ξ^2, ξ^3 be the Lagrangian coordinates of the fixed points of the medium.

In order to establish the quantitative characteristics of the motion, various equations, and the functional relationships, it is possible and convenient to use various moving or stationary coordinate systems.

Consider three basic coordinate systems (Fig. 5).

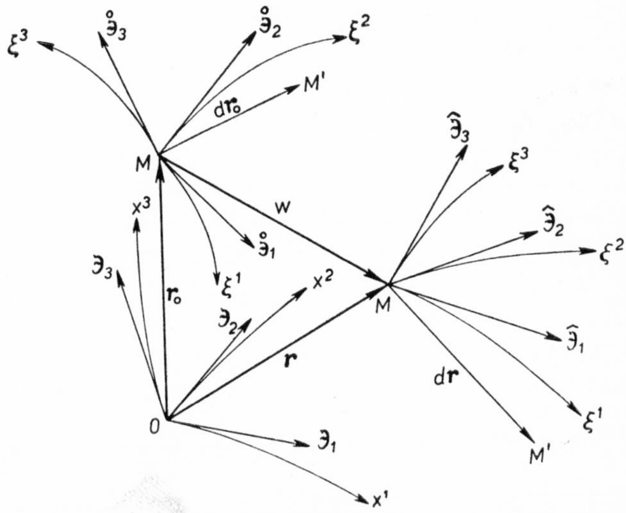

Figure 5

1. The system $Ox^1 x^2 x^3$ with basis vectors $\boldsymbol{\ni}_i$ is chosen as a reference system in which the displacement or motion is defined.

2. The Lagrangian stationary system $M\xi^1\xi^2\xi^3$ with basis vectors $\mathring{\boldsymbol{\ni}}_i$ corresponds to positions of points of the medium at some initial instant of time; in this system, the images of the moving points are fixed for all instants of time.

3. The moving Lagrangian system $M\xi^1\xi^2\xi^3$ is displaced together with those points of the medium with basis vectors $\hat{\boldsymbol{\ni}}_i$ that correspond to the changed positions of the points at the instant of time t in question.

From the one-to-one correspondence, it follows that if the $\mathring{\boldsymbol{\ni}}_i$ are noncoplanar, the $\hat{\boldsymbol{\ni}}_i$ are also noncoplanar (Fig. 5).

In the study of finite displacements using the coordinate systems indicated, it is necessary to employ the most general form of curvilinear coordinates. Indeed, the basis $\boldsymbol{\ni}_i$ can be fixed by choice; one of the systems with bases $\mathring{\boldsymbol{\ni}}_i$ or $\hat{\boldsymbol{\ni}}_i$ can also be fixed by choice. If the basis $\mathring{\boldsymbol{\ni}}_i$ is established, the basis $\hat{\boldsymbol{\ni}}_i$ will correspond to a curvilinear system defined by the displacements. The basis $\hat{\boldsymbol{\ni}}_i$ can be chosen arbitrarily; in that case, the basis $\mathring{\boldsymbol{\ni}}_i$ for the initial position is defined by the properties of the displacement.

If only two positions of the medium are to be considered, there is no point in introducing the reference system $\boldsymbol{\ni}_i$ independently of $\mathring{\boldsymbol{\ni}}_i$ or $\hat{\boldsymbol{\ni}}_i$. In considering the motion of the continuum, all three bases can coincide at some instant of time, but these bases and their variation will be different for the motion of fixed points of the medium (see § 10, Chapter I).

In considering a single finite displacement, the basis $\boldsymbol{\ni}_i$ can coincide either with $\mathring{\boldsymbol{\ni}}_i$ or with $\hat{\boldsymbol{\ni}}_i$.

Let us consider two infinitely close points of a moving continuum $M(\xi^1, \xi^2, \xi^3)$ and $M'(\xi^1 + d\xi^1, \xi^2 + d\xi^2, \xi^3 + d\xi^3)$ (see Fig. 5). The position of the point M' relative to the point M is determined initially by an infinitesimal vector $d\boldsymbol{r}_0$, and in the displaced position by an infinitesimal (because of the continuity) vector $d\boldsymbol{r}$.

From the definition of the bases $\mathring{\boldsymbol{\ni}}_i$ and $\hat{\boldsymbol{\ni}}_i$ [see formula (1.3), Chapter I], we have

$$d\boldsymbol{r}_0 = \frac{\partial \boldsymbol{r}_0}{\partial \xi^\alpha} d\xi^\alpha = \mathring{\boldsymbol{\ni}}_\alpha d\xi^\alpha \quad \text{and} \quad d\boldsymbol{r} = \frac{\partial \boldsymbol{r}}{\partial \xi^\alpha} d\xi^\alpha = \hat{\boldsymbol{\ni}}_\alpha d\xi^\alpha . \tag{3.1}$$

The elements $d\boldsymbol{r}_0$ and $d\boldsymbol{r}$ can be resolved along the base vectors of a single basis. These resolutions can be conveniently obtained by using the tensors

$$\boldsymbol{C} = C^{k\cdot}_{\cdot j} \mathring{\boldsymbol{\ni}}_k \mathring{\boldsymbol{\ni}}^j \quad \text{and} \quad \hat{\boldsymbol{C}} = \hat{C}^{k\cdot}_{\cdot j} \hat{\boldsymbol{\ni}}_k \hat{\boldsymbol{\ni}}^j , \tag{3.2}$$

related to the representation of the basis $\hat{\mathbf{Э}}_i$ in terms of the basis $\mathring{\mathbf{Э}}_i$. In fact, the components of the tensors $\boldsymbol{C}$ and $\hat{\boldsymbol{C}}$ are defined as the coefficients of the following vector-functions:

$$\hat{\mathbf{Э}}_i = \boldsymbol{C}\cdot\mathring{\mathbf{Э}}_i = C^{k\cdot}_{\cdot i}\mathring{\mathbf{Э}}_k, \qquad \mathring{\mathbf{Э}}_i = \hat{\boldsymbol{C}}\cdot\hat{\mathbf{Э}}_i = \hat{C}^{k\cdot}_{\cdot i}\hat{\mathbf{Э}}_k. \tag{3.3}$$

It is easy to see that the matrices $\|C^{k\cdot}_{\cdot i}\|$ and $\|\hat{C}^{k\cdot}_{\cdot i}\|$ are one another's inverses because $C^{k\cdot}_{\cdot\alpha}\hat{C}^{\alpha\cdot}_{\cdot i} = \delta^{k\cdot}_{\cdot i}$.

Let $d\eta^i$ be the components of $d\boldsymbol{r}$ in the system $\mathring{\mathbf{Э}}_i$, and let $d\zeta^i$ be the components of $d\boldsymbol{r}_0$ in system $\hat{\mathbf{Э}}_i$. We have

$$d\boldsymbol{r} = \mathring{\mathbf{Э}}_i d\eta^i \qquad \text{and} \qquad d\boldsymbol{r}_0 = \hat{\mathbf{Э}}_i d\zeta^i. \tag{3.4}$$

From (3.1), (3.3), and (3.4), we find

$$d\eta^i = C^{i\cdot}_{\cdot\alpha}d\xi^\alpha \qquad \text{and} \qquad d\zeta^i = \hat{C}^{i\cdot}_{\cdot\alpha}d\xi^\alpha. \tag{3.5}$$

Formulas (3.3) and (3.5) define an affine transformation in a small region around the point M for infinitesimal $d\boldsymbol{r}_0$ and $d\boldsymbol{r}$ and also for bases $\mathring{\mathbf{Э}}_i$ and $\hat{\mathbf{Э}}_i$. This affine transformation is called tangential with respect to the generally nonlinear finite transformation close to the considered point M.

In the basis $\mathring{\mathbf{Э}}_i$, the tangential affine transformation is defined by the tensor $\boldsymbol{C}$, and in the basis $\hat{\mathbf{Э}}_i$ by $\hat{\boldsymbol{C}}$.

The components of tensors $\boldsymbol{C}$ and $\hat{\boldsymbol{C}}$ can easily be expressed in terms of the displacement vector $\boldsymbol{w}$ for the various points in the medium. It is defined as the difference $\boldsymbol{r} - \boldsymbol{r}_0$:

$$\boldsymbol{r} - \boldsymbol{r}_0 = \boldsymbol{w} = \mathring{w}^\alpha\mathring{\mathbf{Э}}_\alpha = \hat{w}^\alpha\hat{\mathbf{Э}}_\alpha, \tag{3.6}$$

where the $\mathring{w}^\alpha$ are the components of the vector $\boldsymbol{w}$ in the coordinate system with basis $\mathring{\mathbf{Э}}_\alpha$ and the $\hat{w}^\alpha$ are the components in the system with basis $\hat{\mathbf{Э}}_\alpha$.

After differentiating equations (3.6) with respect to ξ^i, we obtain

$$\hat{\mathbf{Э}}_i = (\delta^{\alpha\cdot}_{\cdot i} + \nabla_i\mathring{w}^\alpha)\,\mathring{\mathbf{Э}}_\alpha$$

or

$$\mathring{\mathbf{Э}}_i = (\delta^{\alpha\cdot}_{\cdot i} - \nabla_i\hat{w}^\alpha)\,\hat{\mathbf{Э}}_\alpha. \tag{3.7}$$

On the basis of (3.7) and (3.3), we can write

$$C^{k\cdot}_{\cdot i} = \delta^{k\cdot}_{\cdot i} + \nabla_i\mathring{w}^k = \delta^{k\cdot}_{\cdot i} + \frac{\partial\mathring{w}^k}{\partial\xi^i} + \mathring{\Gamma}^k_{\beta i}\mathring{w}^\beta,$$

$$\hat{C}^{k\cdot}_{\cdot i} = \delta^{k\cdot}_{\cdot i} - \nabla_i\hat{w}^k = \delta^{k\cdot}_{\cdot i} - \frac{\partial\hat{w}^k}{\partial\xi^i} - \hat{\Gamma}^k_{\beta i}\hat{w}^\beta. \tag{3.8}$$

In formulas (3.8), for the Christoffel symbols, we have, according to (1.19) of Chapter I,

$$\mathring{\Gamma}^k_{ij} = \tfrac{1}{2}\mathring{g}^{ks}\left(\frac{\partial \mathring{g}_{is}}{\partial \xi^j} + \frac{\partial \mathring{g}_{js}}{\partial \xi^i} - \frac{\partial \mathring{g}_{ij}}{\partial \xi^s}\right), \qquad \text{where} \qquad \mathring{g}_{ij} = (\mathring{\mathfrak{Z}}_i, \mathring{\mathfrak{Z}}_j), \tag{3.9}$$

and

$$\hat{\Gamma}^k_{ij} = \tfrac{1}{2}\hat{g}^{ks}\left(\frac{\partial \hat{g}_{is}}{\partial \xi^j} + \frac{\partial \hat{g}_{js}}{\partial \xi^i} - \frac{\partial \hat{g}_{ij}}{\partial \xi^s}\right), \qquad \text{where} \qquad \hat{g}_{ij} = (\hat{\mathfrak{Z}}_i, \hat{\mathfrak{Z}}_j). \tag{3.10}$$

In formulas (3.7) and (3.8), the vector $\boldsymbol{w}$ can be replaced by the vector $\boldsymbol{w}_1$ if $\boldsymbol{w} = \boldsymbol{w}_1 + \boldsymbol{a}$, where $\boldsymbol{a}$ is any constant vector, i.e., $\partial \boldsymbol{a}/\partial \xi^i = 0$. We may take $\boldsymbol{a}$ equal to the displacement of the point M; then $\boldsymbol{w}_1$ is the supplementary displacement of the point M' with respect to M.

Formulas (3.8) are true for any finite displacement, and in particular for the finite affine displacements examined in § 2. The coordinate systems $\mathring{\mathfrak{Z}}_i$ or $\hat{\mathfrak{Z}}_i$ can be chosen rectilinear but, generally, oblique throughout the entire volume of the medium. In this case, all the corresponding Christoffel symbols are zero.

In the general case, one of the bases $\hat{\mathfrak{Z}}_i$, $\mathring{\mathfrak{Z}}_i$ can always be taken as cartesian.

If the displacements are infinitesimal, $\nabla_i \mathring{w}^\alpha$ and $\nabla_i w^\alpha$ are infinitesimal.

If the motion is continuous, for a small time increment Δt, we have

$$\boldsymbol{w} = \mathbf{v} \cdot \Delta t,$$

where $\mathbf{v}$ is the velocity vector of the various points of the medium.

4. The tensor characteristics of a deformation

For the initial and deformed states, we have

$$ds_0^2 = (d\boldsymbol{r}_0, d\boldsymbol{r}_0) = \mathring{g}_{\alpha\beta} d\xi^\alpha d\xi^\beta \qquad \text{and} \qquad ds^2 = (d\boldsymbol{r}, d\boldsymbol{r}) = \hat{g}_{\alpha\beta} d\xi^\alpha d\xi^\beta .$$

The condition for the existence of deformation (or change in length) is that the difference

$$ds^2 - ds_0^2 = (\hat{g}_{\alpha\beta} - \mathring{g}_{\alpha\beta})\, d\xi^\alpha d\xi^\beta \tag{4.1}$$

be nonzero.

We define

$$\hat{g}_{\alpha\beta} - \mathring{g}_{\alpha\beta} = (\hat{\mathfrak{Z}}_\alpha, \hat{\mathfrak{Z}}_\beta) - (\mathring{\mathfrak{Z}}_\alpha, \mathring{\mathfrak{Z}}_\beta) = 2\varepsilon_{\alpha\beta} . \tag{4.2}$$

It is obvious that we can introduce two symmetric tensors $\mathring{\mathscr{E}}$ and $\hat{\mathscr{E}}$ with identical covariant components, equal to $\varepsilon_{\alpha\beta}$ in the different bases:

$$\mathring{\mathscr{E}} = \varepsilon_{\alpha\beta} \mathring{\mathfrak{Z}}^\alpha \mathring{\mathfrak{Z}}^\beta \qquad \text{and} \qquad \hat{\mathscr{E}} = \varepsilon_{\alpha\beta} \hat{\mathfrak{Z}}^\alpha \hat{\mathfrak{Z}}^\beta . \tag{4.3}$$

The corresponding components with contravariant indices will be different. For the tensor $\mathring{\mathscr{E}}$, the raising of the indices must be carried out with the aid of the tensor $\mathring{g}^{ij}$, and for the tensor $\hat{\mathscr{E}}$, with the aid of $\hat{g}^{ij}$.

The tensor $\mathring{\mathscr{E}}$ is defined in the space of the initial states; $\hat{\mathscr{E}}$, in the deformed space.

It is evident that for a tangential affine transformation, the necessary and sufficient condition for the absence of deformation is that all the components $\varepsilon_{\alpha\beta}$, and consequently, the tensors $\mathring{\mathscr{E}}$ and $\hat{\mathscr{E}}$ vanish. The tensors $\mathring{\mathscr{E}}$ and $\hat{\mathscr{E}}$ are called tensors of finite deformations.

A mechanical interpretation of the covariant components of $\mathring{\mathscr{E}}$ and $\hat{\mathscr{E}}$ follows from the equation

$$2\varepsilon_{ik} = |\hat{\text{Э}}_i|\,|\hat{\text{Э}}_k| \cos \psi_{ik} - |\mathring{\text{Э}}_i|\,|\mathring{\text{Э}}_k| \cos \mathring{\psi}_{ik}, \tag{4.4}$$

where $\mathring{\psi}_{ik}$ is the angle between the basis vectors $\mathring{\text{Э}}_i$, $\mathring{\text{Э}}_k$ and ψ_{ik} is the angle between their images $\hat{\text{Э}}_i$, $\hat{\text{Э}}_k$.

The coefficients of the elongation of the element $d\boldsymbol{r}_0$ are defined by the formula

$$\frac{|d\boldsymbol{r}| - |d\boldsymbol{r}_0|}{|d\boldsymbol{r}_0|} = l \qquad \text{or} \qquad \frac{|\,d\boldsymbol{r}\,|}{|d\boldsymbol{r}_0|} = 1 + l\,. \tag{4.5}$$

According to the general conclusions of § 2, the elongation depends only on the orientation of the segment and not on its initial length in the case of an affine transformation.

We denote by l_i the elongations in the direction of the basis vectors $\mathring{\text{Э}}_i$. We have

$$|\hat{\text{Э}}_i| = |\mathring{\text{Э}}_i|\,(1 + l_i) \qquad \text{or} \qquad \hat{g}_{ii} = (1 + l_i)^2\, \mathring{g}_{ii}\,. \tag{4.6}$$

Formula (4.4) can be rewritten as

$$\frac{2\varepsilon_{ik}}{\sqrt{\mathring{g}_{ii}}\sqrt{\mathring{g}_{kk}}} = (1 + l_i)(1 + l_k)\cos \psi_{ik} - \cos \mathring{\psi}_{ik}\,. \tag{4.7}$$

If $i = k$, then $\mathring{\psi}_{ik} = 0$ and $\psi_{ik} = 0$; therefore,*

$$2\varepsilon_{ii}/\mathring{g}_{ii} = (1 + l_i)^2 - 1 \qquad \text{or} \qquad l_i = \sqrt{1 + 2\varepsilon_{ii}/\mathring{g}_{ii}} - 1\,. \tag{4.8}$$

Thus the components ε_{ii} define the elongations in the direction of the coordinate axes.

The mechanical significance of the components with mixed indices ε_{ik}, $i \neq k$ is demonstrated in formula (4.7). If the vectors $\mathring{\text{Э}}_i$ and $\mathring{\text{Э}}_k$ are or-

---

* The root should be taken as positive because $l = 0$ for $\varepsilon_{ii} = 0$.

thogonal, $\mathring{\psi}_{ik} = \pi/2$, and in this case the deviation of the ε_{ik} from zero is related to the pinching of the original right angle. Let $\psi_{ik} = \pi/2 - \chi_{ik}$. If $\mathring{\mathbf{\vartheta}}_i$ and $\mathring{\mathbf{\vartheta}}_k$ are orthogonal unit vectors, equation (4.7) gives

$$2\varepsilon_{ik} = (1 + l_i)(1 + l_k)\sin\chi_{ik}. \tag{4.9}$$

If the coordinate system with basis $\mathring{\mathbf{\vartheta}}_i$ coincides with the principal axes of the tensor $\mathring{\mathscr{E}}$, then all $\varepsilon_{ik} = 0$ for $i \neq k$, and, consequently, the basis $\hat{\mathbf{\vartheta}}_i$ is also orthogonal. Therefore, in these bases, the matrices of the symmetric tensors $\mathring{\mathscr{E}}$ and $\hat{\mathscr{E}}$ having arbitrary index structures are diagonal. The corresponding orthogonal trihedrals of the bases $\mathring{\mathbf{\vartheta}}_i$ and $\hat{\mathbf{\vartheta}}_i$ coincide with the principal axes of the tensors $\mathring{\mathscr{E}}$ and $\hat{\mathscr{E}}$, which are generally rotated with respect to one another.

In the coordinate system coinciding with the principal axes, the following holds:

$$\begin{aligned}\tfrac{1}{2}(ds^2 - ds_0^2) &= \varepsilon_{11}(d\xi^1)^2 + \varepsilon_{22}(d\xi^2)^2 + \varepsilon_{33}(d\xi^3)^2 \\ &= \mathring{\varepsilon}_1(ds_0^1)^2 + \mathring{\varepsilon}_2(ds_0^2)^2 + \mathring{\varepsilon}_3(ds_0^3)^2 = \hat{\varepsilon}_1(ds^1)^2 + \hat{\varepsilon}_2(ds^2)^2 + \hat{\varepsilon}_3(ds^3)^2,\end{aligned} \tag{4.10}$$

where the ds_0^i are elements of length parallel to the principal axes of the deformation tensor $\mathring{\mathscr{E}}$ located in the space of the initial states and ds^i are the corresponding elements parallel to the principal axes of the tensor in the deformed state. (It is obvious that $\mathring{\varepsilon}_1 = \mathring{g}^{11}\varepsilon_{11} = \varepsilon_{11}/\mathring{g}_{11}$ and $\hat{\varepsilon}_1 = \hat{g}^{11}\varepsilon_{11} = \varepsilon_{11}/\hat{g}_{11}$.)

The principal components $\mathring{\varepsilon}_1, \mathring{\varepsilon}_2, \mathring{\varepsilon}_3$ of $\mathring{\mathscr{E}}$ are defined as the roots of the characteristic equation

$$|\lambda\delta^{i}_{\cdot j} - \mathring{\varepsilon}^{i}_{\cdot j}| = 0, \qquad \text{where} \qquad \mathring{\varepsilon}^{i}_{\cdot j} = \mathring{g}^{i\alpha}\varepsilon_{\alpha j}, \tag{4.11}$$

and the principal components $\hat{\varepsilon}_1, \hat{\varepsilon}_2, \hat{\varepsilon}_3$ of $\hat{\mathscr{E}}$ are defined as the roots of the characteristic equation

$$|\lambda\delta^{i}_{\cdot j} - \hat{\varepsilon}^{i}_{\cdot j}| = 0, \qquad \text{where} \qquad \hat{\varepsilon}^{i}_{\cdot j} = \hat{g}^{i\alpha}\varepsilon_{\alpha j}. \tag{4.12}$$

From equations (4.10), we obtain

$$\mathring{E}_i = \frac{ds^i - ds_0^i}{ds_0^i} = \sqrt{1 + 2\mathring{\varepsilon}_i} - 1 \qquad \text{and} \qquad \hat{E}_i = \frac{ds^i - ds_0^i}{ds^i} = 1 - \sqrt{1 - 2\hat{\varepsilon}_i}. \tag{4.13}$$

The quantities $\mathring{E}_i$ are the elongations along the principal axes of deformation calculated in terms of unit length in the original state; $\hat{E}_i$ are the elongations calculated in terms of unit length in the deformed state.

From equations (4.13), it follows that

$$1 + \mathring{E}_i = \frac{1}{1 - \hat{E}_i} \qquad \text{and} \qquad 1 + 2\mathring{\varepsilon}_i = \frac{1}{1 - 2\hat{\varepsilon}_i}$$

or (4.14)

$$\mathring{\varepsilon}_i = \frac{\hat{\varepsilon}_i}{1 - 2\hat{\varepsilon}_i} \qquad \text{and} \qquad \hat{\varepsilon}_i = \frac{\mathring{\varepsilon}_i}{1 + 2\mathring{\varepsilon}_i}.$$

The characteristic equations (4.11) and (4.12) can be written respectively as

$$\lambda^3 - \mathring{\mathscr{I}}_1\lambda^2 + \mathring{\mathscr{I}}_2\lambda - \mathring{\mathscr{I}}_3 = 0 \qquad \text{and} \qquad \lambda^3 - \hat{\mathscr{I}}_1\lambda^2 + \hat{\mathscr{I}}_2\lambda - \hat{\mathscr{I}}_3 = 0,$$

where $\mathring{\mathscr{I}}_1, \mathring{\mathscr{I}}_2, \mathring{\mathscr{I}}_3$ are the invariants of the coordinate transformation for the tensor $\mathring{\mathscr{E}}$ in the undeformed space, and $\hat{\mathscr{I}}_1, \hat{\mathscr{I}}_2, \hat{\mathscr{I}}_3$ are the invariants of the coordinate transformation for the tensor $\hat{\mathscr{E}}$ in the deformed space. On the basis of the equalities (4.14), it is easy to derive

$$\begin{aligned}
\hat{\mathscr{I}}_1 &= \hat{\varepsilon}_1 + \hat{\varepsilon}_2 + \hat{\varepsilon}_3 = \frac{\mathring{\mathscr{I}}_1 + 4\mathring{\mathscr{I}}_2 + 12\mathring{\mathscr{I}}_3}{1 + 2\mathring{\mathscr{I}}_1 + 4\mathring{\mathscr{I}}_2 + 8\mathring{\mathscr{I}}_3}, \\
\hat{\mathscr{I}}_2 &= \hat{\varepsilon}_1\hat{\varepsilon}_2 + \hat{\varepsilon}_2\hat{\varepsilon}_3 + \hat{\varepsilon}_3\hat{\varepsilon}_1 = \frac{\mathring{\mathscr{I}}_2 + 6\mathring{\mathscr{I}}_3}{1 + 2\mathring{\mathscr{I}}_1 + 4\mathring{\mathscr{I}}_2 + 8\mathring{\mathscr{I}}_3}, \qquad (4.15) \\
\hat{\mathscr{I}}_3 &= \hat{\varepsilon}_1\hat{\varepsilon}_2\hat{\varepsilon}_3 = \frac{\mathring{\mathscr{I}}_3}{1 + 2\mathring{\mathscr{I}}_1 + 4\mathring{\mathscr{I}}_2 + 8\mathring{\mathscr{I}}_3}.
\end{aligned}$$

It is also possible to express $\mathring{\mathscr{I}}_1$, $\mathring{\mathscr{I}}_2$, and $\mathring{\mathscr{I}}_3$ in terms of $\hat{\mathscr{I}}_1$, $\hat{\mathscr{I}}_2$, and $\hat{\mathscr{I}}_3$. The corresponding formulas are analogous to (4.15), but $\hat{\mathscr{I}}_1$ and $\hat{\mathscr{I}}_3$ have minus signs. It is obvious that if $\mathring{\mathscr{E}}$ is a deviator, $\hat{\mathscr{E}}$ will not in general be a deviator. The converse is also true.

From (4.10), it follows that if $\mathring{\mathscr{E}}$ is spherical, $\hat{\mathscr{E}}$ is also spherical. In this case,

$$\varepsilon_{ik} = a\mathring{g}_{ik} = b\hat{g}_{ik}$$

and

$$\mathring{\varepsilon}^{i\cdot}_{\cdot k} = a\delta^{i\cdot}_{\cdot k}, \qquad \hat{\varepsilon}^{i\cdot}_{\cdot k} = b\delta^{i\cdot}_{\cdot k},$$

where

$$a = \frac{b}{1 - 2b}.$$

Hence, it follows that if $\mathring{\mathscr{E}}$ is spherical, then

$$\mathring{g}_{i\alpha}\hat{g}^{\alpha k} = \frac{b}{a}\delta_{i\cdot}^{\cdot k} = (1 - 2b)\,\delta_{i\cdot}^{\cdot k} = (1 + 2a)\,\delta_{i\cdot}^{\cdot k} \qquad (4.16)$$

must be satisfied. Let us consider the tensors

$$\mathring{\boldsymbol{T}} = \mathring{T}_{ij}\mathring{\boldsymbol{\ni}}^i\mathring{\boldsymbol{\ni}}^j = \mathring{T}^{ij}\mathring{\boldsymbol{\ni}}_i\mathring{\boldsymbol{\ni}}_j \qquad \text{and} \qquad \hat{\boldsymbol{T}} = \hat{T}_{ij}\hat{\boldsymbol{\ni}}^i\hat{\boldsymbol{\ni}}^j = \hat{T}^{ij}\hat{\boldsymbol{\ni}}_i\hat{\boldsymbol{\ni}}_j,$$

defined respectively in the initial and deformed spaces, and suppose that one of the equations

$$\mathring{T}_{ij} = \hat{T}_{ij} \qquad \text{or} \qquad \mathring{T}^{ij} = \hat{T}^{ij}$$

is fulfilled.

For an arbitrary deformation equation, (4.16) will not be satisfied, and, therefore, we can make the following assumption.

If one of the tensors $\mathring{\boldsymbol{T}}$ or $\hat{\boldsymbol{T}}$ is spherical, the other tensor will not be spherical.

If the deformation tensors are spherical, equation (4.16) will be satisfied. If one of tensors $\mathring{\boldsymbol{T}}$ or $\hat{\boldsymbol{T}}$ is spherical, the other is also spherical, but their scalar magnitudes will usually be different.

To the elementary parallelepiped $dV_0 = ds_0^1\, ds_0^2\, ds_0^3$ in the initial state corresponds the parallelepiped $dV = ds^1\, ds^2\, ds^3$ in the deformed state.

On the basis of (4.13), we may write

$$\frac{dV}{dV_0} = \sqrt{(1+2\mathring{\varepsilon}_1)(1+2\mathring{\varepsilon}_2)(1+2\mathring{\varepsilon}_3)} = \frac{1}{\sqrt{(1-2\hat{\varepsilon}_1)(1-2\hat{\varepsilon}_2)(1-2\hat{\varepsilon}_3)}}$$

or (4.17a)

$$\frac{dV}{dV_0} = \sqrt{1+2\mathring{\mathscr{I}}_1+4\mathring{\mathscr{I}}_2+8\mathring{\mathscr{I}}_3} = \frac{1}{\sqrt{1-2\hat{\mathscr{I}}_1+4\hat{\mathscr{I}}_2-8\hat{\mathscr{I}}_3}}.$$

If the deformations $\mathring{\varepsilon}_1, \mathring{\varepsilon}_2, \mathring{\varepsilon}_3$ are small, the following equations are valid up to infinitesimals of first-order:

$$\mathring{\varepsilon}_i \approx \hat{\varepsilon}_i, \qquad \mathring{\mathscr{I}}_1 \approx \hat{\mathscr{I}}_1, \qquad \frac{dV - dV_0}{dV_0} = \mathring{\mathscr{I}}_1 = \mathring{\varepsilon}^{\alpha\cdot}_{\cdot\alpha} = \hat{\varepsilon}^{\alpha\cdot}_{\cdot\alpha}. \tag{4.17b}$$

The tensors $\mathring{\mathscr{E}}$ and $\hat{\mathscr{E}}$ are the same for small deformations. The mechanical significance of the first invariant $\mathring{\mathscr{I}}_1$ follows from (4.17b). However, for finite deformations, the first invariants $\mathring{\mathscr{I}}_1$ and $\hat{\mathscr{I}}_1$ are unequal scalars, and they do not have a simple mechanical meaning.

Let us examine the variation in area for corresponding flat elements of area when a deformation takes place. We take an arbitrary plane s_0 in the original state, the orientation of which is given by the direction cosines l, m, n of the normal in a cartesian coordinate system which coincides with the principal axes of the tensor $\mathring{\mathscr{E}}$. Let there be in the deformed state an element of area s_0 which corresponds to s (Fig. 6). It is obvious that for an arbitrary affine transformation, the ratio $s/s_0 = \omega$ depends only on the orientation of s_0, and not on the shape or position of the plane s_0 in space.

Let s_{01}, s_{02}, and s_{03} be the projections of s_0 onto the planes which pass through the principal axes in the initial state, and let s_1, s_2, and s_3 be the corresponding projections of s onto the planes in the deformed state. It is immediately obvious that

$$s_{01} = ls_0\,, \qquad s_{02} = ms_0\,, \qquad s_{03} = ns_0\,, \qquad s^2 = s_1^2 + s_2^2 + s_3^2\,,$$

and

$$\omega^2 = \frac{s^2}{s_0^2} = \frac{s_1^2}{s_{01}^2}\cdot\frac{s_{01}^2}{s_0^2} + \frac{s_2^2}{s_{02}^2}\cdot\frac{s_{02}^2}{s_0^2} + \frac{s_3^2}{s_{03}^2}\cdot\frac{s_{03}^2}{s_0^2}\,.$$

From (4.13), we obtain

$$\omega^2 = s^2/s_0^2 = (1 + 2\mathring{\varepsilon}_2)(1 + 2\mathring{\varepsilon}_3)\,l^2 + (1 + 2\mathring{\varepsilon}_3)(1 + 2\mathring{\varepsilon}_1)\,m^2 + (1 + 2\mathring{\varepsilon}_1)(1 + 2\mathring{\varepsilon}_2)\,n^2\,. \tag{4.18}$$

Formula (4.18) allows the ratio (s/s_0) to be found if the principal components of $\mathring{\mathscr{E}}$ are known and the orientation of s_0 is given.

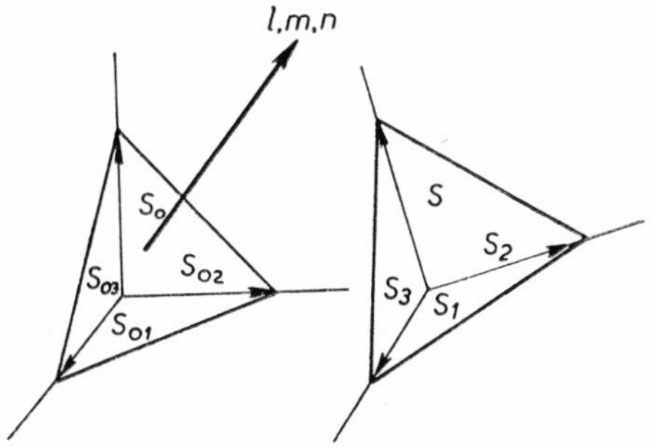

Figure 6

Let us find the values of l, m, n at which ω^2 attains an extremum. Lagrange's equations for a relative extremum $(l^2 + m^2 + n^2 = 1)$ are of the form

$$\begin{aligned} [(1 + 2\mathring{\varepsilon}_2)(1 + 2\mathring{\varepsilon}_3) - \Lambda]\,2l &= 0\,, \\ [(1 + 2\mathring{\varepsilon}_3)(1 + 2\mathring{\varepsilon}_1) - \Lambda]\,2m &= 0\,, \\ [(1 + 2\mathring{\varepsilon}_1)(1 + 2\mathring{\varepsilon}_2) - \Lambda]\,2n &= 0\,, \end{aligned} \tag{4.19}$$

and

$$l^2 + m^2 + n^2 = 1\,.$$

The following three solutions to these equations are possible:

$$\begin{aligned} &\omega_1^2 = \Lambda_1 = (1 + 2\mathring{\varepsilon}_2)(1 + 2\mathring{\varepsilon}_3)\,, && l^2 = 1\,, && m = n = 0\,, \\ &\omega_2^2 = \Lambda_2 = (1 + 2\mathring{\varepsilon}_3)(1 + 2\mathring{\varepsilon}_1)\,, && l = 0\,, && m^2 = 1\,, \quad n = 0\,, \\ &\omega_3^2 = \Lambda_3 = (1 + 2\mathring{\varepsilon}_1)(1 + 2\mathring{\varepsilon}_2)\,, && l = m = 0\,, && n^2 = 1\,. \end{aligned}$$

It is clear that the stationary values of ω^2 are attained for surfaces parallel to the planes passing through the principal axes of deformation.

If $\mathring{\varepsilon}_1 > \mathring{\varepsilon}_2 > \mathring{\varepsilon}_3$, then $\omega_{\max}$ corresponds to a surface perpendicular to the ξ^3-axis and $\omega_{\min}$ to a surface perpendicular to the ξ^1-axis.

Besides the tensors $\mathring{\mathscr{E}}$ and $\hat{\mathscr{E}}$, we can examine other tensors that are functions of $\mathring{\mathscr{E}}$ and $\hat{\mathscr{E}}$. For example,

$$\mathring{\boldsymbol{E}} = \mathring{E}_{ij}\mathring{\boldsymbol{\vartheta}}^i\mathring{\boldsymbol{\vartheta}}^j = \sqrt{\mathring{\boldsymbol{G}} + 2\mathring{\mathscr{E}}} - \mathring{\boldsymbol{G}}$$

and (4.20)

$$\hat{\boldsymbol{E}} = \hat{E}_{ij}\boldsymbol{\vartheta}^i\boldsymbol{\vartheta}^j = \hat{\boldsymbol{G}} - \sqrt{\hat{\boldsymbol{G}} - 2\hat{\mathscr{E}}},$$

where

$$\mathring{\boldsymbol{G}} = \mathring{g}_{ij}\mathring{\boldsymbol{\vartheta}}^i\mathring{\boldsymbol{\vartheta}}^j \qquad \text{and} \qquad \hat{\boldsymbol{G}} = \hat{g}_{ij}\hat{\boldsymbol{\vartheta}}^i\hat{\boldsymbol{\vartheta}}^j,$$

or

$$\mathring{\boldsymbol{H}} = \mathring{H}_{ij}\mathring{\boldsymbol{\vartheta}}^i\mathring{\boldsymbol{\vartheta}}^j = \ln\sqrt{\mathring{\boldsymbol{G}} + 2\mathring{\mathscr{E}}}$$

and (4.21)

$$\hat{\boldsymbol{H}} = \hat{H}_{ij}\boldsymbol{\vartheta}^i\boldsymbol{\vartheta}^j = -\ln\sqrt{\hat{\boldsymbol{G}} - 2\hat{\mathscr{E}}}.$$

The tensors $\mathring{\mathscr{E}}$, $\mathring{\boldsymbol{E}}$, and $\mathring{\boldsymbol{H}}$ have common principal axes, and the formulas

$$\mathring{H}_i = \tfrac{1}{2}\ln(1 + 2\mathring{\varepsilon}_i) \qquad \text{and} \qquad \mathring{E}_i = \sqrt{1 + 2\mathring{\varepsilon}_i} - 1 \tag{4.22}$$

hold for the principal components.

On the basis of (4.14), it follows that the principal components of the tensors $\mathring{\boldsymbol{H}}$ and $\hat{\boldsymbol{H}}$ are identical; therefore, the components with mixed indices of the tensor $\mathring{\boldsymbol{H}}$ in the basis $\mathring{\boldsymbol{\vartheta}}_i$ and of the tensor $\hat{\boldsymbol{H}}$ in the basis $\hat{\boldsymbol{\vartheta}}^i$ are identical.

The principal components $\mathring{E}_i$ are determined by the simple formulas

$$\mathring{E}_i = \Delta l/l, \tag{4.23}$$

where l is the initial length of a segment in the considered direction of the principal axis of deformation, Δl is the total increment of the length, and the components $\mathring{H}_i$ are defined by

$$\begin{aligned}\mathring{H}_i &= \frac{\Delta l_1}{l} + \frac{\Delta l_2}{l + \Delta l_1} + \frac{\Delta l_3}{l + \Delta l_1 + \Delta l_2} + \cdots \\ &= \int_l^{l+\Delta l} \frac{dl}{l} = \ln\left(1 + \frac{\Delta l}{l}\right) = \ln(1 + \mathring{E}_i) = \ln\sqrt{1 + 2\mathring{\varepsilon}_i}.\end{aligned} \tag{4.24}$$

It is obvious that $\mathring{H}_i$ can be considered as an elongation equal to the sum of the elementary elongations. For fixed axes of deformation and for deformations carried out successively one after another, the principal components of the tensor $\boldsymbol{H}$ for the resultant deformation are equal to the sum of the principal components of successive deformations. This property does not hold for tensors $\mathring{\mathscr{E}}$, $\mathring{\boldsymbol{E}}$ and $\hat{\mathscr{E}}$, $\hat{\boldsymbol{E}}$.

Formulas (4.22), (4.23), and (4.24) are true only for directions along the principal deformation axes. For segments with an arbitrary direction, these formulas do not hold.

For arbitrary deformations in the ranges of variation of the principal components,

$$-\tfrac{1}{2} < \mathring{\varepsilon}_1 < +\infty, \qquad -1 < \mathring{E}_i < +\infty, \qquad -\infty < \mathring{H}_i = \hat{H}_i < +\infty,$$

and, correspondingly,

$$\tfrac{1}{2} > \hat{\varepsilon}_i > -\infty, \qquad 1 > \hat{E}_i > -\infty.$$

If an initial length l increases to$l + \Delta l$ and $\Delta l = 0.5l$, the following are true:

$$\mathring{\varepsilon}_i = 0.625, \qquad \mathring{E}_i = 0.5, \qquad \mathring{H}_i = \hat{H}_i = \ln 1.5,$$
$$\hat{\varepsilon}_i = 0.277, \qquad \hat{E}_i = \tfrac{1}{3} = 0.33\ldots.$$

The components of the tensors $\mathring{\boldsymbol{E}}$ and $\mathring{\boldsymbol{H}}$ in any coordinate system can be expressed in terms of the components of tensor $\mathring{\mathscr{E}}$ by formulas (4.20) and (4.21). The components of $\mathring{\mathscr{E}}$ can be replaced by the corresponding tensor polynomials of second degree by using the Lagrange-Sylvester formulas, a fact involving the necessity of knowing the principal components of the tensor $\mathring{\mathscr{E}}$. It is not difficult to see that one of the equations

$$\mathring{\mathscr{E}} = 0, \qquad \mathring{\boldsymbol{E}} = 0, \qquad \mathring{\boldsymbol{H}} = 0, \qquad \hat{\mathscr{E}} = 0, \qquad \hat{\boldsymbol{E}} = 0, \qquad \hat{\boldsymbol{H}} = 0$$

implies the remaining ones.

Clearly, for small deformations, we have

$$\mathring{\mathscr{E}} = \mathring{\boldsymbol{E}} = \mathring{\boldsymbol{H}} = \hat{\mathscr{E}} = \hat{\boldsymbol{E}} = \hat{\boldsymbol{H}}.$$

The difference between the tensors and bases $\mathring{\text{Э}}_i$ and $\hat{\text{Э}}_i$ vanishes when quantities of order higher than one are neglected.

Problems in mechanics in which the deformations associated with finite displacements can be considered small are said to be geometrically linear. It is obvious that cases can arise in which the displacements are finite and the deformations small.

In geometrically linear problems, all the deformation tensors considered above are equal with accuracy up to first-order infinitesimals, but differ by higher orders.

In considering finite deformations and in establishing the generalized linear theory of infinitesimal deformations, the question naturally arises as to what tensor we must substitute for the tensor of infinitesimal deformations in various applications. Obviously this question must be solved on the basis of supplementary data of a geometrical or mechanical nature.

In § 3 it was shown that every displacement of a continuum can be defined for every point by the generally nonsymmetric tensors $\boldsymbol{C}$ or $\hat{\boldsymbol{C}}$ [formulas (3.2) and (3.3)]. It is now shown that the deformation is defined by the symmetric tensors $\mathring{\mathscr{E}}$ or $\hat{\mathscr{E}}$, and formulas expressing the components of these tensors in terms of the components of $\boldsymbol{C}$ and $\hat{\boldsymbol{C}}$ can easily be found.

It immediately follows from (3.3) that

$$g_{ik} = C^{\beta\cdot}_{\cdot k} C^{\alpha\cdot}_{\cdot i} \mathring{g}_{\alpha\beta} \qquad \text{and} \qquad \mathring{g}_{ik} = \hat{C}^{\beta\cdot}_{\cdot k} \hat{C}^{\alpha\cdot}_{\cdot i} \hat{g}_{\alpha\beta},$$

and therefore according to (4.2), we obtain

$$\varepsilon_{ik} = \tfrac{1}{2}(\hat{g}_{ik} - \mathring{g}_{ik}) = \tfrac{1}{2}(C^{\beta\cdot}_{\cdot k} C^{\alpha\cdot}_{\cdot i} - \delta^{\beta\cdot}_{\cdot k}\delta^{\alpha\cdot}_{\cdot i})\mathring{g}_{\alpha\beta} = \tfrac{1}{2}(\delta^{\beta\cdot}_{\cdot k}\delta^{\alpha\cdot}_{\cdot i} - \hat{C}^{\beta\cdot}_{\cdot k}\hat{C}^{\alpha\cdot}_{\cdot i})\hat{g}_{\alpha\beta}. \quad (4.25)$$

It then follows that

$$\mathring{\varepsilon}^{i\cdot}_{\cdot k} = \tfrac{1}{2}(C_{\alpha k} C^{\alpha i} - \delta^{i\cdot}_{\cdot k}) \qquad \text{and} \qquad \hat{\varepsilon}^{i\cdot}_{\cdot k} = \tfrac{1}{2}(\delta^{i\cdot}_{\cdot k} - \hat{C}_{\alpha k}\hat{C}^{\alpha i}). \quad (4.26)$$

If, in addition to the tensors $\boldsymbol{C}$ and $\hat{\boldsymbol{C}}$, we introduce the tensors $\boldsymbol{C}^*$ and $\hat{\boldsymbol{C}}^*$ whose components are defined by

$$C^*_{k\alpha} = C_{\alpha k} \qquad \text{and} \qquad \hat{C}^*_{k\alpha} = C_{\alpha k}, \quad (4.27)$$

then formulas (4.25) in terms of components can be replaced by tensor (and at the same time matrix) equations that are valid in any coordinate system

$$2\mathring{\mathscr{E}} = \boldsymbol{C}^*\boldsymbol{C} - \boldsymbol{G} \qquad \text{and} \qquad 2\hat{\mathscr{E}} = \hat{\boldsymbol{G}} - \hat{\boldsymbol{C}}^*\hat{\boldsymbol{C}} = \hat{\boldsymbol{G}} - (\boldsymbol{C}\boldsymbol{C}^*)^{-1}, \quad (4.28)$$

because

$$\hat{\boldsymbol{C}}^*\hat{\boldsymbol{C}} = \boldsymbol{C}^{*-1}\boldsymbol{C}^{-1} = (\boldsymbol{C}\boldsymbol{C}^*)^{-1}.$$

On the basis of (4.28), the tensors $\mathring{\boldsymbol{E}}$ and $\mathring{\boldsymbol{H}}$ can also be expressed in terms of $\boldsymbol{C}$ and $\boldsymbol{C}^*$, which appear only in the combination $\boldsymbol{C}^*\boldsymbol{C}$.

If in cartesian coordinates $\boldsymbol{C}^*\boldsymbol{C} = \boldsymbol{C}\boldsymbol{C}^*$, the corresponding matrix of $\boldsymbol{C}$ is normal (see § 5, Chapter I). In this case, we have $\boldsymbol{C}^* = f(\boldsymbol{C})$, and therefore the tensors $\mathring{\mathscr{E}}$, $\mathring{\boldsymbol{E}}$, and $\mathring{\boldsymbol{H}}$ can be represented as tensor functions of only one tensor $\boldsymbol{C}$.

The components of $\mathring{\mathscr{E}}$ and $\hat{\mathscr{E}}$ can be expressed in terms of the displacement vector $\boldsymbol{w}$. On the basis of (3.8) and (4.25), and by using (8.4) of Chapter I, we obtain

$$\begin{aligned} \varepsilon_{ik} &= \tfrac{1}{2}(\nabla_i \mathring{w}_k + \nabla_k \mathring{w}_i + \nabla_i \mathring{w}^\alpha \nabla_k \mathring{w}_\alpha) \\ &= \tfrac{1}{2}(\nabla_i \hat{w}_k + \nabla_k \hat{w}_i - \nabla_i \hat{w}^\alpha \nabla_k \hat{w}_\alpha). \end{aligned} \quad (4.29)$$

If the bases $\mathring{Э}_i$ and $\hat{Э}_i$ are orthogonal and cartesian, the symbols $\nabla_j \mathring{w}_\beta$ and $\nabla_j \mathring{w}^\beta$ coincide with the usual derivatives $\partial \mathring{w}_\beta / \partial s_0^j$. In this case, the following are true:

$$\varepsilon_{ij} = \frac{1}{2}\left(\frac{\partial \mathring{w}_i}{\partial s_0^j} + \frac{\partial \mathring{w}_j}{\partial s_0^i}\right) + \frac{1}{2}\left(\frac{\partial \mathring{w}_1}{\partial s_0^i}\frac{\partial \mathring{w}_1}{\partial s_0^j} + \frac{\partial \mathring{w}_2}{\partial s_0^i}\frac{\partial \mathring{w}_2}{\partial s_0^j} + \frac{\partial \mathring{w}_3}{\partial s_0^i}\frac{\partial \mathring{w}_3}{\partial s_0^j}\right) \tag{4.30}$$

or

$$\varepsilon_{ij} = \frac{1}{2}\left(\frac{\partial \hat{w}_i}{\partial s^j} + \frac{\partial \hat{w}_j}{\partial s^i}\right) - \frac{1}{2}\left(\frac{\partial \hat{w}_1}{\partial s^i}\frac{\partial \hat{w}_1}{\partial s^j} + \frac{\partial \hat{w}_2}{\partial s^i}\frac{\partial \hat{w}_2}{\partial s^j} + \frac{\partial \hat{w}_3}{\partial s^i}\frac{\partial \hat{w}_3}{\partial s^j}\right). \tag{4.31}$$

If the displacements are infinitesimal, the components ε_{ij} in any coordinate system are given by

$$\begin{aligned} \varepsilon_{ij} &= \tfrac{1}{2}(\nabla_i \mathring{w}_j + \nabla_j \mathring{w}_i) = \mathring{w}_{ij}, \\ \varepsilon_{ij} &= \tfrac{1}{2}(\nabla_i \hat{w}_j + \nabla_j \hat{w}_i) = \hat{w}_{ij}. \end{aligned} \tag{4.32}$$

For finite displacements, $\mathring{w}_{ij} \neq \hat{w}_{ij}$. The quantities $\mathring{w}_{ij}$ and $\hat{w}_{ij}$ also define the covariant components of two new symmetric tensors $\mathring{\mathfrak{W}} = \mathring{w}_{ij}\, \mathring{Э}^i \mathring{Э}^j$ and $\hat{\mathfrak{W}} = \hat{w}_{ij}\, \hat{Э}^i \hat{Э}^j$. However, for finite displacements, these tensors are generally defined by displacements, and not just by the deformation of a continuum. For arbitrary finite rigid-body displacements of a medium, the tensor equations $\mathring{\mathscr{E}} = \hat{\mathscr{E}} = 0$ apply, and the tensors $\mathring{\mathfrak{W}}$ and $\hat{\mathfrak{W}}$ are usually nonzero.

It is not difficult to verify that if $\mathring{\mathfrak{W}} = 0$, the deformations are generally different from zero and $\mathring{\mathscr{E}} \neq 0$. In fact, we have

$$\mathring{\mathfrak{W}} = \boldsymbol{C} + \boldsymbol{C}^* - 2\mathring{\boldsymbol{G}}.$$

If $\mathring{\mathfrak{W}} = 0$, then $\boldsymbol{C}^* = 2\boldsymbol{G} - \boldsymbol{C}$, and if we let $\boldsymbol{C} = \mathring{\boldsymbol{G}} + \boldsymbol{\Delta}$, then $\boldsymbol{C}^* = \mathring{\boldsymbol{G}} - \boldsymbol{\Delta}$. It then follows that the equation $\mathring{\mathfrak{W}} = 0$ is satisfied if the tensor $\boldsymbol{\Delta}$ is any skew-symmetric tensor. In this case, for $\mathring{\mathscr{E}}$ we have

$$2\mathring{\mathscr{E}} = \boldsymbol{C}^*\boldsymbol{C} - \mathring{\boldsymbol{G}} = (\mathring{\boldsymbol{G}} - \boldsymbol{\Delta})(\mathring{\boldsymbol{G}} + \boldsymbol{\Delta}) - \mathring{\boldsymbol{G}} = -\boldsymbol{\Delta}^2 \neq 0.$$

It is also obvious that if the tensor $\mathring{\mathscr{E}}$, or correspondingly, the tensor $\hat{\mathscr{E}}$, vanishes at an arbitrary point in the body, then $\mathring{g}_{ik} = \hat{g}_{ik}$, and therefore the body can be displaced only as a rigid body.

From this it follows that if the determinant of the corresponding transformation is positive, the necessary and sufficient conditions for the continuum to displace in rigid-body motion are given by the tensor identity $\mathring{\mathscr{E}} = 0$.

5. The rotation vector of the axes of deformation

From formulas (5.40) and (5.42) of Chapter I, it is possible to write

$$\begin{aligned} \boldsymbol{C} &= e^{\mathring{\boldsymbol{K}}}\sqrt{\boldsymbol{C}^*\boldsymbol{C}} = e^{\mathring{\boldsymbol{K}}}\sqrt{\mathring{\boldsymbol{G}} + 2\mathring{\mathscr{E}}}, \\ \hat{\boldsymbol{C}} &= e^{\hat{\boldsymbol{K}}}\sqrt{\hat{\boldsymbol{C}}^*\hat{\boldsymbol{C}}} = e^{\hat{\boldsymbol{K}}}\sqrt{\hat{\boldsymbol{G}} - 2\hat{\mathscr{E}}}, \end{aligned} \tag{5.1}$$

where $\mathring{\boldsymbol{K}}$ and $\hat{\boldsymbol{K}}$ are skew-symmetric tensors corresponding to the rotation vectors of the principal axes of deformation.

An affine displacement of a continuous medium defined by the tensor $\boldsymbol{C}$ in the basis $\mathring{\mathrm{Э}}_i$, or by the tensor $\hat{\boldsymbol{C}}$ in basis $\hat{\mathrm{Э}}_i$, is described by the formulas (5.1) as the consequence of a pure deformation which consists of an elongation along the principal axes of deformation and of a rotation of the trihedral of the principal axes of deformation.

The tensor $\boldsymbol{C}$ defines the transition from basis $\mathring{\mathrm{Э}}_i$ to the basis $\hat{\mathrm{Э}}_i$, and the tensor $\hat{\boldsymbol{C}}$ defines the inverse transformation from $\hat{\mathrm{Э}}_i$ to $\mathring{\mathrm{Э}}_i$. From formulas (5.1), it follows that

$$\begin{aligned} \mathring{\boldsymbol{K}} &= -\ln[\sqrt{\boldsymbol{C}^*\boldsymbol{C}}\,\boldsymbol{C}^{-1}] = -\ln[\sqrt{\mathring{\boldsymbol{G}} + 2\mathring{\mathcal{E}}}\,\boldsymbol{C}^{-1}], \\ \hat{\boldsymbol{K}} &= -\ln[\sqrt{\hat{\boldsymbol{C}}^*\hat{\boldsymbol{C}}}\,\hat{\boldsymbol{C}}^{-1}] = -\ln[\sqrt{\hat{\boldsymbol{G}} - 2\hat{\mathcal{E}}}\,\hat{\boldsymbol{C}}^{-1}]. \end{aligned} \tag{5.2}$$

By using the Lagrange-Sylvester formula, the tensors $\sqrt{\boldsymbol{C}^*\boldsymbol{C}}$ and $\sqrt{\hat{\boldsymbol{C}}^*\hat{\boldsymbol{C}}}$ in (5.2) can be replaced by tensors of the type

$$\begin{aligned} \sqrt{\boldsymbol{C}^*\boldsymbol{C}} &= m_0\mathring{\boldsymbol{G}} + m_1\boldsymbol{C}^*\boldsymbol{C} + m_2\boldsymbol{C}^*\boldsymbol{C}\boldsymbol{C}^*\boldsymbol{C}, \\ \sqrt{\hat{\boldsymbol{C}}^*\hat{\boldsymbol{C}}} &= \hat{m}_0\hat{\boldsymbol{G}} + \hat{m}_1\hat{\boldsymbol{C}}^*\hat{\boldsymbol{C}} + \hat{m}_2\hat{\boldsymbol{C}}^*\hat{\boldsymbol{C}}\hat{\boldsymbol{C}}^*\hat{\boldsymbol{C}}, \end{aligned}$$

where m_0, m_1, m_2, and correspondingly $\hat{m}_0$, $\hat{m}_1$, $\hat{m}_2$, are known functions of the principal components of tensors $\mathring{\mathcal{E}}$ or $\hat{\mathcal{E}}$.

If the displacements are finite but the deformations small, that is, if the components of the tensor $\boldsymbol{C}$ are finite, and the components of the tensor $\mathring{\mathcal{E}}$ are small, then, with accuracy to second-order quantities, the following formula is valid:

$$\begin{aligned} \sqrt{\mathring{\boldsymbol{G}} + 2\mathring{\mathcal{E}}}\,\boldsymbol{C}^{-1} &= [\mathring{\boldsymbol{G}} + \mathring{\mathcal{E}} - \tfrac{1}{2}\mathring{\mathcal{E}}\mathring{\mathcal{E}} + \dots]\boldsymbol{C}^{-1} \\ &= \tfrac{1}{2}(\boldsymbol{C}^{-1} + \boldsymbol{C}^*) - \tfrac{1}{8}(\boldsymbol{C}^*\boldsymbol{C} - \mathring{\boldsymbol{G}})^2\boldsymbol{C}^{-1} + \cdots \end{aligned}$$

and

$$\begin{aligned} \sqrt{\hat{\boldsymbol{G}} - 2\hat{\mathcal{E}}}\,\boldsymbol{C}^{-1} &= [\hat{\boldsymbol{G}} - \hat{\mathcal{E}} - \tfrac{1}{2}\hat{\mathcal{E}}\hat{\mathcal{E}} + \dots]\hat{\boldsymbol{C}}^{-1} \\ &= \tfrac{1}{2}(\hat{\boldsymbol{C}}^{-1} + \hat{\boldsymbol{C}}^*) - \tfrac{1}{8}(\boldsymbol{C}^*\hat{\boldsymbol{C}} - \hat{\boldsymbol{G}})^2\boldsymbol{C}^{-1} + \cdots. \end{aligned}$$

In such a case, for $\mathring{\boldsymbol{K}}$ and $\hat{\boldsymbol{K}}$, the following approximating formulas are accurate to first-order infinitesimals inclusively:

$$\mathring{\boldsymbol{K}} = -\ln\tfrac{1}{2}(\boldsymbol{C}^{-1} + \boldsymbol{C}^*), \qquad \hat{\boldsymbol{K}} = -\ln\tfrac{1}{2}(\hat{\boldsymbol{C}}^{-1} + \hat{\boldsymbol{C}}^*). \tag{5.3}$$

If the total displacements are infinitesimal, we have

$$\begin{aligned} \boldsymbol{C} &= \mathring{\boldsymbol{G}} + \boldsymbol{S}, \\ \boldsymbol{C}^{-1} &= \mathring{\boldsymbol{G}} - \boldsymbol{S} = 2\mathring{\boldsymbol{G}} - \boldsymbol{C}, \\ \hat{\boldsymbol{C}}^{-1} &= 2\hat{\boldsymbol{G}} - \hat{\boldsymbol{C}}, \end{aligned} \tag{5.4}$$

where $\boldsymbol{S}$ is a tensor with infinitesimal components. These formulas are valid with accuracy to first-order infinitesimals inclusively.

On the basis of (5.4), formulas (5.3) give, with accuracy to first-order infinitesimals,

$$\begin{aligned} \mathring{K} &= -\ln\left[\mathring{G} + \tfrac{1}{2}(C^* - C)\right] \approx \tfrac{1}{2}(C - C^*), \\ \hat{K} &= -\ln\left[\hat{G} + \tfrac{1}{2}(\hat{C}^* - \hat{C})\right] \approx \tfrac{1}{2}(\hat{C} - \hat{C}^*). \end{aligned} \tag{5.5}$$

If the tensor C is represented as a sum of a symmetric tensor N and a skew-symmetric tensor Ω, that is, if

$$C = N + \Omega, \qquad C^* = N - \Omega,$$

then for infinitesimal deformations, (3.8) can be used to reduce (5.5) to

$$\begin{aligned} \mathring{K} &= \Omega = \tfrac{1}{2}(\nabla_j \mathring{w}_i - \nabla_i \mathring{w}_j)\,\mathring{\mathfrak{I}}^i\mathring{\mathfrak{I}}^j = \tfrac{1}{2}\left(\frac{\partial \mathring{w}_i}{\partial \xi^j} - \frac{\partial \mathring{w}_j}{\partial \xi^i}\right)\mathring{\mathfrak{I}}^i\mathring{\mathfrak{I}}^j, \\ \hat{K} &= \tfrac{1}{2}(\nabla_i \hat{w}_j - \nabla_j \hat{w}_i)\,\hat{\mathfrak{I}}^i\hat{\mathfrak{I}}^j = \tfrac{1}{2}\left(\frac{\partial \hat{w}_j}{\partial \xi^i} - \frac{\partial \hat{w}_i}{\partial \xi^j}\right)\hat{\mathfrak{I}}^i\hat{\mathfrak{I}}^j; \end{aligned} \tag{5.6}$$

since the displacements are small, we have $\mathring{K} = -\hat{K}$.

If a small deformation under scrutiny corresponds to a continuous motion during the time dt, we get $w_i = v_i\, dt$, where the v_i are the covariant components of the velocity vector. Therefore,

$$\mathring{K} = \tfrac{1}{2}(\nabla_j v_i - \nabla_i v_j)\,\Delta t\,\mathring{\mathfrak{I}}^i\mathring{\mathfrak{I}}^j. \tag{5.7}$$

Formulas (5.5) and (5.6) can be used for the rotation vector in connection with infinitesimal displacements. If the deformations are small but the displacements are finite, equations (5.3) must be used. For small displacements, by using the first of equations (5.2) and equations (4.29), we can, by expanding the matrices into series, write the following exact formula [38] for the components $\mathring{K}^i_j$ of the tensor K:

$$\begin{aligned} \mathring{K}^{i}_{\cdot j} &= \tfrac{1}{2}(\nabla_j \mathring{w}^i - \nabla^i \mathring{w}_j) - \tfrac{1}{4}(\nabla_\alpha \mathring{w}^i \nabla_j \mathring{w}^\alpha - \nabla^i \mathring{w}_\alpha \nabla^\alpha \mathring{w}_j) \\ &+ \tfrac{1}{6}(\nabla_\alpha \mathring{w}^i \nabla_\beta \mathring{w}^\alpha \nabla_j \mathring{w}^\beta - \nabla^i \mathring{w}_\alpha \nabla^\alpha \mathring{w}_\beta \nabla^\beta \mathring{w}_j) + \tfrac{1}{48}(\nabla_\alpha \mathring{w}^i \nabla_\beta \mathring{w}^\alpha \nabla^\beta \mathring{w}_j \\ &- \nabla_\alpha \mathring{w}^i \nabla^\alpha \mathring{w}_\beta \nabla^\beta \mathring{w}_j + \nabla^i \mathring{w}_\alpha \nabla_\beta \mathring{w}^\alpha \nabla_j \mathring{w}^\beta - \nabla^i \mathring{w}_\alpha \nabla^\alpha \mathring{w}_\beta \nabla_j \mathring{w}^\beta) \\ &+ \tfrac{1}{24}(\nabla^i \mathring{w}_\beta \nabla_\alpha \mathring{w}^\beta \nabla^\alpha \mathring{w}_j - \nabla_\alpha \mathring{w}^i \nabla^\alpha \mathring{w}_\beta \nabla_j \mathring{w}^\beta) + \cdots. \end{aligned} \tag{5.8}$$

Formula (5.8) is true in any curvilinear coordinate system. The discarded remaining terms are of the fourth order of magnitude.

6. Kinematic tensors characterizing a deformation

In § 4 and § 5, various tensors were introduced which can characterize the geometrical properties of finite displacements and deformations of a continuum.

In this Section, we shall be considering tensors which represent the kinematic characteristics of the displacements and deformations.

The displacement $d\boldsymbol{r}$ of points of the continuum during the time interval dt can be represented in the form

$$d\boldsymbol{r} = dx^1(\xi^1, \xi^2, \xi^3, t)\,\boldsymbol{\vartheta}_1 + dx^2(\xi^1, \xi^2, \xi^3, t)\,\boldsymbol{\vartheta}_2 + dx^3(\xi^1, \xi^2, \xi^3, t)\,\boldsymbol{\vartheta}_3, \quad (6.1)$$

in which the displacement vector $d\boldsymbol{r}$ and its components dx^1, dx^2, dx^3 refer to a fixed particle at constant values of ξ^i.

Obviously, the velocity vector of the various particles is defined by the formula

$$\mathbf{v} = \frac{d\boldsymbol{r}}{dt} = v^\alpha \boldsymbol{\vartheta}_\alpha, \qquad v^\alpha = \left(\frac{dx^\alpha}{\partial t}\right)_{\xi^i = \mathrm{const}}. \quad (6.2)$$

The acceleration vector is defined by

$$\boldsymbol{j} = \left(\frac{d\mathbf{v}}{dt}\right)_{\xi^i = \mathrm{const}} = \left(\frac{\partial v^\alpha}{\partial t}\right)_{\xi^i = \mathrm{const}} \boldsymbol{\vartheta}_\alpha + v^\lambda \left(\frac{d\boldsymbol{\vartheta}_\lambda}{dt}\right)_{\substack{\xi^i = \mathrm{const} \\ x^i = \mathrm{variable}}}.$$

Using formulas (10.5) and (10.18) of Chapter I, we obtain

$$\boldsymbol{j} = \left[\left(\frac{\partial v^\alpha}{\partial t}\right)_{\xi^i = \mathrm{const}} + v^\omega v^\lambda \Gamma^\alpha_{\lambda\omega}\right] \boldsymbol{\vartheta}_\alpha$$

$$= \left[\left(\frac{\partial v^\alpha}{\partial t}\right)_{x^i = \mathrm{const}} + v^\omega \nabla_\omega v^\alpha\right] \boldsymbol{\vartheta}_\alpha = \left(\frac{dv^\alpha}{dt}\right)_{\mathrm{total}} \boldsymbol{\vartheta}_\alpha, \quad (6.3)$$

where $(dv^\alpha/dt)_{\mathrm{total}}$ is the total derivative with respect to time t.

Formulas (6.2) and (6.3) define the components of velocity and acceleration in any curvilinear Eulerian coordinate system.

In an analogous way, we can define the acceleration vector of higher order.

For example, the components of the derivative $d\boldsymbol{j}/dt = \boldsymbol{\Omega}$ can be expressed in terms of the components j^α in accordance with a formula of the type (6.3), in which v^λ and v^α must be replaced by j^λ and j^α, and these in turn can be replaced by the components of $\mathbf{v}$ according to formulas (6.3).

If the velocity vector $\mathbf{v}$ is defined in the bases $\mathring{\boldsymbol{\vartheta}}_i$ or $\hat{\boldsymbol{\vartheta}}_i$, then, when all three bases coincide at a particular instant of time t, we get

$$\mathbf{v} = v^\alpha \boldsymbol{\vartheta}_\alpha = v^\alpha \mathring{\boldsymbol{\vartheta}}_\alpha = v^\alpha \hat{\boldsymbol{\vartheta}}_\alpha. \quad (6.4)$$

However, at subsequent instants of time, the bases $\hat{\boldsymbol{\vartheta}}_\alpha$ and $\boldsymbol{\vartheta}_\alpha$ will be different, and a moving point will be displaced to a different position in the stationary basis $\boldsymbol{\vartheta}_\alpha$.

The basis $\mathring{\boldsymbol{\vartheta}}_\alpha$ is taken in the space of initial states. The bases $\hat{\boldsymbol{\vartheta}}_\alpha$ and $\boldsymbol{\vartheta}_\alpha$ are taken in a single space. The correspondence between these bases is established by the transformation of coordinates. Therefore, for all instants of time

$t' > t$, we have

$$\mathbf{v} = \hat{v}^\alpha \hat{\mathfrak{I}}_\alpha = v^\alpha \mathfrak{I}_\alpha, \qquad \mathbf{v} \neq \hat{v}^\alpha \mathring{\mathfrak{I}}_\alpha = \mathring{\mathbf{v}}; \tag{6.5}$$

by using for the acceleration the moving Lagrangian basis $\hat{\mathfrak{I}}_\alpha$ and equations (10.4) of Chapter I, we have

$$\boldsymbol{j} = \frac{d\mathbf{v}}{dt} = \left[\left(\frac{\partial \hat{v}^\alpha}{\partial t}\right)_{\xi^i = \text{const}} + \hat{v}^\omega \nabla_\omega \hat{v}^\alpha\right] \hat{\mathfrak{I}}_\alpha. \tag{6.6}$$

Since at the instant t we can take $\mathfrak{I}_\alpha = \hat{\mathfrak{I}}_\alpha$, it follows from (6.3) and (6.6) that

$$\left(\frac{\partial v^\alpha}{\partial t}\right)_{x^i = \text{const}} = \left(\frac{\partial \hat{v}^\alpha}{\partial t}\right)_{\xi^i = \text{const}}. \tag{6.7}$$

Formula (6.7) is valid only for the velocity components; for the other vectors, an analogous formula would not hold [see formula (10.13) of Chapter I].

Let us also define a vector $\boldsymbol{j}_0 = d\mathbf{v}_0/dt \neq \boldsymbol{j}$. On the basis of equation (6.7) for $\mathfrak{I}_\alpha = \hat{\mathfrak{I}}_\alpha = \mathring{\mathfrak{I}}_\alpha$, we may write for the vector $\boldsymbol{j}_0$ the following:

$$\boldsymbol{j}_0 = \left(\frac{\partial v^\alpha}{\partial t}\right)_{x^i = \text{const}} \mathfrak{I}_\alpha = \left(\frac{\partial \hat{v}^\alpha}{\partial t}\right)_{\xi^i = \text{const}} \hat{\mathfrak{I}}_\alpha = \left(\frac{\partial \hat{v}^\alpha}{\partial t}\right)_{\xi^i = \text{const}} \mathring{\mathfrak{I}}_\alpha.$$

Obviously, for constant motion, $\boldsymbol{j}_0 = 0$.

We now consider a change in the length of elementary segments in unit time. We have $ds^2 - ds_0^2 = 2\varepsilon_{\alpha\beta} d\xi^\alpha d\xi^\beta$. Differentiating this with respect to time, we obtain

$$\frac{d}{dt}(ds^2) = 2e_{\alpha\beta} d\xi^\alpha d\xi^\beta, \qquad \text{where} \qquad e_{\alpha\beta} = \left(\frac{\partial \varepsilon_{\alpha\beta}}{\partial t}\right)_{\xi^i = \text{const}},$$

$$\frac{d^2}{dt^2}(ds^2) = 2j_{\alpha\beta} d\xi^\alpha d\xi^\beta, \qquad \text{where} \qquad j_{\alpha\beta} = \frac{\partial e_{\alpha\beta}}{\partial t} = \left(\frac{\partial^2 \varepsilon_{\alpha\beta}}{\partial t^2}\right)_{\xi^i = \text{const}}.$$

Obviously, the quantities $e_{\alpha\beta}$ and $j_{\alpha\beta}$ can be thought of as the covariant components of tensors

$$\mathring{\mathfrak{E}} = e_{\alpha\beta} \mathring{\mathfrak{I}}^\alpha \mathring{\mathfrak{I}}^\beta, \qquad \mathring{J} = j_{\alpha\beta} \mathring{\mathfrak{I}}^\alpha \mathring{\mathfrak{I}}^\beta,$$
$$\mathfrak{E} = e_{\alpha\beta} \hat{\mathfrak{I}}^\alpha \hat{\mathfrak{I}}^\beta, \qquad J = j_{\alpha\beta} \hat{\mathfrak{I}}^\alpha \hat{\mathfrak{I}}^\beta,$$

where also

$$\begin{aligned} \mathring{\mathfrak{E}} &= \frac{d\mathring{\mathscr{E}}}{dt}, \qquad \mathring{J} = \frac{d\mathring{\mathfrak{E}}}{dt} = \frac{d^2\mathring{\mathscr{E}}}{dt^2}, \\ \mathfrak{E} &\neq \frac{d\hat{\mathscr{E}}}{dt}, \qquad J \neq \frac{d\mathfrak{E}}{dt}. \end{aligned} \tag{6.8}$$

The symmetric tensor $\mathfrak{E}$ is called the tensor of the velocity of deformation. The product $\mathfrak{E}dt$ can be considered, for infinitesimal dt, as an infinitesimal deformation tensor $d\mathscr{E}$ for a displacement taking place in time dt. From this, in particular, follows the mechanical significance of all the components of $\mathfrak{E}$.

The symmetric tensor $\boldsymbol{J}$ characterizes the accelerations of a pure deformation.

Let us give formulas for the components $e_{\alpha\beta}$ and $j_{\alpha\beta}$ in terms of the components of the velocity vector $\mathbf{v}$. We have

$$\varepsilon_{\alpha\beta} = \tfrac{1}{2}(\hat{\mathfrak{Z}}_\alpha, \hat{\mathfrak{Z}}_\beta) - \tfrac{1}{2}(\mathring{\mathfrak{Z}}_\alpha, \mathring{\mathfrak{Z}}_\beta), \qquad e_{\alpha\beta} = \tfrac{1}{2}\left[\left(\hat{\mathfrak{Z}}_\alpha, \frac{d\hat{\mathfrak{Z}}_\beta}{dt}\right) + \left(\frac{d\hat{\mathfrak{Z}}_\alpha}{dt}, \hat{\mathfrak{Z}}_\beta\right)\right].$$

Then, since

$$d\hat{\mathfrak{Z}}_i/dt = d\mathbf{v}/d\xi^i = \nabla_j v_\omega \hat{\mathfrak{Z}}^\omega,$$

we have

$$e_{\alpha\beta} = \tfrac{1}{2}(\nabla_\beta v_\alpha + \nabla_\alpha v_\beta). \tag{6.9}$$

It is obvious that if at a given moment of time an infinitesimal rigid-body displacement takes place in the medium, then $e_{\alpha\beta} = 0$; that is, the velocity tensor of the deformation equals zero. Conversely, if at every point of the body $e_{\alpha\beta} = 0$, the corresponding velocity field and the infinitesimal displacement of the medium are the same as in a rigid body. Further, for $j_{\alpha\beta}$, we have

$$j_{\alpha\beta} = \tfrac{1}{2}\left[\left(\mathfrak{Z}_\alpha, \frac{\partial \boldsymbol{j}}{\partial \xi^\beta}\right) + 2\left(\frac{\partial \mathbf{v}}{\partial \xi^\alpha}, \frac{\partial \mathbf{v}}{\partial \xi^\beta}\right) + \left(\frac{\partial \boldsymbol{j}}{\partial \xi^\alpha}, \mathfrak{Z}_\beta\right)\right].$$

From this, we obtain

$$j_{\alpha\beta} = \tfrac{1}{2}[\nabla_\beta j_\alpha + 2\nabla_\alpha v^\omega \nabla_\beta v_\omega + \nabla_\alpha j_\beta]. \tag{6.10}$$

In this formula, the components of the acceleration j_k can be replaced by the corresponding velocity components according to (6.6).

Formulas (6.9) contain only derivatives with respect to the coordinates and they are true in any curvilinear coordinate system, more particularly, in systems with the bases $\hat{\mathfrak{Z}}_i$ and $\mathfrak{Z}_i$.

We can introduce a tensor $\hat{\mathfrak{E}}$, in addition to the velocity of deformation tensor $\mathfrak{E}$, and define it as the individual time derivatives of the tensor

$$\mathscr{E} = \varepsilon_{\alpha\beta}\hat{\mathfrak{Z}}^\alpha\hat{\mathfrak{Z}}^\beta = \varepsilon'_{\alpha\beta}\mathfrak{Z}^\alpha\mathfrak{Z}^\beta.$$

We have

$$\hat{\mathfrak{E}} = \left(\frac{d\mathscr{E}}{dt}\right)_{\xi^i} = \hat{e}_{\alpha\beta}\hat{\mathfrak{Z}}^\alpha\hat{\mathfrak{Z}}^\beta = e'_{\alpha\beta}\mathfrak{Z}^\alpha\mathfrak{Z}^\beta.$$

For the components $\hat{e}_{\alpha\beta}$ and $e'_{\alpha\beta}$, we have

$$\hat{e}_{\alpha\beta} = e_{\alpha\beta} - \varepsilon_{\lambda\beta}\nabla_{\alpha}\hat{v}^{\lambda} - \varepsilon_{\alpha\lambda}\nabla_{\beta}\hat{v}^{\lambda},$$

$$e'_{\alpha\beta} = \left(\frac{\partial\varepsilon'_{\alpha\beta}}{\partial t}\right)_{\xi^i} - \varepsilon'_{\alpha\omega}\Gamma^{\omega}_{\lambda\beta}v^{\lambda} - \varepsilon'_{\omega\beta}\Gamma^{\omega}_{\lambda\alpha}v^{\lambda} = \left(\frac{\partial\varepsilon'_{\alpha\beta}}{\partial t}\right)_{x^i} + v^{\lambda}\nabla_{\lambda}\varepsilon'_{\alpha\beta} = \left(\frac{d\varepsilon'_{\alpha\beta}}{dt}\right)_{\xi^i}, \tag{6.11}$$

where $(d\varepsilon'_{\alpha\beta}/dt)_{\xi^i}$ is the total individual derivative of $\varepsilon'_{\alpha\beta}$ with respect to time and $\hat{v}^i$ and v^i are the components of the velocity vector $\mathbf{v}$ in the bases $\hat{\mathfrak{I}}_i$ and $\mathfrak{I}_i$.

Formulas (6.11) are valid in any curvilinear coordinate system; as a special case, assuming that at some instant the bases $\hat{\mathfrak{I}}_i$ and $\mathfrak{I}_i$ coincide, we obtain

$$e_{\alpha\beta} = \left(\frac{\partial\varepsilon'_{\alpha\beta}}{\partial t}\right)_{\xi^i} + \varepsilon_{\lambda\beta}\frac{\partial\hat{v}^{\lambda}}{\partial\xi^{\alpha}} + \varepsilon_{\alpha\lambda}\frac{\partial\hat{v}^{\lambda}}{\partial\xi^{\beta}} = \left(\frac{\partial\varepsilon'_{\alpha\beta}}{\partial t}\right)_{\xi^i} + \varepsilon_{\lambda\beta}\frac{\partial v^{\lambda}}{\partial x^{\alpha}} + \varepsilon_{\alpha\lambda}\frac{\partial\hat{v}^{\lambda}}{\partial x^{\beta}}$$

$$= \left(\frac{d\varepsilon'_{\alpha\beta}}{dt}\right)_{\xi^i} + \varepsilon_{\lambda\beta}\nabla_{\alpha}v^{\lambda} + \varepsilon_{\alpha\lambda}\nabla_{\beta}v^{\lambda}. \tag{6.12}$$

The derivatives $(\partial\varepsilon'_{\alpha\beta}/\partial t)_{\xi^i}$ and $(d\varepsilon'_{\alpha\beta}/dt)_{\xi^i}$ coincide when the reference system is cartesian.

The tensor $\mathring{\mathfrak{E}} = d\mathscr{E}/dt$ represents the kinematic characteristic of the motion of a continuum, which is connected with the velocities of the deformation and the velocities of the motion of points of the medium.

In a similar way, one can introduce tensors obtained as the second derivatives of the tensor $\mathscr{E}$, $d^2\mathscr{E}/dt^2$ and higher-order derivatives.

The components with the contravariant indices of the tensor $\mathring{\mathfrak{E}}$ are obtained from (6.11) by raising the indices with the aid of the tensors $\hat{g}^{ik}(\xi^i, t)$ in the basis $\hat{\mathfrak{I}}_i$ and with the aid of the tensor $g^{ik}(x^i)$ in the basis $\mathfrak{I}_i$.

If the velocities and deformations are small, then, after retaining only first-order terms, we see that the above-introduced tensors $\mathfrak{E}$ and $\mathring{\mathfrak{E}}$ are identical. In accordance with equation (5.7) for the skew-symmetric tensor $d\mathring{\mathbf{K}}/dt$ and in accordance with equation (3.14) of Chapter I, the components of the vector of rotation, which is equal to the angular velocity of rotation of the axes of deformation, are given by

$$\omega^i = \tfrac{1}{2}\sqrt{g_1}\left(\frac{\partial v_k}{\partial\eta^j} - \frac{\partial v_i}{\partial\eta^k}\right), \qquad g_1 = \frac{1}{g} = |g^{ik}|. \tag{6.13}$$

This formula defines the components of the vector of rotation in an arbitrary curvilinear coordinate system; the indices i, j, k, are taken in a cyclic permutation of 1, 2, and 3.

7. The differentiation of nonlinear tensor functions

In formulas (10.26) and (10.29) of Chapter I, the quantities $\nabla_i v^j$ can be replaced by the components e_{ij} of the velocity of deformation tensor and the components Ω_{ij} of the rotation tensor by means of the formula

$$\tfrac{1}{2}(\nabla_i v_j + \nabla_j v_i) = e_{ij} \qquad \text{and} \qquad \tfrac{1}{2}(\nabla_i v_j - \nabla_j v_i) = \Omega_{ij},$$

where the components of velocity v^i, the components e_{ij} of the velocity of deformation tensor, and the components of rotation Ω_{ij} are taken for the motion of some basis $\hat{\text{Э}}_i$ with respect to some generally moving reference system with basis $\mathring{\text{Э}}_i$ (see § 10, Chapter I).

In particular, the basis $\hat{\text{Э}}_i$ can be associated with a coordinate system frozen into the medium, and $\mathring{\text{Э}}_i$ can be a moving basis, its given equations of motion being defined with respect to a stationary coordinate system with basis Э_i.

Using the laws for "juggling" indices for e_{ij} and Ω_{ij}, formulas (10.26) to (10.29) of Chapter I can be written in the form

$$\frac{d\hat{h}^{\alpha\beta}}{dt} = \left(\frac{dh^{\alpha\beta}}{dt}\right)_{\text{total}} - h^{\omega\beta}\Omega_{\omega\cdot}^{\cdot\alpha} - h^{\alpha\omega}\Omega_{\omega\cdot}^{\cdot\beta} - h^{\omega\beta}e_{\omega\cdot}^{\cdot\alpha} - h^{\alpha\omega}e_{\omega\cdot}^{\cdot\beta}, \tag{7.1}$$

$$\frac{d\hat{h}^{\alpha\cdot}_{\cdot\beta}}{dt} = \left(\frac{dh^{\alpha\cdot}_{\cdot\beta}}{dt}\right)_{\text{total}} - h^{\omega\cdot}_{\cdot\beta}\Omega_{\omega\cdot}^{\cdot\alpha} + h^{\alpha\cdot}_{\cdot\omega}\Omega_{\beta\cdot}^{\cdot\omega} - h^{\omega\cdot}_{\cdot\beta}e_{\omega\cdot}^{\cdot\alpha} + h^{\alpha\cdot}_{\cdot\omega}e_{\beta\cdot}^{\cdot\omega}, \tag{7.2}$$

$$\frac{d\hat{h}_{\alpha\cdot}^{\cdot\beta}}{dt} = \left(\frac{dh_{\alpha\cdot}^{\cdot\beta}}{dt}\right)_{\text{total}} + h_{\omega\cdot}^{\cdot\beta}\Omega_{\alpha\cdot}^{\cdot\omega} - h_{\alpha\cdot}^{\cdot\omega}\Omega_{\omega\cdot}^{\cdot\beta} + h_{\omega\cdot}^{\cdot\beta}e_{\alpha\cdot}^{\cdot\omega} - h_{\alpha\cdot}^{\cdot\omega}e_{\omega\cdot}^{\cdot\beta}, \tag{7.3}$$

$$\frac{d\hat{h}_{\alpha\beta}}{dt} = \left(\frac{dh_{\alpha\beta}}{dt}\right)_{\text{total}} + h_{\omega\beta}\Omega_{\alpha\cdot}^{\cdot\omega} + h_{\alpha\omega}\Omega_{\beta\cdot}^{\cdot\omega} + h_{\omega\beta}e_{\alpha\cdot}^{\cdot\omega} + h_{\alpha\omega}e_{\beta\cdot}^{\cdot\omega}. \tag{7.4}$$

If the coordinate system with basis $\mathring{\text{Э}}_i$ is cartesian, at every instant of time we have $h^{ij} = h_{ij} = h^{i\cdot}_{\cdot j} = h_{i\cdot}^{\cdot j}$, and, moreover, $\Omega_{i\cdot}^{\cdot j} = \Omega^{i\cdot}_{\cdot j} = \Omega_{ij} = -\Omega_{ji}$. Using the tensor properties of the quantities in question, we obtain for any curvilinear coordinate system corresponding to the bases $\mathring{\text{Э}}_i$ or $\hat{\text{Э}}_i$,

$$\begin{aligned}(h_{\omega\beta}\Omega_{\alpha\cdot}^{\cdot\omega} + h_{\alpha\omega}\Omega_{\beta\cdot}^{\cdot\omega})\,\mathring{\text{Э}}^{\alpha}\mathring{\text{Э}}^{\beta} &= (h_{\omega\cdot}^{\cdot\beta}\Omega_{\alpha\cdot}^{\cdot\omega} - h_{\alpha\cdot}^{\cdot\omega}\Omega_{\omega\cdot}^{\cdot\beta})\,\mathring{\text{Э}}^{\alpha}\mathring{\text{Э}}_{\beta}\\ &= (-h^{\omega\cdot}_{\cdot\beta}\Omega_{\omega\cdot}^{\cdot\alpha} + h^{\alpha\cdot}_{\cdot\omega}\Omega_{\beta\cdot}^{\cdot\omega})\,\mathring{\text{Э}}_{\alpha}\mathring{\text{Э}}^{\beta} = (-h^{\omega\beta}\Omega_{\omega\cdot}^{\cdot\alpha} - h^{\alpha\omega}\Omega_{\omega\cdot}^{\cdot\beta})\,\mathring{\text{Э}}_{\alpha}\mathring{\text{Э}}_{\beta}.\end{aligned}$$

The derivatives of the components $d\hat{h}^{\alpha\beta}/dt$, $d\hat{h}^{\alpha\cdot}_{\cdot\beta}/dt$, etc., generally form different tensors. This also applies to derivatives of the type $(dh^{\alpha\beta}/dt)_{\text{total}}$ and $(dh^{\alpha\cdot}_{\cdot\beta}/dt)_{\text{total}}$, etc. If, however, the basis $\mathring{\text{Э}}_i$ is rigid, i.e., $(\mathring{\text{Э}}_i, \mathring{\text{Э}}_j) = \mathring{g}_{ij} = \text{const}$, we quite obviously have

$$\left(\frac{dh^{\alpha\beta}}{dt}\right)_{\text{total}} \hat{\mathfrak{I}}_\alpha \hat{\mathfrak{I}}_\beta = \left(\frac{dh^{\alpha\cdot}_{\cdot\beta}}{dt}\right)_{\text{total}} \hat{\mathfrak{I}}_\alpha \hat{\mathfrak{I}}^\beta = \left(\frac{dh^{\cdot\beta}_{\alpha\cdot}}{dt}\right)_{\text{total}} \hat{\mathfrak{I}}^\alpha \hat{\mathfrak{I}}_\beta = \left(\frac{dh_{\alpha\beta}}{dt}\right)_{\text{total}} \hat{\mathfrak{I}}^\alpha \hat{\mathfrak{I}}^\beta .$$

Consequently, in this case the total derivatives of tensor $\boldsymbol{H}$ of the type $(dh^{\alpha\beta}/dt)_{\text{total}}$ define one and the same tensor.

If the basis $\hat{\mathfrak{I}}_i = \mathfrak{I}_i$ is stationary and $\hat{\mathfrak{I}}_i$ is frozen into the medium ($e_{ik} \neq 0$), the tensor given by

$$\left[\left(\frac{dh^{\alpha\beta}}{dt}\right)_{\text{total}} - h^{\omega\beta}\Omega^{\cdot\alpha}_{\omega\cdot} - h^{\alpha\omega}\Omega^{\cdot\beta}_{\omega\cdot}\right]\mathfrak{I}_\alpha \mathfrak{I}_\beta$$

$$= \left[\left(\frac{dh^{\alpha\cdot}_{\cdot\beta}}{dt}\right)_{\text{total}} - h^{\omega\cdot}_{\cdot\beta}\Omega^{\cdot\alpha}_{\omega\cdot} + h^{\alpha\cdot}_{\cdot\omega}\Omega^{\cdot\omega}_{\beta\cdot}\right]\mathfrak{I}_\alpha \mathfrak{I}^\beta$$

$$= \left[\left(\frac{dh^{\cdot\beta}_{\alpha\cdot}}{dt}\right)_{\text{total}} + h^{\cdot\beta}_{\omega\cdot}\Omega^{\cdot\omega}_{\alpha\cdot} - h^{\cdot\omega}_{\alpha\cdot}\Omega^{\cdot\beta}_{\omega\cdot}\right]\mathfrak{I}^\alpha \mathfrak{I}_\beta$$

$$= \left[\left(\frac{dh_{\alpha\beta}}{dt}\right)_{\text{total}} + h_{\omega\beta}\Omega^{\cdot\omega}_{\alpha\cdot} + h_{\alpha\omega}\Omega^{\cdot\omega}_{\beta\cdot}\right]\mathfrak{I}^\alpha \mathfrak{I}^\beta$$

represents the relative derivative in the context of Jaumann (see § 10, Chapter I).

If bases $\hat{\mathfrak{I}}_i$, $\hat{\mathfrak{I}}_i$ move as a rigid body, the derivatives of the type $d\hat{h}^{\alpha\beta}/dt$, $dh^{\alpha\cdot}_{\cdot\beta}/dt$, etc., also form a system of components of one and the same tensor, since $e_{ik} \equiv 0$.

Hence in this case, instead of four different tensors V_1, V_2, V_3, V_4, we obtain only one, and formulas (7.1) to (7.4) together with $e_{ik} = 0$ give the components of this tensor, which has a different index structure in an arbitrary curvilinear system. These components are equal to the components of the derivative of a tensor of the Jaumann type when $\hat{\mathfrak{I}}_i$ is a stationary basis and the Ω_{ij} are the tensor components of the rotation vector.

Let us also consider the special case when the basis $\hat{\mathfrak{I}}_i$ is stationary and the tensor $\boldsymbol{H}$ is symmetric but varying with time. The principal axes of $\boldsymbol{H}$ form an orthogonal trihedral. We direct the unit vectors $\hat{\mathfrak{I}}_i$ of the cartesian system along the principal axes of the tensor $\boldsymbol{H}$.

The cartesian basis $\hat{\mathfrak{I}}_i$, generally speaking, rotates with some angular velocity $\boldsymbol{\omega} = \omega^\alpha \hat{\mathfrak{I}}_\alpha = \omega^\alpha \hat{\mathfrak{I}}_\alpha$ (we assume that $\hat{\mathfrak{I}}_i$ and $\hat{\mathfrak{I}}_i$ coincide at the instant of time under consideration).

To the angular velocity $\boldsymbol{\omega}$ there corresponds the skew-symmetric tensor with matrix

$$\|\omega_{\alpha\beta}\| = \left\| \begin{matrix} 0 & -\omega^3 & \omega^2 \\ \omega^3 & 0 & -\omega^1 \\ -\omega^2 & \omega^1 & 0 \end{matrix} \right\| .$$

At a given instant in the basis $\hat{\mathfrak{Э}}_i$, the components of the tensor $\boldsymbol{H}$ with any arrangement of the indices in the basis $\hat{\mathfrak{Э}}_i$ form one and the same canonical matrix

$$\begin{Vmatrix} h_1(t) & 0 & 0 \\ 0 & h_2(t) & 0 \\ 0 & 0 & h_3(t) \end{Vmatrix},$$

where h_i are the roots of the characteristic equation.

Since the basis $\hat{\mathfrak{Э}}_i$ is cartesian, the derivatives $d\hat{h}^{\alpha\beta}/dt$, $d\hat{h}^{\alpha\cdot}_{\cdot\beta}/dt$, and $d\hat{h}_{\alpha\beta}/dt$ form one and the same matrix.

From formulas (7.1), (7.2), and (7.4) and from the rules for the addition of velocities [(10.30) of Chapter I], we obtain for these components

$$\frac{d\hat{h}^{\alpha\beta}}{dt} = \frac{d\hat{h}^{\alpha\cdot}_{\cdot\beta}}{dt} = \frac{dh_{\alpha\beta}}{dt} = \frac{dh_\alpha}{dt}\delta^{\alpha\cdot}_{\cdot\beta} - (h_\beta - h_\alpha)\,\omega_{\alpha\beta}. \tag{7.5}$$

In this formula the indices α and β are fixed (there is no summation over the same indices).

It is obvious that, in general, the principal axes of $\boldsymbol{H}$ are not the principal axes of the tensor derivative $d\boldsymbol{H}/dt$. The principal axes of $d\boldsymbol{H}/dt$ and $\boldsymbol{H}$ coincide only when $\omega = 0$, i.e., when the principal axes of the tensor retain their directions in space.

We now assume that tensor $\boldsymbol{H}$ is an isotropic function of some symmetric tensor $\boldsymbol{T}$ which is time-dependent in the stationary basis $\hat{\mathfrak{Э}}_i$:

$$\boldsymbol{H} = f(\boldsymbol{T}).$$

From this assumption, it follows that the principal axes of the tensors $\boldsymbol{H}$ and $\boldsymbol{T}$ coincide. Consequently, the principal axes of tensors $\boldsymbol{T}$ and $\boldsymbol{H}$ rotate at the same angular velocity $\boldsymbol{\omega}$.

Besides (7.5), we can also write in the basis $\hat{\mathfrak{Э}}_i$

$$\frac{d\hat{T}^{\alpha\beta}}{dt} = \frac{d\hat{T}^{\alpha\cdot}_{\cdot\beta}}{dt} = \frac{dT_{\alpha\beta}}{dt} = \frac{dT_\alpha}{dt}\delta^{\alpha\cdot}_{\cdot\beta} - (T_\beta - T_\alpha)\,\omega_{\alpha\beta}, \tag{7.6}$$

where T_i are the principal components of $\boldsymbol{T}$.

Because $h_i = f(T_i)$, on the basis of (7.5) and (7.6), we obtain

$$\frac{d\hat{h}^{\alpha\cdot}_{\cdot\beta}}{dt} = f'(T_\alpha)\frac{dT_\alpha}{dt}\delta^{\alpha\cdot}_{\cdot\beta} + \frac{f(T_\beta) - f(T_\alpha)}{T_\beta - T_\alpha}\left[\frac{d\hat{T}^{\alpha\cdot}_{\cdot\beta}}{dt} - \frac{dT_\alpha}{dt}\delta^{\alpha\cdot}_{\cdot\beta}\right]. \tag{7.7}$$

Using (7.6), the diagonal elements with $\alpha = \beta$ are given by

$$\frac{d\hat{h}^{\alpha\cdot}_{\cdot\beta}}{dt} = f'(T_\alpha)\frac{dT_\alpha}{dt} = f'(T_\alpha)\frac{d\hat{T}^{\alpha\cdot}_{\cdot\beta}}{dt}. \tag{7.8}$$

If $\alpha \neq \beta$, we get

$$\frac{d\hat{h}^{\alpha\cdot}_{\cdot\beta}}{dt} = \frac{f(T_\beta) - f(T_\alpha)}{T_\beta - T_\alpha} \frac{d\hat{T}^{\alpha\cdot}_{\cdot\beta}}{dt}. \tag{7.9}$$

Thus for isotropic tensor functions in stationary cartesian coordinate systems in which the principal axes coincide at the given instant of time, formulas (7.8) and (7.9) can be written in differential form as

$$dh^{\alpha\cdot}_{\cdot\beta} = f'(T_\alpha)\, dT^{\alpha\cdot}_{\cdot\beta} \quad \text{and} \quad dh^{\alpha\cdot}_{\cdot\beta} = \frac{f(T_\beta) - f(T_\alpha)}{T_\beta - T_\alpha} dT^{\alpha\cdot}_{\cdot\beta}. \tag{7.10}$$

The first of these formulas is obtained from the second by formally going to the limit as $\beta \to 0$.

Obviously, equations analogous to (7.10) can be written for the differentials of tensors with a different arrangement of the indices.

The relationship between the differentials of the tensor $dh^{i\cdot}_{\cdot j}$ and $dT^{i\cdot}_{\cdot j}$ in any stationary curvilinear coordinate system can be obtained from (7.10) by using the formulas for the transformation of tensor components.

Let us now consider the relative derivatives and differentials of symmetrical second-rank tensors in a coordinate system with basis $\hat{\mathrm{Э}}_i$ frozen into the moving deformable medium. It is obvious that, in the general case, the motion of the medium and the rotation of the principal axes of a particular tensor are different and independent of one another.

Choosing all bases to be coincident and directed along the principal axes of the tensor, we may use formulas (7.1), (7.2), (7.3), and (7.4) for the required derivatives. Formula (7.5) gives derivatives of the type $(dh^{\alpha\beta}/dt)_{\text{total}}$ with respect to the stationary coordinate system with basis $\mathrm{Э}_i$, which appear as the first terms in formulas (7.1) to (7.4).

Carrying out the substitution, we obtain

$$\frac{d\hat{h}^{\alpha\beta}}{dt} = \frac{dh_\alpha}{dt}\delta^{\alpha\cdot}_{\cdot\beta} + (h_\beta - h_\alpha)(\Omega_{\alpha\beta} - \omega_{\alpha\beta}) - (h_\beta + h_\alpha)e_{\alpha\beta}, \tag{7.11}$$

$$\frac{d\hat{h}^{\alpha\cdot}_{\cdot\beta}}{dt} = \frac{dh_\alpha}{dt}\delta^{\alpha\cdot}_{\cdot\beta} + (h_\beta - h_\alpha)(\Omega_{\alpha\beta} - \omega_{\alpha\beta}) - (h_\beta - h_\alpha)e_{\alpha\beta}, \tag{7.12}$$

$$\frac{d\hat{h}^{\cdot\beta}_{\alpha\cdot}}{dt} = \frac{dh_\alpha}{dt}\delta^{\alpha\cdot}_{\cdot\beta} + (h_\beta - h_\alpha)(\Omega_{\alpha\beta} - \omega_{\alpha\beta}) + (h_\beta - h_\alpha)e_{\alpha\beta}, \tag{7.13}$$

$$\frac{d\hat{h}_{\alpha\beta}}{dt} = \frac{dh_\alpha}{dt}\delta^{\alpha\cdot}_{\cdot\beta} + (h_\beta - h_\alpha)(\Omega_{\alpha\beta} - \omega_{\alpha\beta}) + (h_\beta + h_\alpha)e_{\alpha\beta}. \tag{7.14}$$

In these formulas, the indices α and β are fixed. It is also obvious that the components $\Omega_{\alpha\beta}$ and $\omega_{\alpha\beta}$ generally define different skew-symmetric tensors.

Because of the terms which contain the components of the velocity of deformation tensor, the four derivatives (7.11) to (7.14) define four different tensors.

If a tensor $\boldsymbol{H} = f(\boldsymbol{T})$ is an isotropic function of the tensor $\boldsymbol{T}$, we can write for $\boldsymbol{T}$ formulas analogous to (7.11) through (7.14). Using the formulas for the relative derivatives of the tensors $\boldsymbol{T}$ and $\boldsymbol{H}$, it is possible to eliminate the quantity $\Omega_{\alpha\beta} - \omega_{\alpha\beta}$; we then obtain

$$\frac{d\hat{h}^{\alpha\beta}}{dt} = \frac{dh_\alpha}{dt}\delta^{\alpha\cdot}_{\cdot\beta} + \frac{h_\beta - h_\alpha}{T_\beta - T_\alpha}\left[\frac{d\hat{T}^{\alpha\beta}}{dt} - \frac{dT_\alpha}{dt}\delta^{\alpha\cdot}_{\cdot\beta}\right] - 2\frac{h_\alpha T_\beta - h_\beta T_\alpha}{T_\beta - T_\alpha}e_{\alpha\beta}, \tag{7.15}$$

$$\frac{d\hat{h}^{\alpha\cdot}_{\cdot\beta}}{dt} = \frac{dh_\alpha}{dt}\delta^{\alpha\cdot}_{\cdot\beta} + \frac{h_\beta - h_\alpha}{T_\beta - T_\alpha}\left[\frac{d\hat{T}^{\alpha\cdot}_{\cdot\beta}}{dt} - \frac{dT_\alpha}{dt}\delta^{\alpha\cdot}_{\cdot\beta}\right], \tag{7.16}$$

$$\frac{d\hat{h}^{\cdot\beta}_{\alpha\cdot}}{dt} = \frac{dh_\alpha}{dt}\delta^{\beta\cdot}_{\cdot\alpha} + \frac{h_\beta - h_\alpha}{T_\beta - T_\alpha}\left[\frac{d\hat{T}^{\cdot\beta}_{\alpha\cdot}}{dt} - \frac{dT_\alpha}{dt}\delta^{\beta\cdot}_{\cdot\alpha}\right], \tag{7.17}$$

$$\frac{d\hat{h}_{\alpha\beta}}{dt} = \frac{dh_\alpha}{dt}\delta^{\alpha\cdot}_{\cdot\beta} + \frac{h_\beta - h_\alpha}{T_\beta - T_\alpha}\left[\frac{d\hat{T}_{\alpha\beta}}{dt} - \frac{dT_\alpha}{dt}\delta^{\alpha\cdot}_{\cdot\beta}\right] + 2\frac{h_\alpha T_\beta - h_\beta T_\alpha}{T_\beta - T_\alpha}e_{\alpha\beta}. \tag{7.18}$$

Because the derivatives $d\hat{T}^{\alpha\beta}/dt$, $d\hat{T}^{\alpha\cdot}_{\cdot\beta}/dt$, $d\hat{T}^{\cdot\beta}_{\alpha\cdot}/dt$, and $d\hat{T}_{\alpha\beta}/dt$ are all different from each other, the terms that are independent of $e_{\alpha\beta}$ in formulas (7.15) to (7.18) are all different; however, they become equal for $e_{\alpha\beta} = 0$.

If the principal axes of tensors $\boldsymbol{T}$, $\boldsymbol{H}$, and the finite deformation tensor $\mathscr{E} = \varepsilon_{\alpha\beta}\hat{\boldsymbol{\partial}}^\alpha\hat{\boldsymbol{\partial}}^\beta$ coincide, then $\Omega_{\alpha\beta} = \omega_{\alpha\beta}$.

In this case, one can eliminate the components e_{ij}, after which we see that equations (7.16) and (7.17) preserve their form; then, together with formulas (7.15) and (7.18), we can write

$$\frac{d\hat{h}^{\alpha\beta}}{dt} = \frac{dh_\alpha}{dt}\delta^{\alpha\cdot}_{\cdot\beta} + \frac{h_\beta + h_\alpha}{T_\beta + T_\alpha}\left(\frac{d\hat{T}^{\alpha\beta}}{dt} - \frac{dT_\alpha}{dt}\delta^{\alpha\cdot}_{\cdot\beta}\right), \tag{7.19}$$

$$\frac{d\hat{h}_{\alpha\beta}}{dt} = \frac{dh_\alpha}{dt}\delta^{\alpha\cdot}_{\cdot\beta} + \frac{h_\beta + h_\alpha}{T_\beta + T_\alpha}\left(\frac{d\hat{T}_{\alpha\beta}}{dt} - \frac{dT_\alpha}{dt}\delta^{\alpha\cdot}_{\cdot\beta}\right). \tag{7.20}$$

Evidently, if the principal axes of the finite deformation tensor $\mathscr{E}$ maintain their direction in space relative to a stationary reference system, the principal axes of the velocity of deformation tensor coincide with the principal axes of the finite deformation tensor; therefore, in the system of the principal axes we find we have $e_{\alpha\beta} = 0$ for $\alpha \neq \beta$. Consequently, it follows that if the principal axes of $\boldsymbol{H}$, $\boldsymbol{T}$, and $\mathscr{E}$ coincide and keep their directions in space, then

$$\frac{d\hat{T}^{\alpha\cdot}_{\cdot\beta}}{dt} = \frac{d\hat{T}^{\cdot\beta}_{\alpha\cdot}}{dt} = \frac{dT_\alpha}{dt}\delta^{\alpha\cdot}_{\cdot\beta} \quad \text{and} \quad \frac{d\hat{h}^{\alpha\cdot}_{\cdot\beta}}{dt} = \frac{d\hat{h}^{\cdot\beta}_{\alpha\cdot}}{dt} = f'(T_\alpha)\frac{dT_\alpha}{dt}\delta^{\alpha\cdot}_{\cdot\beta}. \tag{7.21}$$

For example, for the Hencky tensor defined by the formula

$$\boldsymbol{H} = -\ln\sqrt{\hat{G} - 2\mathscr{E}} \tag{7.22}$$

for a fixed direction of the axes of deformation in the principal axes, the following matrix formulas are valid:

$$\|dh_i\delta^{i\cdot}_{\cdot j}\| = \left\|\frac{d\hat{\varepsilon}_i}{1-2\hat{\varepsilon}}\delta^{i\cdot}_{\cdot j}\right\| = \left\|\frac{\delta^{i\cdot}_{\cdot\beta}}{1-2\hat{\varepsilon}_i}\right\|\cdot\|d\hat{\varepsilon}_\beta\delta^{\beta\cdot}_{\cdot j}\| = \|(1-2\hat{\varepsilon}_i)\,\delta^{i\cdot}_{\cdot\beta}\|^{-1}\cdot\|d\hat{\varepsilon}_\beta\delta^{\beta\cdot}_{\cdot j}\|.$$

On the basis of the rules for the transformation of coordinates (independent of time), it is easy to see that when we use arbitrary curvilinear coordinate systems, these formula are equivalent to

$$\|dh^{i\cdot}_{\cdot j}\| = \|\delta^{i\cdot}_{\cdot\beta} - 2\varepsilon^{i\cdot}_{\cdot\beta}\|^{-1}\,\|d\varepsilon^{\beta\cdot}_{\cdot j}\|. \tag{7.23}$$

This formula is obtained from (7.22) by applying to matrices the general rule for the differentiation of functions.

We note, however, that this differentiation rule is true only in the case in which the axes of deformation retain their directions in space.

If the principal axes of the deformation tensor and the velocity of deformation tensor do not coincide when $e_{\alpha\beta} \neq 0$ for $\alpha \neq \beta$ (which can occur only in the presence of rotation of the axes of deformation), then, if $h_\beta \neq h_\alpha$ for $\alpha \neq \beta$, we find that formulas (7.21) are not valid, and consequently the matrix formulas (7.23) do not follow from formula (7.22).

Let us also define for every point of the moving medium a rigid moving basis $\mathfrak{I}_i$ related to the principal axes of the tensors $\boldsymbol{T}$ and $\boldsymbol{H}$ ($\boldsymbol{H} = f(\boldsymbol{T})$) in some fixed manner and consider the derivatives $d\boldsymbol{T}/dt$ and $d\boldsymbol{H}/dt$ taken with respect to this basis. The expression for the components of these tensors in terms of the components of the derivatives in the stationary system is given by the right-hand members of formulas (7.1) through (7.4), in which we must put $e_{\alpha\beta} = 0$ and $\Omega_{ij} = \omega_{ij}$, where ω_{ij} is the instantaneous angular velocity of rotation of the principal axes of $\boldsymbol{T}$ and $\boldsymbol{H}$.

If the principal axes of tensors $\boldsymbol{H}$ and $\boldsymbol{T}$ coincide with those of the deformation tensor $\mathscr{E} = \varepsilon_{\alpha\beta}\,\mathfrak{I}^\alpha\mathfrak{I}^\beta$, the tensor derivatives $d\boldsymbol{T}/dt$ and $d\boldsymbol{H}/dt$ are the relative derivatives in the Jaumann sense.

It is obvious that the matrices of the tensors $\boldsymbol{T}$ and $d\boldsymbol{T}/dt$, $\boldsymbol{H}$ and $d\boldsymbol{H}/dt$ always have the same principal axes, which can change their directions in stationary space.

It is also clear that together with the functional relationship

$$H = f(T) \tag{7.24}$$

the following differentiation rule for the relative derivatives dH/dt and dT/dt will exist:

$$\frac{dH}{dt} = f'(T)\frac{dT}{dt} \quad \text{or} \quad dH = f'(T)\,dT. \tag{7.25}$$

The above can be regarded as either matrix or tensor equations.

Thus, in general, the relative derivatives dT/dt and dH/dt are always related to one another in the same way as derivatives relative to stationary axes are related when the principal axes of T and H keep their direction in space.

8. Compatibility conditions

The six covariant components $\varepsilon_{\alpha\beta}$ of the tensors $\mathring{\mathscr{E}}$ and $\hat{\mathscr{E}}$ cannot be arbitrary functions of the Lagrangian coordinates ξ^1, ξ^2, ξ^3 of the Eulerian coordinates x^1, x^2, x^3.

We have

$$2\varepsilon_{\alpha\beta} = \hat{g}_{\alpha\beta} - \mathring{g}_{\alpha\beta}\,.$$

Because the quadratic forms

$$ds^2 = \hat{g}_{\alpha\beta}\, d\xi^\alpha\, d\xi^\beta \quad \text{and} \quad ds_0^2 = \mathring{g}_{\alpha\beta}\, d\xi^\alpha\, d\xi^\beta \tag{8.1}$$

define the square of an element of arc in Euclidean space, on the basis of the theory developed in Chapter I, § 9, it follows that the Riemannian tensors formulated for the fundamental tensor $\mathring{g}_{\alpha\beta}$ or $\hat{g}_{\alpha\beta}$ must be zero. This leads to the equations

$$\hat{R}_{ij\mu\nu} = 0 \quad \text{and} \quad \mathring{R}_{ij\mu\nu} = 0\,. \tag{8.2}$$

One of the coordinate bases in the deformed space $\hat{\mathfrak{I}}_i$ or in the space of initial states $\mathring{\mathfrak{I}}_i$ can be chosen arbitrarily. The second of these bases, however, will then be completely defined by the deformation.

One of the equations (8.2) will be satisfied by choosing the appropriate base in Euclidean space. The second can be thought of as the equation for the components $\varepsilon_{\alpha\beta}$.

The corresponding equations can easily be written in unfolded form by using formulas (9.8) and (9.9) of Chapter I.

In particular, if in the deformed state the coordinate system is rectilinear cartesian (generally nonorthogonal), $\partial \hat{g}_{\alpha\beta}/\partial \xi^i = 0$, and therefore the compatibility equations $\mathring{R}_{ij\mu\nu} = 0$ can be written in the form

$$\frac{\partial^2 \varepsilon_{\nu i}}{\partial \xi^j \partial \xi^\mu} + \frac{\partial^2 \varepsilon_{\mu j}}{\partial \xi^i \partial \xi^\nu} - \frac{\partial^2 \varepsilon_{\mu i}}{\partial \xi^j \partial \xi^\nu} - \frac{\partial^2 \varepsilon_{\nu j}}{\partial \xi^i \partial \xi^\mu} + \mathring{g}^{\alpha\omega}\left[G_{\omega\mu j}G_{\alpha\nu i} - G_{\omega\mu i}G_{\alpha\nu j}\right] = 0, \quad (8.3)$$

where

$$G_{\nu\alpha j} = \frac{\partial \varepsilon_{\alpha\nu}}{\partial \xi^j} + \frac{\partial \varepsilon_{j\nu}}{\partial \xi^\alpha} - \frac{\partial \varepsilon_{\alpha j}}{\partial \xi^\nu}, \quad (8.4)$$

and the components $\mathring{g}^{\alpha\omega}$ are defined as the elements of the matrix inverse to the matrix with components $\hat{g}_{\alpha\omega} - 2\varepsilon_{\alpha\omega}$:

$$\|\mathring{g}^{\alpha\omega}\| = \|\hat{g}_{\alpha\omega} - 2\varepsilon_{\alpha\omega}\|^{-1}. \quad (8.5)$$

We can write the compatibility equations $R_{ij\mu\nu} = 0$ in a similar fashion if the Lagrangian system is rectilinear in the original state when $\mathring{g}_{\alpha\beta} = \text{const.}$

The fact that the forms (8.1) are positive definite imposes an additional condition on the components ε_{ij}.

Equations (8.3) for the six functions $\varepsilon_{\alpha\beta}(\xi^1, \xi^2, \xi^3)$ are second-order partial differential equations that are linear with respect to the second derivatives, and nonlinear with respect to the first derivatives.

For all possible combinations of the values 1, 2, 3 for i, j, μ, ν the system (8.3) consists, in all, of six independent equations. These six independent equations correspond to the combinations of indices mentioned in (9.12) of Chapter I ($ij\mu\nu$ = 1212, 1313, 2323, 1213, 2123, 3132).

It is obvious that the formulas (4.31) give the general integral of the system of equations (8.3).

In § 6, by differentiating with respect to time, we introduced tensors which characterize the kinematic properties of the displacements and deformations.

It is obvious that the components of these tensors must also satisfy certain compatibility equations. For example, the components of the velocity of deformation tensor are given by

$$\varepsilon_{\alpha\beta} = e_{\alpha\beta}\Delta t, \quad (8.6)$$

where the $\varepsilon_{\alpha\beta}$ are the components of an infinitesimal deformation corresponding to an infinitesimal time interval Δt. Substituting (8.6) in (8.3) and taking the limit as $\Delta t \to 0$, we obtain

$$\frac{\partial^2 e_{\nu i}}{\partial \xi^j \partial \xi^\mu} + \frac{\partial^2 e_{\mu j}}{\partial \xi^i \partial \xi^\nu} - \frac{\partial^2 e_{\mu i}}{\partial \xi^j \partial \xi^\nu} - \frac{\partial^2 e_{\nu j}}{\partial \xi^i \partial \xi^\mu} = 0. \quad (8.7)$$

In equations (8.7), the coordinate system ξ^1, ξ^2, ξ^3 is cartesian because in equations (8.3) the coordinate system $\hat{\mathfrak{Z}}_i$ is cartesian, and, on taking the limit, $\mathring{\mathfrak{Z}}_i = \hat{\mathfrak{Z}}_i$ identically.

Analogously to (8.3), the system (8.7) contains six independent second-order partial differential equations linear in second derivatives of the quantities e_{ik}.

The corresponding independent equations can be obtained for the combinations of indices indicated above.

It is easy to see that for any three functions v_1, v_2, v_3, formulas (6.9) give the general integral of the system of equations (8.7).

It is obvious that for small deformations, when the components and their first and second derivatives with respect to the coordinates are of the same order, the nonlinear terms in (8.3) are second-order infinitesimals, because $\mathring{g}^{\alpha\omega}$ is a finite quantity of the order of unity. If the second-order terms in equations (8.3) are dropped, the components of the deformation tensor defined by the equation assume the form (8.7), which are the exact equations for the components of the tensor of velocity of deformation.

It is not difficult to verify [31] that if the functions

$$\varepsilon_{ij}(\xi^1, \xi^2, \xi^3)$$

are defined as some general solution of the system of equations (8.3), then the functions

$$\mathring{\varepsilon}_{ij} = \lambda \varepsilon_{ij}(\xi^1, \xi^2, \xi^3),$$

in which λ is a time-dependent variable, do not satisfy the compatibility equations (8.3).

It thus follows that for finite deformations, a proportional variation in the components of the deformation tensor is not in general geometrically possible for a finite body.

For particular types of functions ε_{ij}, such a proportional variation is possible [2]. In particular, a proportional change of the components of the tensor is possible for finite affine deformations when $\varepsilon_{ij} = \text{const}$; however, the positive-definite nature of the compatibility equations (8.1) may restrict the significance of λ.

It is easy to see that proportional variation in the velocity tensor components is always possible.

In the linearized theory for small deformations, only the linear terms in (8.3) are preserved. Therefore, the compatibility conditions are satisfied for proportional variation in the components of the deformation tensor for any distribution of deformations that is admissible under the compatibility conditions.

CHAPTER III

DYNAMIC AND THERMODYNAMIC EQUATIONS

1. Physical foundations

The mechanics of material bodies is related to the generalization of observations and experimental data on the property of inertia. For any body of small dimensions which can be considered as a point mass, its interaction with other bodies is related to its inertial properties, which can be determined in theory and practical calculations with the aid of one physical constant – the mass.

Every point mass can be associated with a basic mechanical characteristic – its mass.

Experiment shows that for any body of finite dimensions, the mass can be taken as the sum of all its constituent parts.

In physics, gases, liquids, and solids under normal conditions can be thought of as sets of moving and interacting molecules and atoms.

In constructing models of material bodies, it is necessary to be guided by the experimental data obtained from physical investigation.

The motion of a material body can be considered as the average macroscopic motion of a large number of particles in a physically small volume, and as a microscopic random thermal motion of the individual particles (molecules, atoms, electrons, etc.). The internal physical properties of a body include the statistical mean characteristics and the laws for the random microscopic phenomena associated with them, which are determined by the form of the relative distribution of the particles, the strength of their interactions, and their kinetic energy in random motions.

The features of the internal properties of a body may differ according to the class of phenomena considered; certain properties of a solid may not need to be taken into account if they are not essential to the problems in question.

It is very important for the dimensions and masses of the individual particles (molecules, atoms, nuclei, electrons, etc.) of which the body is made up to be extremely small, and therefore in many important cases we have to deal with bodies which have a large number of separate particles in the particular volume we are investigating.

The following are some important known physical data.

The light quantum – the photon – is a radiation particle moving in a vacuum with the speed of light, having a rest mass of zero, with an energy E equal to $h\nu$, and a momentum p different from zero and equal to $h\nu/c$; $|E = pc|$, where $h = 6.62 \times 10^{-27}$ erg·sec is Planck's constant, c is the velocity of light, and ν is the frequency.

For a photon in the visible region, $\nu \approx 4$ to 8×10^{14} cycles per second and $h\nu = 1.65$ to 3.3 ev; for high-energy gamma radiation $\nu > 10^{19}$ cycles per second, and $h\nu > 40$ kev. A volume filled with light can be thought of as a material body possessing energy and momentum. The model of such a continuum continuously filling space is based on electromagnetic field theory.

The rest mass of an electron $m_e = 9.1066 \times 10^{-28}$ gm; the charge of an electron is $e = 4.802 \times 10^{-10}$ esu; the radius of an electron is about 2.81×10^{-13} cm; the mass of the proton $m_n = 1.6724 \times 10^{24}$ gm, and its radius about 10^{-13} cm.

The macroscopic theory of the motion and interaction of charges with electromagnetic fields is the basis of the subject of electrodynamics.

For the hydrogen molecule, we have $m_{H_2} = 3.3466 \times 10^{-24}$ gm, $r_{H_2} \approx 1.15 \times 10^{-8}$ cm, and for iron, $m_{Fe} = 92.98 \times 10^{-24}$ gm and $r_{Fe} \approx 1.26 \times 10^{-8}$ cm.

The density ρ and the number of particles N in one cubic centimeter are given as follows.

For air in the Earth's atmosphere under normal conditions:
at sea level, $\rho = 0.00122$ gm/cm^3; $N = 2.687 \times 10^{19}$ cm^{-3};
at 10 km, $\rho = 0.00044$ gm/cm^3; $N = 9 \times 10^{18}$ cm^{-3};
at 60 km, $\rho = 2.6 \times 10^{-7}$ gm/cm^3; $N = 8 \times 10^{15}$ cm^{-3};
at 120 km, $\rho = 1.8 \times 10^{-10}$ gm/cm^3; $N = 6 \times 10^{12}$ cm^{-3}.

For interstellar gas, $\rho \approx 3 \times 10^{-24}$ gm/cm^3 and $N \approx 1$ cm$^{-3} = 10^{15}$ km^{-3}. The mean density of a red giant is $\rho \approx 10^{-7}$ gm/cm^3 and $N \approx 10^{17}$ cm^{-3}; the mean density of a white dwarf is $\rho \approx 10^6$ to 10^8 gm/cm^3 and $N \approx 3 \times 10^{28}$ to 3×10^{30} cm^{-3}.

Under normal conditions, the density of iron $\rho = 7.86$ gm/cm^3, $N = 8.622 \times 10^{22}$ cm^{-3}, and finally the density of its nucleus is $\rho = 1.16 \times 10^{14}$ gm/cm^3.

The data above clearly indicate that densities can vary between very wide limits; however, it is characteristic that in all known cases the density of the nuclear matter is much greater than the macroscopic density of the various bodies. For example, for iron we have

$$\frac{\rho_{\text{iron}}}{\rho_{\text{nucleus}}} = 7 \times 10^{-14},$$

and consequently a volume made up of iron atoms constitutes an insignificant fraction of the volume occupied by a piece of iron. A piece of iron of finite volume, similarly to finite volumes of other substances, is practically empty space, an insignificant part of which is filled with the crystal lattice formed from a very large number of atoms.

On the other hand, data on the number of particles N in a unit volume show that ordinarily the number of particles is extremely large in physically small volumes. This factor allows a mathematical abstraction to be introduced which supposes that a mass exists in any volume occupied by a body, no matter how small, and so a continuous medium can be represented as a material continuum filling space continuously.

Apart from the inertial property, characterized by the density, other properties of a body due to the interaction between the elementary particles, atoms and molecules, and their internal microscopic motions are important.

Some of the characteristics of such processes for gases can be listed as follows.

For the random motion of gas molecules at zero degrees celsius (273° K) and atmospheric pressure, molecules of hydrogen H_2 move with a mean velocity of 1692 m/sec and have a mean free path between two collisions equal to 11.2×10^{-6} cm, and each molecule undergoes 15×10^9 collisions per second. An oxygen molecule O_2 has a mean velocity of 425 m/sec (mean free path 6.5×10^{-6} cm) and undergoes 6.55×10^9 collisions per second.

The motion and interaction between molecules in liquids and solids has a more complicated nature, but the mean energy of the random motion for a molecule with one degree of freedom, which determines the temperature of the body, is exactly the same as for gases.

To construct material continua models of real bodies, it is necessary to consider the various structural features of the bodies. Bodies can be gaseous, liquid, solid, or crystalline, and can have various phases. When the temperature and pressure are increased, states can occur which can be considered simultaneously as a gas, a liquid, or a solid.

Apart from the structure, the nature of a material is of great importance, along with the properties of mixtures, solutions, and alloys.

In many cases, mechanical problems arise on the motion of the bodies due to a change in the properties and relative numbers of constituent parts. As an example we can cite the motion of gases undergoing nuclear and chemical reactions and in particular, combustion, dissociation, recombination, ionization, etc. Phase transitions play an important part in the motion of material bodies, e.g., condensation, vaporization, melting, solidification, polymerization, recrystallization, etc.

It is necessary to introduce internal stresses for the study of material continua. In bodies with discrete molecular structures, the internal stresses are defined by statistical averages; these stresses are due to the direct interaction of forces between molecules distributed on the different sides of the cross section considered, and to the transport of macroscopic momentum across this cross section caused by the thermal motion of the molecules. For example, the viscosity in gases is explained by the effect of the thermal motion of the molecules averaging out the macroscopic velocities of neighboring particles of the gas. Thus, the properties of the internal stresses in material media can be expressed in terms of the molecular state of the media, in terms of the interaction forces between molecules and atoms occurring only over the very small distances between them, and in terms of the thermal motion characterized by the temperature.

Thermal conductivity is explained in a similar way. For any two neighboring particles in the medium that come into contact, an energy transfer takes place either through collisions or directly by a transfer of rapid and slow particles. The statistical mean of the energy of thermal motion described as the temperature tends toward the equilibrium value.

Diffusion in mixtures can be expressed in terms of molecular kinetic processes which mix the molecules by thermal motion.

Radiation phenomena, which occur because of quantum effects associated with changes in the energy levels of molecules, atoms, or nuclei, and also because of the acceleration of charged particles, can be described in a somewhat more complex manner. The phenomenon of radiation, which can be considered as the emission of photons, is closely connected with the random thermal motion and essentially depends on the temperature, which defines the possible excitation energy levels for the collision of particles. The motion of material media at high temperatures is studied by considering the effects of energy transfer and variation in temperature due to the accompanying processes of absorption and dispersion of radiant energy. In the phenomena listed above, the formulation of the macroscopic laws on the basis of a rigorous analysis of the physical microscopic mechanisms and the properties of elementary particles is one of the major areas of physical investigation.

2. The concept of a material continuum

In order to simplify the setting up of mechanical problems, to give a clear definition of the ideal properties of material bodies, and to make formulation of the mechanics possible with the aid of differential and integral calculus, ideal physical-mechanical models, which can be used to describe the states and processes of motion of real bodies both in nature and in engineering structures are introduced into mechanics.

For this, we introduce into general mechanics the concepts of point masses and absolutely rigid bodies; it is well known that in this way it is possible to describe with great accuracy many phenomena and solve many important problems.

In order to study mechanical problems on the motion of gases, liquids, and solids, we must consider a continuum as a medium continuously filling space and possessing inertial and other physical properties which reflect statistical relationships for certain classes of physical bodies composed of a large number of interacting particles.

In accordance with additional definitions, material continua with diverse properties are considered in mechanics. It is possible to introduce different models of deformed media applicable to real bodies with different properties.

In mechanics, however, one property is common to all material continua, namely, the property of inertia, which is characterized by the mass. For a material continuum it is assumed that any part of the medium has a mass which is a positive and additive function of the volume.

Let us consider a certain volume V within a body and let m denote its mass.

The ratio

$$\frac{m}{V} = \rho^*$$

is called the average density. For the usual models of continuous media we assume that ρ^* has some limit when the volume V is reduced to a point

$$\rho = \lim_{V \to 0} \rho^* = \lim_{V \to 0} \frac{m}{V}. \tag{2.1}$$

The limit of ρ^* denoted by ρ is called the density at a given point to which the volume V is being reduced.

If the density ρ is known at every point, the mass m for any finite volume V can be obtained by means of the following integral taken over the volume V:

$$m = \int_V \rho \, d\tau. \tag{2.2}$$

The intertial properties of a point mass are fully defined by the value of its mass. The intertial properties of a body of finite dimensions are defined by the law for the distribution of the density throughout the volume of the body. The situation is greatly simplified for an absolutely rigid body. For an absolutely rigid body, the inertial characteristics can be completely defined by the following: the mass of the body, the position of the center of mass (center of gravity), and the moment-of-inertia tensor at the center of mass.

The experimental law of the conservation of mass for every substantial part of the body has long been one of the fundamental laws of nature. At present, this law is also of great practical importance for the study of many physico-chemical processes. At high velocities approaching the speed of light, however, the laws of Newtonian mechanics must be replaced by the laws of relativity. In this theory, the mass of a body depends on its speed and has different values for observers situated in frames of reference moving with respect to one another. At the same time, the change in mass and the equivalence of mass and energy are significant in nuclear reaction processes.

In practice, one may have occasion to examine the motion of bodies with variable mass within the framework of classical mechanics; in particular, theories on the motion of bodies with variable mass have been developed that are suited for problems on reactive motions. In order to avoid misunderstandings, it is necessary to note that in these theories it is not essentially a given body made up of one and the same set of particles with changing mass that is being examined, but a body in which the composition of the particles changes, some separating from the body and others attaching themselves to it.

For such a type of problem, we can always define and examine a mechanical system with an overall constant mass in accordance with the classical laws.

Moreover, when we study the motions of bodies with "changing" mass, we have to take into consideration in a very real way the law of conservation of mass for the system made up of individualized material particles.

3. The continuity equations

Let ξ^1, ξ^2, ξ^3 be the Lagrangian coordinates and x^1, x^2, x^3 the coordinates of points in the reference system with respect to which the motion is considered (see Chapter II, § 1). The law of motion appears in the form

$$x^i = f^i(\xi^1, \xi^2, \xi^3, t) \qquad (i = 1, 2, 3), \tag{3.1}$$

where the functions f^i, by hypothesis, contain partial derivatives with respect to all the arguments in the region under consideration.

Without losing generality, we assume that at the instant $t = t_0$

$$x_i|_{t=t_0} = x_0^i = \xi^i.$$

The law of the conservation of mass for any moving body made up of identical material particles can be written in the forms

$$m = \int_{V(\xi, t_0)} \rho(\xi, t_0)\, d\tau = \int_{V(\xi, t)} \rho(\xi, t)\, d\tau = \text{const} \tag{3.2}$$

or

$$\frac{d}{dt} \int_{V(\xi, t)} \rho(\xi, t)\, d\tau = \int_V \frac{\partial \rho(x, t)}{\partial t}\, d\tau + \int_\Sigma \rho \mathbf{v}_n\, d\sigma = 0, \tag{3.3}$$

where V is a moving volume of space occupied by particles of the body and Σ is the surface enclosing volume V. In equation (3.3), the motion and deformation of the volume V are significant only on the left-hand side of the equation before differentiation of the integral with respect to time. After differentiation, one obtains an integral equation valid for any volume V at any fixed instant t.

Equations (3.2) and (3.3) can be applied to arbitrary motions of a material medium, and in particular to discontinuous motions. When the volume V is in motion, it can be divided into separate parts; inside the volume V, the field of the density, velocity, and other mechanical characteristics can be nonanalytical and discontinuous.

For continuous motion described by smooth functions, the integral equations (3.2) and (3.3) can be replaced by partial differential equations.

For any infinitesimal particle, equation (3.2) becomes

$$\rho_0\, dV_0 = \rho\, dV = dm\,; \tag{3.4}$$

ρ and dV_0 are the density and volume of the particle at time t_0, and ρ and dV are the same quantities at time t.

For an infinitesimal particle, the deformation can be considered as affine, and therefore the ratio dV/dV_0 does not depend on the form of the original volume dV_0 (see § 2, Chapter II).

On the basis of formulas (1.6), (2.11), and (4.17) of Chapter II, equation (3.4) is equivalent to

$$\frac{\rho_0}{\rho} = \frac{\sqrt{g}}{\sqrt{g_0}} = \left| \frac{\partial x^i}{\partial \xi^j} \right| = \Delta$$

or

$$\frac{\rho}{\rho_0} = \frac{1}{\sqrt{1 + 2\mathring{\mathscr{I}}_1 + 4\mathring{\mathscr{I}}_2 + 8\mathring{\mathscr{I}}_3}} = \sqrt{1 - 2\hat{\mathscr{I}}_1 + 4\hat{\mathscr{I}}_2 - 8\hat{\mathscr{I}}_3}, \tag{3.5}$$

where Δ is the determinant for a tangential affine transformation, $\mathring{\mathscr{I}}_1, \mathring{\mathscr{I}}_2, \mathring{\mathscr{I}}_3$ are the invariants of the tensor of the finite deformation $\mathring{\mathscr{E}}$, and $\hat{\mathscr{I}}_1$, $\hat{\mathscr{I}}_2$, $\hat{\mathscr{I}}_3$ are the invariants of the tensor of the finite deformation $\hat{\mathscr{E}}$.

The differential equation (3.5) is called the continuity equation in the Lagrangian form. This equation has been established for any curvilinear coordinate system, and the essential feature is that it contains derivatives of the functions, defined in equations (3.1), which give the law of motion at time t, while the difference $t - t_0$ is finite and arbitrary.

A differential continuity equation, analogous to equation (3.3), which depends only on one instant of time t, can be found from the integral relationship (3.3). However, we shall establish this equation using (3.4) by means of the limiting transition when $t_0 \to t$.

Equation (3.4) can be rewritten as

$$\frac{\rho(\xi^i, t_0) - \rho(\xi^i, t)}{\rho(\xi^i, t_0)\,\Delta t} = \frac{dV - dV_0}{dV_0 \Delta t},$$

where

$$\Delta t = t - t_0 .$$

If $\Delta t \to 0$ and the deformation is infinitesimal, from (4.17a) and (4.32) of Chapter II, we obtain

$$-\frac{\Delta\rho}{\rho\Delta t} = \frac{\varepsilon^{\alpha\cdot}_{\cdot\alpha}}{\Delta t} = \frac{\nabla_\alpha w^\alpha}{\Delta t}. \tag{3.6}$$

It is obvious that for an infinitesimal deformation we may assume that $\mathring{\mathscr{I}}_1 = \hat{\mathscr{I}}_1 = \varepsilon^{\alpha\cdot}_{\cdot\alpha}$ and that the bases $\mathring{\mathfrak{I}}_i$, $\hat{\mathfrak{I}}_i$ are coincident; the w^α denote the components of the infinitesimal displacement, while $w^\alpha = v^\alpha \Delta t$, where v^α are the components of the velocity vector of the particles. Equation (3.6) becomes in the limit, as $\Delta t \to 0$,

$$\frac{1}{\rho}\left(\frac{d\rho}{dt}\right)_{\xi^i = \text{const}} + \nabla_\alpha v^\alpha = 0. \tag{3.7}$$

Equation (3.7) can be rewritten in still another form:

$$\left(\frac{\partial\rho}{\partial t}\right)_{x^i = \text{const}} + v^\alpha \frac{\partial\rho}{\partial x^\alpha} + \rho\nabla_\alpha v^\alpha = 0$$

or

$$\frac{\partial\rho}{\partial t} + \nabla_\alpha \rho v^\alpha = 0. \tag{3.8}$$

Equation (3.8) represents the continuity equation in an arbitrary curvilinear coordinate system.

If we write the covariant derivatives in open form, equation (3.8) becomes

$$\frac{\partial\rho}{\partial t} + \frac{\partial\rho v^\alpha}{\partial x^\alpha} + \rho v^\alpha \Gamma^\beta_{\alpha\beta} = 0. \tag{3.9}$$

This can be transformed with the aid of the formulas

$$\Gamma^{\beta}_{\alpha\beta} = \frac{1}{\sqrt{g}}\frac{\partial\sqrt{g}}{\partial x^{\alpha}}, \tag{3.10}$$

which follow from the equations

$$g = |(\mathfrak{Э}_i, \mathfrak{Э}_j)| \qquad \text{and} \qquad \frac{\partial \mathfrak{Э}}{\partial x^s} = \Gamma^{\omega}_{ks}\mathfrak{Э}_{\omega}.$$

In fact, the derivative with respect to x^{α} of determinant g can be written as the sum of the determinants with derivatives of the first factors in the rows and the determinants with derivatives of the second factors in the columns. It is obvious that each determinant of this type will equal $g\Gamma^{i}_{i\alpha}$ with a fixed indices i, and therefore,

$$\frac{\partial g}{\partial x^{\alpha}} = 2g\Gamma^{\beta}_{\beta\alpha} = 2g\Gamma^{\beta}_{\alpha\beta}.$$

Formula (3.10) follows from this.

On the basis of (3.10), the continuity equation (3.9) may be written in the form

$$\frac{\partial\rho}{\partial t} + \frac{1}{\sqrt{g}}\frac{\partial\rho\sqrt{g}\,v^{\alpha}}{\partial x^{\alpha}} = 0. \tag{3.11}$$

For the velocity vector $\mathbf{v}$, we can write the formula

$$\mathbf{v} = v^1\mathfrak{Э}_1 + v^2\mathfrak{Э}_2 + v^3\mathfrak{Э}_3 = u^1\frac{\mathfrak{Э}_1}{\sqrt{g_{11}}} + u^2\frac{\mathfrak{Э}_2}{\sqrt{g_{22}}} + u^3\frac{\mathfrak{Э}_3}{\sqrt{g_{33}}}, \tag{3.12}$$

where the vectors $\mathfrak{Э}_i/\sqrt{g_{ii}}$ form a basis with unit vectors. If the coordinate system is orthogonal, the quantities u^i are equal to the projections of the velocity onto the coordinate axes; in this case, $\sqrt{g} = \sqrt{g_{11}\,g_{22}\,g_{33}}$ because $g_{ik} = 0$ for $i \neq k$. The continuity equation (3.11) in an arbitrary orthogonal coordinate system will have the form

$$\sqrt{g_{11}g_{22}g_{33}}\frac{\partial\rho}{\partial t} + \frac{\partial\sqrt{g_{22}g_{33}}\rho u^1}{\partial x^1} + \frac{\partial\sqrt{g_{33}g_{11}}\rho u^2}{\partial x^2} + \frac{\partial\sqrt{g_{11}g_{22}}\rho u^3}{\partial x^3} = 0. \tag{3.13}$$

For any vector $A = A^{\alpha}\,\mathfrak{Э}_{\alpha}$, the invariant quantity is called the divergence of the vector A. For an arbitrary curvilinear coordinate system, we have

$$\operatorname{div} A = \frac{\partial A^{\alpha}}{\partial x^{\alpha}} + A^{\alpha}\Gamma^{\beta}_{\alpha\beta} = \frac{1}{\sqrt{g}}\frac{\partial\sqrt{g}\,A^{\alpha}}{\partial x^{\alpha}}. \tag{3.14}$$

The corresponding simplifications of this expression for orthogonal coordinate systems are obvious from the foregoing conclusions. Formula

(3.14) will conserve its form if the components A^α are considered as vectors or tensors of arbitrary rank. It is obvious in this case the quantity $A = A^\alpha Э_\alpha$ is a tensor of rank exceeding that of the tensor A^α by one.

4. The dynamic equations

The subject of dynamics is concerned with the study and methods of solving problems on the motion of material bodies with respect to the causes producing the motion.

The most varied forms of experiments and observations show that the motion of material bodies is dependent on the interaction of various bodies. The concept of motion is kinematic and in an essential way rests on the geometric concepts of space and time.

In classical Newtonian mechanics, it is assumed that space is Euclidean and that time flows the same for all observers irrespective of their relative motions. Motion is investigated by supposing that an inertial coordinate system exists. In an inertial coordinate system, an isolated point (not interacting with other bodies) is at rest or in a state of uniform and rectilinear motion. Any motion of a material point with respect to an accelerating inertial system is considered the result of the interaction of this point with other bodies.

Experiment shows that for any two interacting material points M_1 and M_2, there always exists the following relationship between accelerations $\boldsymbol{a}_1$ and $\boldsymbol{a}_2$ of these points:

$$m_1 \boldsymbol{a}_1 = -m_2 \boldsymbol{a}_2, \tag{4.1}$$

and for the interaction of point M_1 or point M_2 with another material point M_3, the following equations are always valid:

$$m_1 \boldsymbol{a}_1' = -m_3 \boldsymbol{a}_3' \quad \text{and} \quad m_2 \boldsymbol{a}_2'' = -m_3 \boldsymbol{a}''. \tag{4.2}$$

The vector equation (4.1) constitutes the law of equality of action and reaction.

Equations (4.1) and (4.2) provide the basis for introducing the scalar characteristic m of the mass of a material point. For any two interacting material points, the ratio of their accelerations equals the ratio of their masses. The values of the accelerations of two such points are inversely proportional to their masses, and therefore we say that the mass characterizes the inertial property of material points, which consists of the tendency for a material point to conserve a state of motion at constant velocity.

The interaction between point masses can be found from the product

$\boldsymbol{ma}$, which cannot be zero if an interaction exists. It is of fundamental significance that the magnitude and direction of the product $\boldsymbol{ma}$, called force, can in many practical cases be immediately detected by our senses or measured by means of the effects observed on many types of apparatus, particularly dynamometers or balances.

We first experience the concept of force in our early childhood. The extent of the many phenomena in life and technology in which force effects are of primary importance make this concept fundamental to science and engineering.

The force vector defined by the formula

$$\mathscr{F} = m\boldsymbol{a} \tag{4.3}$$

completely defines, from the mechanical point of view, the interaction of material bodies which results in a corresponding motion of a given point mass.

Clearly, the laws of interaction of bodies form the foundation of our knowledge and the basis for describing the motions of mechanical systems, which are considered in mechanics as an array of point masses interacting among themselves and with other material systems.

It is necessary to emphasize from the very start that all the physical laws connected with the interaction of bodies, or, in other words, connected with the properties of forces, are obtained either directly from experiment or from theoretical generalizations of experimental facts and supplementary hypotheses which must be tested experimentally.

It is important, however, to understand clearly that the properties of forces are always experimentally established by use of the basic equation (4.3), or, in the case of several simultaneous interactions, by use of the equation

$$\mathscr{F}_1 + \mathscr{F}_2 + \cdots + \mathscr{F}_n = m\boldsymbol{a}\,, \tag{4.4}$$

where some of the forces $\mathscr{F}_i$ are determined *a priori* from previous experiments.

In particular, the right-hand side of (4.4) can be equal to zero. In this case, we can say that some of the unknowns on the left-hand side are determined from static experiments. However, it is not always possible to determine forces by the static method.

The results of a description of the properties of forces are reduced in many cases to establishing functional relationships between the forces of the interaction and the geometric and kinematic characteristics of the bodies and their relative position and motion.

The number of physical laws for forces is not very great. In various special cases the explanation of the corresponding laws is the subject of contemporary investigations.

This question will be considered in greater detail below for the models of material continua.

We shall confine ourselves to these general remarks about the concept of force; this question is dealt with in more detail in our book *Similitude and Dimensional Analysis Methods in Mechanics.**

In the study of material continua, it is necessary to consider forces concentrated at a point, spread over a surface, or distributed throughout the volume of the body.

Let us examine a material continuum filling a certain volume V in space. Special cases are possible in which at certain indicated points of the volume V external concentrated finite forces are applied to the material points of the medium which pass through these isolated points.

If the density is finite throughout the medium, at the points of application of the concentrated forces the acceleration must be infinite. In idealized theoretical models of motion, such cases can be encountered both within the actual volume occupied by the moving medium, and also, under a mathematical analytical extension, in certain regions of space (outside the boundaries of the medium) not occupied by the actual material medium. However, from mathematical considerations it is clear that in these regions one may introduce a conceptually auxiliary material medium and corresponding auxiliary forces.

To explain and describe such a fictitious material medium, one may need to consider finite concentrated forces, infinite accelerations, etc.

In a similar way, one can introduce and consider (for certain ideal theoretical schemes) external concentrated forces distributed along lines or surfaces.

Mass (volume) and surface forces are the physically natural and basic types of actual forces for an uninterrupted continuum, which serves as a model for actual bodies.

Mass forces are finite for bodies of finite mass, and as the volume of the particle is reduced to zero, these forces also approach zero.

Let $d\tau$ be an infinitesimal volume element occupied by a moving continuum. The mass force acting on the masses inside the volume can by definition be put in the form

$$d\mathcal{F} = \boldsymbol{F}\rho\, d\tau\,,$$

where $\boldsymbol{F}$ is finite with the dimensions of acceleration.

* See [32], Chapter I, Section 5, pp. 19–25.

Forces of a Newtonian attraction, specifically ordinary gravity forces, electromagnetic forces, and inertial forces encountered in the study of relative motions, are basic examples of mass forces. The acting forces calculated from the given motions or the forces introduced in theory as mathematical extensions of real motions can also be mass forces.

In considering the motions of finite volumes of material media, one can introduce the principal vector and the principal moment with respect to a certain point (e.g., the origin) of the mass forces which are acting on the particles of the volume. The following formulas can be used for these quantities:

$$\mathscr{F} = \int_V \boldsymbol{F}\rho\, d\tau\,, \qquad \mathfrak{M} = \int_V [\boldsymbol{r}, \boldsymbol{F}]\,\rho\, d\tau\,. \tag{4.5}$$

As a rule, surface forces are the principal form of forces of interaction in models of material continua.

Surface forces can be external forces acting over the boundary of a liquid, or internal forces which must be introduced over any dividing surface of a body, which surface may be mentally introduced in any manner in the vicinity of any interior point of the medium.*

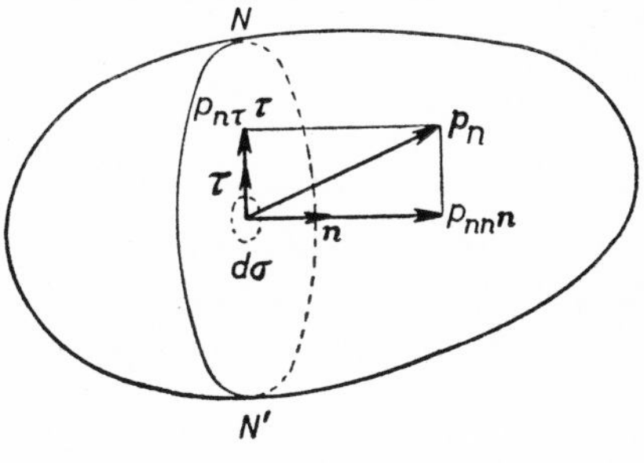

Figure 7

Let NN' be some imaginary cross section dividing the body into two parts (Fig. 7). In an arbitrary state of motion and equilibrium, each part of the volume can be considered separately. The interaction of the separate parts can be attained by means of the mass forces distributed throughout their volumes, and by means of the forces distributed along the cross section NN'.

* In some cases, external surface forces can also act along certain isolated surfaces inside the continuum (a face, a disk, a screw, etc.). Such surfaces can be considered as two-sided and included in the boundaries. This is usually done when the mass of the medium is flowing through the surface.

Let $d\sigma$ be an infinitesimal element of the dividing surface considered as an element of the boundary of the left-hand part, and let $\boldsymbol{n}$ be the unit vector of the outwardly directed normal to the element $d\sigma$. Let $d\boldsymbol{P}_n$ be the force acting from the right part toward the left, and let us define a finite vector $\boldsymbol{p}_n$ by

$$d\boldsymbol{P}_n = \boldsymbol{p}_n \, d\sigma \, .$$

The forces $\boldsymbol{p}_n$ distributed over a unit of surface are called the internal stress forces. At every internal point, the magnitude and direction of a stress force $\boldsymbol{p}_n$ depend on the direction of the normal $\boldsymbol{n}$ to the infinitesimal element of area along which the interaction of the medium divided by the area into two separate parts is being examined.

The vector $\boldsymbol{p}_n$ can be resolved into components normal and tangential to the element of area on which the force of the stress $\boldsymbol{p}_n$ is given:

$$\boldsymbol{p}_n = p_{nn}\boldsymbol{n} + p_{n\tau}\boldsymbol{\tau} \, .$$

Here, p_{nn} is the projection of the stress onto the normal, and $p_{n\tau}$ the projection onto the plane of the element of area. In the general case of an arbitrary element of area, at equilibrium, and with motion of the material medium, p_{nn} and $p_{n\tau}$ are both different from zero and depend on the orientation of the element of area.

The surface stress forces acting on the boundary Σ of an element of volume of the medium must be considered as external forces.

It is obvious that the principal vector and the principal moment of external surface forces are represented by the integrals

$$\boldsymbol{P} = \int_{\Sigma} \boldsymbol{p}_n \, d\sigma \qquad \text{and} \qquad \boldsymbol{M} = \int_{\Sigma} [\boldsymbol{r}, \boldsymbol{p}_n] \, d\sigma \, . \tag{4.6}$$

The surface forces of internal interaction have certain universal properties which apply to any body and to any mechanical or other type of processes taking place in the body.

Moreover, stress forces also have certain general characteristics which are defined by the particular form of the material continuum (in theory, characteristics which correspond to a particular continuum model), and these characteristics represent the specific physical relationships of the various types of processes and motions.

The basic difference between the various continuum models lies in the difference in the properties and laws governing the dependence of the internal stresses on the characteristics of the deformation and the motion of the medium. This question will be studied in more detail.

Let us now clarify the universal properties of stresses. These properties follow from equations (4.2), (4.3), and (4.4), which contain the definitions of mass and force for point masses, and hence the general dynamic equations for systems of point masses distributed through any material continuum. Such a generalization follows from the fact that any material body can be considered as a point mass under certain conditions.

These general dynamic equations for the charge in linear and angular momentum for any material media and for arbitrary motions are of the form

$$\int_V \boldsymbol{a}\rho\, d\tau = \frac{d}{dt}\int_V \mathbf{v}\rho\, d\tau = \int_V \boldsymbol{F}\rho\, d\tau + \int_\Sigma \boldsymbol{p}_n\, d\sigma, \tag{4.7}$$

$$\int_V [\boldsymbol{r}, \boldsymbol{a}]\, \rho\, d\tau = \frac{d}{dt}\int_V [\boldsymbol{r}, \mathbf{v}]\, \rho\, d\tau = \int_V [\boldsymbol{r}, \boldsymbol{F}]\, \rho\, d\tau + \int_\Sigma [\boldsymbol{r}, \boldsymbol{p}_n]\, d\sigma, \tag{4.8}$$

where $\mathbf{v}$ is the velocity vector, $\boldsymbol{a}$ is the acceleration vector of the particles, and $\boldsymbol{r}$ is the radius vector from some stationary point (or from a point moving uniformly in a straight line).

The volume V is an arbitrary, material, and generally movable volume consisting of one and the same type of particles.

Equations (4.7) and (4.8), representing a theorem on the changes in linear and angular momentum of a mechanical system,* are valid for any motion including discontinuous motion, in which the distributions of the characteristics of the motion and state within the volume V can be step functions of the time t (shock processes).

In the region of continuous smooth motions, the integral relationships (4.7) and (4.8) are equivalent to differential equations which we shall establish further on in this section.

The satisfying of equations (4.7) and (4.8) sets restrictions on the possible form of the dependence of stresses $\boldsymbol{p}_n$ on the orientation of the corresponding area element. These restrictions are as follows.

1. In the neighborhood of points in the medium for which the acceleration is finite, for any direction of the normal $\boldsymbol{n}$, the following equation is valid:

$$\boldsymbol{p}_n = -\boldsymbol{p}_{-n}. \tag{4.9}$$

In fact, let us take a small simply connected volume V and let us imagine a plane Σ cutting it into two volumes V_1 and V_2 (Fig. 8). The boundary of volume V_1 will be designated by $S_1 + \Sigma$ and that of V_2 by $S_2 + \Sigma$. The

---

* The angular momentum equation (4.8) is written in a form applicable for ordinarily attainable internal momenta and external torques.

unit vector normal to Σ directed outward from V_1 is denoted by $\boldsymbol{n}$; then, the unit vector of the normal directed outward from V_2 will be equal to $-\boldsymbol{n}$. Equation (4.7) gives for the volumes V_1, V_2, and $V_1 + V_2$:

$$\int_{V_1} \rho \boldsymbol{a}\, d\tau = \int_{V_2} \rho \boldsymbol{F}\, d\tau + \int_{S_1} \boldsymbol{p}_n\, d\sigma + \int_{\Sigma} \boldsymbol{p}_n\, d\sigma,$$

$$\int_{V_2} \rho \boldsymbol{a}\, d\tau = \int_{V_2} \rho \boldsymbol{F}\, d\tau + \int_{S_2} \boldsymbol{p}_n\, d\sigma + \int_{\Sigma} \boldsymbol{p}_{-n}\, d\sigma,$$

$$\int_{V_1+V_2} \rho \boldsymbol{a}\, d\tau = \int_{V_1+V_2} \rho \boldsymbol{F}\, d\tau + \int_{S_1+S_2} \boldsymbol{p}_n\, d\sigma.$$

After adding the first two equations and subtracting the third, we have

$$\int_{\Sigma} (\boldsymbol{p}_n + \boldsymbol{p}_{-n})\, d\sigma = 0.$$

Since the element Σ is arbitrarily oriented and infinitesimal, equation (4.9) follows.

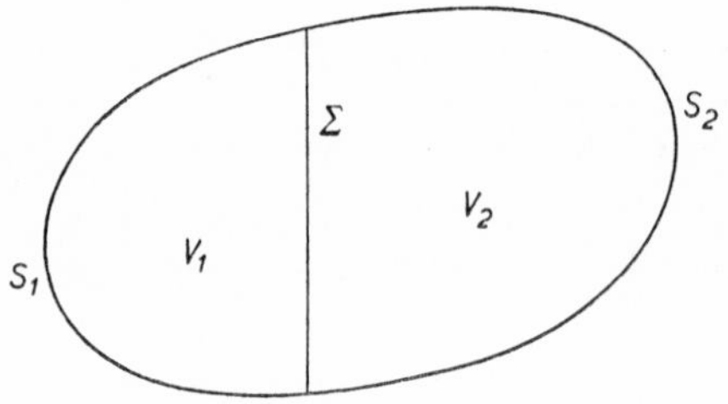

Figure 8

We note that it is essential to assume that the acceleration is finite. If within the volume V there is a surface with a sharp discontinuity in velocity and the points of the medium are flowing through it, (4.9) will not be satisfied.

The property (4.9), which was obtained as a consequence of (4.7), can be considered as an expression of the law of equality of action and reaction under continuous motion in the case of internal surface forces. In the transition from the laws for the motion of individual material points to the law of momenta for the system as a whole, the law of equality of action and reaction must be used. We have already shown that the law of momenta for any finite mass leads in the case of continuous motions to the law of equality of action and reaction for material stresses.

2. We will now consider the stresses on different elements of area near a point M with the assumption that its motion in this region has finite accelerations and that the external mass forces are finite.

Let $Ox^1x^2x^3$ be a rectangular cartesian coordinate system. Consider the volume V as an infinitesimal tetrahedron (Fig. 9) with faces MCB, MAB, and MAC perpendicular to the coordinate axes and with face ABC arbitrarily determined by an externally directed unit normal vector

$$\boldsymbol{n} = \cos(\widehat{\boldsymbol{n}\boldsymbol{x}^1})\,\boldsymbol{Э}_1 + \cos(\widehat{\boldsymbol{n}\boldsymbol{x}^2})\,\boldsymbol{Э}_2 + \cos(\widehat{\boldsymbol{n}\boldsymbol{x}^3})\,\boldsymbol{Э}_3,$$

where $\boldsymbol{Э}_1$, $\boldsymbol{Э}_2$, $\boldsymbol{Э}_3$ are unit vectors directed along the coordinate axes.

The stresses on the areas with the normals $\boldsymbol{Э}_1 = \boldsymbol{Э}^1$, $\boldsymbol{Э}_2 = \boldsymbol{Э}^2$, $\boldsymbol{Э}_3 = \boldsymbol{Э}^3$, and $\boldsymbol{n}$ are denoted by $\boldsymbol{p}^1$, $\boldsymbol{p}^2$, $\boldsymbol{p}^3$, and $\boldsymbol{p}_n$, respectively.

We shall show that the relationship

$$\boldsymbol{p}_n = \boldsymbol{p}^1 \cos(\widehat{\boldsymbol{n}\boldsymbol{Э}_1}) + \boldsymbol{p}^2 \cos(\widehat{\boldsymbol{n}\boldsymbol{Э}_2}) + \boldsymbol{p}^3 \cos(\widehat{\boldsymbol{n}\boldsymbol{Э}_3}) \qquad (4.10)$$

is always valid.

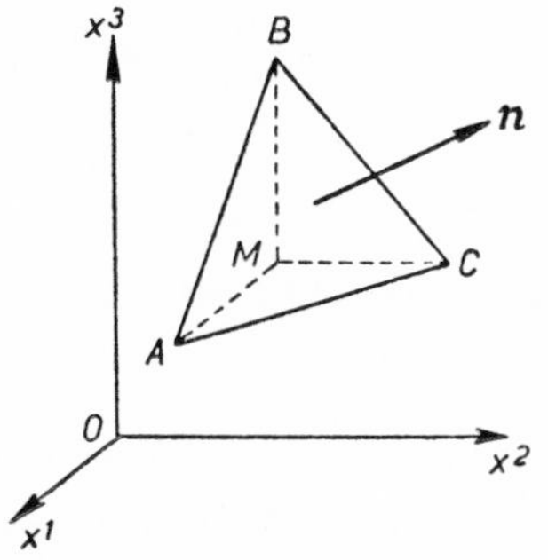

Figure 9

In fact, applying (4.7) to the masses of the volume that are inside the infinitesimal tetrahedron $MABC$ at the instant in question, we obtain

$$(\rho\boldsymbol{a} - \rho\boldsymbol{F})\cdot\tfrac{1}{3}Sh$$
$$= [-\boldsymbol{p}^1 S\cos(\widehat{\boldsymbol{n}\boldsymbol{Э}_1}) - \boldsymbol{p}^2 S\cos(\widehat{\boldsymbol{n}\boldsymbol{Э}_2}) - \boldsymbol{p}^3 S\cos(\widehat{\boldsymbol{n}\boldsymbol{Э}_3}) + \boldsymbol{p}_n\cdot S] + S\cdot O(h),$$

where S is the area of the bounding surface ABC, and h is the infinitesimal height of the tetrahedron; $O(h)$ is a quantity which tends to zero for $h \to 0$.

Approaching the limit, as $h \to 0$, we obtain equation (4.10). This equation shows that the stress pressure $\boldsymbol{p}_n$ on any given element of area can be expressed linearly in terms of the stresses $\boldsymbol{p}^1$, $\boldsymbol{p}^2$, $\boldsymbol{p}^3$ on fixed elements of areas parallel to the coordinate axes. We obtain

$$\begin{aligned}
\boldsymbol{p}^1 &= p^{11}\boldsymbol{Э}_1 + p^{21}\boldsymbol{Э}_2 + p^{31}\boldsymbol{Э}_3,\\
\boldsymbol{p}^2 &= p^{12}\boldsymbol{Э}_1 + p^{22}\boldsymbol{Э}_2 + p^{32}\boldsymbol{Э}_3,\\
\boldsymbol{p}^3 &= p^{13}\boldsymbol{Э}_1 + p^{23}\boldsymbol{Э}_2 + p^{33}\boldsymbol{Э}_3.
\end{aligned}$$

The stress on any element of area defined by the unit vector $\boldsymbol{n}$ can be considered as a linear vector function of the vector $\boldsymbol{n}$, defined by the matrix

$$\| p^{ij} \| .$$

It is obvious that the system of the components of this matrix can be considered as the components of a tensor $\boldsymbol{P}$ defined by the equation

$$\boldsymbol{P} = \boldsymbol{p}^1 \text{Э}_1 + \boldsymbol{p}^2 \text{Э}_2 + \boldsymbol{p}^3 \text{Э}_3 = p^{\alpha\beta} \text{Э}_\alpha \text{Э}_\beta . \tag{4.11}$$

The tensor $\boldsymbol{P}$ is called the stress tensor. Using $\boldsymbol{P}$, equation (4.10) can be written in the invariant form

$$\boldsymbol{p}_n = \boldsymbol{P} \cdot \boldsymbol{n} . \tag{4.12}$$

Equation (4.12) remains valid in the transition to any curvilinear coordinate system.

In the general case, the components of the tensor $\boldsymbol{P}$ and the components of the vector $\boldsymbol{p}_n$ transform according to the general formulas established in § 2, Chapter I.

The components of the tensor $\boldsymbol{P}$ can be considered in any coordinate system and, in particular, in moving Lagrangian, or stationary Lagrangian coordinates (see § 3, Chapter II).

The tensor $\boldsymbol{P}$ in a cartesian system is uniquely defined.

In curvilinear coordinates, the indices can be "juggled" using the fundamental tensor $\boldsymbol{G}$ which is formed by the coefficients in the quadratic form of the square of the element of arc.

In the Lagrangian coordinates ξ^1, ξ^2, ξ^3, the following different fundamental quadratic forms can be used to "juggle" the indices:

$$ds^2 = \hat{g}_{ik}\, d\xi^i\, d\xi^k \qquad \text{or} \qquad ds_0^2 = \mathring{g}_{ik}\, d\xi^i\, d\xi^k ,$$

and corresponding to this, just as in the case of finite deformation tensors, we can consider various stress tensors

$$\mathring{\boldsymbol{P}} = p^{\alpha\beta} \mathring{\text{Э}}_\alpha \mathring{\text{Э}}_\beta$$

and

$$\boldsymbol{P} = p^{\alpha\beta} \text{Э}_\alpha \text{Э}_\beta = p^{\alpha\beta} \hat{\text{Э}}_\alpha \hat{\text{Э}}_\beta = p^{\alpha\beta} C^{\lambda \cdot}_{\cdot \alpha} C^{\omega \cdot}_{\cdot \beta} \mathring{\text{Э}}_\lambda \mathring{\text{Э}}_\omega .$$

The components of the tensor $C^{i \cdot}_{\cdot j}$ are defined by the transformation $\hat{\text{Э}}_i = C^{\alpha \cdot}_{\cdot j} \mathring{\text{Э}}_\alpha$ associated with finite deformations (see § 3, Chapter II).

In curvilinear systems, the contravariant components of the tensors $\mathring{\boldsymbol{P}}$ and $\boldsymbol{P}$ are the same, but the components with mixed indices are different. This difference is revealed in a substantial manner in the differentiation of tensors $\boldsymbol{P}$ and $\mathring{\boldsymbol{P}}$ with respect to time (See § 10, Chapter I).

For a given curvilinear coordinate system, let us consider an element of area defined by vectors of the basis $\mathbf{Э}_{i+1}$ and $\mathbf{Э}_{i+2}$ (the indices are defined according to modulo 3), and let us define the positive direction as that of the contravariant vector of the basis

$$\mathbf{Э}^i = \frac{[\mathbf{Э}_{i+1}, \mathbf{Э}_{i+2}]}{\sqrt{g}},$$

the unit vector of this direction being defined by the formula

$$n = \frac{\mathbf{Э}^i}{\sqrt{g^{ii}}}.$$

According to (4.11) and (4.12), the vector of the stress on this surface will be given by

$$p^{*i} = \frac{p^{\alpha i} \mathbf{Э}_\alpha}{\sqrt{g^{ii}}} = X^{\alpha i} \frac{\mathbf{Э}_\alpha}{\sqrt{g_{\alpha\alpha}}}, \tag{4.13}$$

whence,

$$p^{\alpha i} = X^{\alpha i} \sqrt{\frac{g^{ii}}{g_{\alpha\alpha}}}; \tag{4.14}$$

therefore, in formula (4.13) there is no summation over the index i, and in (4.14) there is no summation over i and α. It is immediately clear that $g^{ii} > 0$ and $g_{\alpha\alpha} > 0$. Here and in the future, the roots $\sqrt{g^{ii}}$ and $\sqrt{g_{\alpha\alpha}}$ are always taken with the plus sign.

It is obvious that for any coordinate system, the vector p^{*i} representing the stress on the coordinate area $\mathbf{Э}_{i+1}$, $\mathbf{Э}_{i+2}$ is not equal to the vector

$$p^i = p^{\alpha i} \mathbf{Э}_\alpha.$$

According to (4.13), vector p^{*i} can be written as the sum of three vectors parallel to the coordinate lines; since the $\mathbf{Э}_\alpha / \sqrt{g_{\alpha\alpha}}$ are unit vectors, it is obvious that the quantities $X^{\alpha i}$ defined by formulas (4.14) are equal to the numerical values of the components taken with the appropriate sign along the coordinate lines for the vector p^{*i}.

The quantities $p^{\alpha i}$ are the components of the stress tensor P, whereas the quantities $X^{\alpha i}$ are not components of any tensor. In line with the simple mechanical view given above, the quantities $X^{\alpha i}$ are called the physical components of the stress vector. It is obvious that in rectangular cartesian coordinates $p^{\alpha i} = X^{\alpha i}$.

3. If the components of the tensor p^{ik} are smooth functions within the volume V, then on the basis of (4.10) in an orthogonal cartesian system of

coordinates using the Gauss-Ostrogradskii theorem, we obtain

$$\int_{\Sigma} \boldsymbol{p}_n \, d\sigma = \int_{V} \left(\frac{\partial \boldsymbol{p}^1}{\partial x^1} + \frac{\partial \boldsymbol{p}^2}{\partial x^2} + \frac{\partial \boldsymbol{p}^3}{\partial x^3} \right) d\tau \tag{4.15}$$

or

$$\int_{\Sigma} \boldsymbol{p}_n \, d\sigma = \int_{V} \nabla_\beta \boldsymbol{p}^\beta d\tau \,. \tag{4.16}$$

Because the quantity $\nabla_\beta \boldsymbol{p}^\beta$ is a vector written in invariant form, it is clear that formula (4.16) will hold in any coordinate system.

On the basis of the transformations (4.16), and because volume V is chosen arbitrarily, we shall obtain from (4.7) the basic dynamic differential equation for the mechanics of continuous media in vector form:

$$\rho \boldsymbol{a} = \rho \boldsymbol{F} + \nabla_\beta \boldsymbol{p}^\beta \,. \tag{4.17}$$

Using the transformation (3.14), equation (4.17) can be written as

$$\rho \boldsymbol{a} = \rho \boldsymbol{F} + \frac{1}{\sqrt{g}} \frac{\partial \sqrt{g} \cdot \boldsymbol{p}^\beta}{\partial \eta^\beta} \,, \tag{4.18}$$

where η^1, η^2, η^3 are the coordinates of points of the space in some arbitrary curvilinear coordinate system, and g is equal to the determinant $|g_{ik}| = |(\mathfrak{Э}_i, \mathfrak{Э}_k)|$ defined for the basis $\mathfrak{Э}_i = \partial \boldsymbol{r} / \partial \eta^i$ of the coordinate system under consideration.

The vector equation (4.17) is equivalent to three scalar equations, which in contravariant components are of the form

$$\rho a^j = \rho F^j + \frac{\partial p^{j\beta}}{\partial \eta^\beta} + p^{j\omega} \Gamma^\beta_{\omega\beta} + p^{\alpha\beta} \Gamma^j_{\alpha\beta} \,, \tag{4.19}$$

and similarly equation (4.18) is equivalent to the scalar equations

$$\rho a^j = \rho F^j + \frac{1}{\sqrt{g}} \left[\frac{\partial \sqrt{g} \cdot p^{j\beta}}{\partial \eta^\beta} + \sqrt{g} \cdot p^{\alpha\beta} \Gamma^j_{\alpha\beta} \right] , \tag{4.20}$$

where Γ^i_{jk} are the Christoffel symbols defined in the coordinate system η^i, and a^j and F^j are the contravariant components of the acceleration and the mass forces. Equations (4.20) also follow directly from equations (4.19). The contravariant components of the tensor of the stresses $p^{\alpha i}$ are connected with physical components of the vector of the stresses $X^{\alpha i}$ by formulas (4.14).

It is also easy to write the dynamic equations in a Lagrangian system of coordinates ξ^1, ξ^2, ξ^3, whose basis $\mathring{\mathfrak{Э}}_i$ is taken in the space of the initial conditions.

If $\eta^i = \xi^i$, we obtain equations (4.17) or (4.18) in a deformed Lagrangian system with basis $\hat{\mathbf{\ni}}_i$.

The change from $\hat{\mathbf{\ni}}_i$ to $\mathring{\mathbf{\ni}}_i$ is determined by the formulas

$$\hat{\mathbf{\ni}}_i = C^{\alpha\cdot}_{\cdot i}\mathring{\mathbf{\ni}}_\alpha,$$

where, according to § 3 of Chapter II,

$$C^{\alpha\cdot}_{\cdot i} = \delta^{\alpha\cdot}_{\cdot i} + \nabla_i w^\alpha = \delta^{\alpha\cdot}_{\cdot i} + \frac{\partial w^\alpha}{\partial \xi^i} + w^\lambda \mathring{\Gamma}^\alpha_{\lambda i},$$

and the contravariant components w^α of the displacement vector are determined by the formula

$$\boldsymbol{r} - \boldsymbol{r}_0 = \boldsymbol{w} = w^\alpha \mathring{\mathbf{\ni}}_\alpha .$$

Using (4.12) and (4.13), we can immediately write the following equations for the vectors $\sqrt{g}\cdot \boldsymbol{p}^\beta$:

$$\sqrt{g}\cdot \boldsymbol{p}^\beta = \sqrt{g}\boldsymbol{P}\cdot\hat{\mathbf{\ni}}^\beta = \boldsymbol{P}\cdot[\hat{\mathbf{\ni}}_{\beta+1}, \hat{\mathbf{\ni}}_{\beta+2}] = S_\beta \boldsymbol{P}\cdot\hat{\boldsymbol{n}}^\beta = S_\beta \overset{*}{\boldsymbol{p}}{}^\beta$$
$$= \frac{S_\beta}{\sqrt{\hat{g}_{jj}}} X^{j\beta}\hat{\mathbf{\ni}}_j = \frac{S_\beta}{\sqrt{\mathring{g}_{jj}}(1+l_j)} X^{j\beta} C^{\omega\cdot}_{\cdot j}\mathring{\mathbf{\ni}}_\omega, \tag{4.21}$$

where $\hat{\boldsymbol{n}}^\beta$ is the unit vector of the direction, S_β is the magnitude of the vector product $[\hat{\mathbf{\ni}}_{\beta+1}, \hat{\mathbf{\ni}}_{\beta+2}]$, and $l_j - [|\hat{\mathbf{\ni}}_j| - |\mathring{\mathbf{\ni}}_j|]/|\mathring{\mathbf{\ni}}_j|$ is the coefficient of the elongation along the jth coordinate axis. In formula (4.21), the summation is carried out only over the indices j and ω. The index β is fixed.

The desired equations with $\xi^i = \eta^i$ are obtained by substituting $\sqrt{g}\cdot \boldsymbol{p}^\beta$ from equation (4.21) into (4.18), after which the scalar equations can be found at once. These equations can be obtained for any curvilinear system of coordinates. If the basis $\mathring{\mathbf{\ni}}_j$ is cartesian, obtaining the corresponding system of equations will be simplified in that the vectors of the basis $\mathring{\mathbf{\ni}}_j$ will be constant with respect to the coordinates ξ^i.

For a set of accompanying Lagrangian coordinates, the equation (4.18), taking into account the continuity equation (3.5), can be written in the form

$$\rho_0\sqrt{g_0}\,\boldsymbol{a} = \rho_0\sqrt{g_0}\,\boldsymbol{F} + \frac{\partial \rho_0\sqrt{g_0}\,(\boldsymbol{p}^\beta/\rho)}{\partial \xi^\beta}.$$

In this equation, the factor $\rho_0\sqrt{g_0}$ can be cancelled when the product $\rho_0\sqrt{g_0}$ does not depend on the coordinates ξ^i. If in the initial state the density ρ_0 is constant and the original Lagrangian coordinate system is cartesian, one may assume that $\rho_0\sqrt{g_0} = \text{const}$. It is obvious that if the accompanying Lagrangian coordinate system in the initial state is fixed, the freedom of choice of the coordinate system in the deformed state is excluded.

4. From the angular momentum equation (4.8), using (4.17), we obtain

$$p^{ij} = p^{ji}. \tag{4.22}$$

Consequently, the angular momentum equation indicates the fundamental property of the stress tensor, namely that it is symmetrical.

We note that the matrix $\|X^{\alpha i}\|$ of the physical components of the stress tensor, defined according to equation (4.14), is not in the general case symmetrical.

If the coordinate system corresponding to basis $\mathbf{Э}_i$ is orthogonal, then $g_{ii} = 1/g^{ii}$, and therefore in this case it follows from (4.14) that the property of symmetry holds:

$$X^{\alpha i} = X^{i\alpha}.$$

5. The tensor of the internal stresses changes on going from one point in the medium to a neighboring point. The variability of the tensor $\boldsymbol{P}$ gives rise to acceleration forces which act on the particles of the medium. For an infinitesimal particle with volume $d\tau$ and mass $dm = \rho d\tau$, this force is given by the expression

$$d\mathscr{F} = \nabla_\beta \boldsymbol{p}^\beta \, d\tau = (\nabla_\beta p^{\alpha\beta})\, \mathbf{Э}_\alpha \, d\tau = \frac{1}{\rho}(\nabla_\beta p^{\alpha\beta})\, \mathbf{Э}_\alpha \, dm. \tag{4.23}$$

In the general case, this force is in equilibrium with the mass forces and the inertial forces.

The dynamic equations established in this section have a much more general character. They are valid for arbitrary motions of any material medium. These equations contain six components of the stress tensor: p^{11}, p^{22}, p^{33}, p^{12}, p^{13}, p^{23}. For the theoretical solution of problems it is necessary to determine the six components of the internal stress tensor as functions of the coordinates and time.

The three general scalar equations equivalent to the vector equations (4.17) and the one scalar continuity equation (3.8) form an open system of equations in general. In order to close the system of equations, relationships which express additional physical laws must be added.

5. The kinetic energy theorem and the work of internal surface forces

One of the most important consequences of the general character of the dynamic equations established in the preceding section is the kinetic energy theorem.

Let V be the volume moving together with the particles of the material medium, and let Σ be the surface enclosing this volume. We suppose that within the volume V, the components of the stress tensor $\boldsymbol{P} = p^{ik}\,\mathfrak{Э}_i\mathfrak{Э}_k$ and of the velocity vector $\mathbf{v} = v_i\,\mathfrak{Э}^i$ are continuous differentiable functions with respect to the space coordinates and time.

For simplicity we take a rectangular cartesian coordinate system. We multiply as scalars both parts of the first of equations (4.17) by $\mathbf{v}\,dt\,d\tau = d\boldsymbol{r}\,d\tau$, where $d\boldsymbol{r}$ is an elementary displacement of points in the volume V, and obtain

$$\rho d\tau\cdot\mathbf{v}\frac{d\mathbf{v}}{dt}dt$$
$$= \rho\boldsymbol{F}\mathbf{v}d\tau dt + \left[\frac{\partial \boldsymbol{p}^1\mathbf{v}}{\partial x^1} + \frac{\partial \boldsymbol{p}^2\mathbf{v}}{\partial x^2} + \frac{\partial \boldsymbol{p}^3\mathbf{v}}{\partial x^3} - \boldsymbol{p}^1\frac{\partial \mathbf{v}}{\partial x^1} - \boldsymbol{p}^2\frac{\partial \mathbf{v}}{\partial x^2} - \boldsymbol{p}^3\frac{\partial \mathbf{v}}{\partial x^3}\right]d\tau dt.$$

We integrate this equation over the volume V. Remembering that

$$\mathbf{v}\frac{d\mathbf{v}}{dt}\rho\,d\tau = \frac{d(\mathbf{v}^2\rho\,d\tau/2)}{dt},$$

and making the obvious Gauss-Ostrogradskii transformation taking into account (4.10), we obtain the kinetic energy equation

$$dE = d\mathscr{A}^e + d\mathscr{A}^i_M + d\mathscr{A}^i, \tag{5.1}$$

where

$$E = \int_V \frac{\rho\mathbf{v}^2}{2}\,d\tau,$$

$$d\mathscr{A}^e = \int_V \rho\boldsymbol{F}^e\,d\boldsymbol{r}\,d\tau + \int_\Sigma (\boldsymbol{p}_n, \mathbf{v})\,d\sigma\,dt,$$

$$d\mathscr{A}^i_{\mathscr{M}} = \int_V \rho\boldsymbol{F}^i d\boldsymbol{r}\,d\tau,$$

and

$$d\mathscr{A}^i = -\int_V\left[p^{11}\frac{\partial v_1}{\partial x^1} + p^{22}\frac{\partial v_2}{\partial x^2} + p^{33}\frac{\partial v_3}{\partial x^3}\right.$$
$$\left. + p^{12}\left(\frac{\partial v_2}{\partial x^1} + \frac{\partial v_1}{\partial x^2}\right) + p^{13}\left(\frac{\partial v_3}{\partial x^1} + \frac{\partial v_1}{\partial x^3}\right) + p^{23}\left(\frac{\partial v_3}{\partial x^2} + \frac{\partial v_2}{\partial x^3}\right)\right]d\tau\,dt.$$

The quantity E is called the kinetic energy of the masses of the medium in the volume V. The quantity $d\mathscr{A}^e$ is equal to the elementary work of all the external volumes ($\boldsymbol{F}^e$) and surface forces. The quantity $d\mathscr{A}^i_M$ is the elementary work of the internal volumetric* macroscopic forces F^i ($\boldsymbol{F}^e + \boldsymbol{F}^i = \boldsymbol{F}$). By

---

* For gravitational forces of type $d\mathscr{A}^i_M = -dV^i$, where V^i is the potential energy of the macroscopic internal forces.

definition $d\mathscr{A}^i$ is called the elementary work of the internal surface forces.

It is obvious that for the invariant quantity $d\mathscr{A}^i$, in any coordinate system, the following formula is valid:

$$d\mathscr{A}^i = -\int_V p^{\alpha\beta} e_{\alpha\beta}\, dt\, d\tau\,, \tag{5.2}$$

where $e_{\alpha\beta}$ are the components of the tensor of the rates of deformation, which according to § 6, Chapter II, are determined by the formulas

$$e_{\alpha\beta} = \tfrac{1}{2}\left[\nabla_\alpha v_\beta + \nabla_\beta v_\alpha\right],$$

The work of the internal forces for a finite deformation of a moving volume of matter is given by the integral

$$\mathscr{A}^i = -\int_{t_0}^{t}\int_V p^{\alpha\beta} e_{\alpha\beta}\, dt\, d\tau = -\int_{t_0}^{t}\int_m p^{\alpha\beta}(\xi^i, t)\, d\varepsilon_{\alpha\beta}(\xi^i, t)\frac{dm}{\rho(\xi^i, t)}, \tag{5.3}$$

where $d\varepsilon_{\alpha\beta} = \dot{\varepsilon}_{\alpha\beta} dt$ is the increment in the covariant components of the tensor of the finite deformation for a fixed particle (ξ^i = const), and ρ is the density of the particle. In accordance with the continuity equation, we note that $d\tau = dm/\rho$, where ρ is the density of the volume element $d\tau$ with mass dm composed of the same material points.

For compressible media, ρ depends on ξ^i and on the time t.

The work $\mathscr{A}^i$ depends on the separated volume V_0 and in a functional manner on the law of change with respect to time of the varying components of the stress and the components of the tensor of the rates of deformation.

For an infinitesimal particle, the expression for $d\mathscr{A}^i$ in (5.2) is reduced to the integrand

$$d\mathscr{A}^i = -\frac{1}{\rho} p^{\alpha\beta} e_{\alpha\beta}\, dt\, dm = -\frac{1}{\rho} p^{\alpha\beta}\, d\varepsilon_{\alpha\beta}\, dm\,. \tag{5.4}$$

The elementary work of the internal surface forces can be considered for all possible displacements $\delta\boldsymbol{r}$ of the points of the continuum, which is equivalent to all possible variations $\delta\varepsilon_{\alpha\beta}$ of the deformation tensor.

For an arbitrary variation $\delta\varepsilon_{\alpha\beta}$, the work of the internal forces will be given by the formula

$$\delta\mathscr{A}^i = -\frac{1}{\rho} p^{\alpha\beta}\, \delta\varepsilon_{\alpha\beta}\, dm\,. \tag{5.5}$$

This expression, in general, is not a total differential of any function.

If the infinitesimal displacements of the medium occur as displacements of a rigid body, then $\delta\varepsilon_{\alpha\beta} = 0$, and therefore the work of the internal surface forces is always equal to zero for infinitesimal displacements with no deformations.

6. Thermodynamic systems and cycles, equations of the law of conservation of energy, and the concept of the internal energy of a system

In order to construct a theoretical model and to obtain a closed system of equations describing the interrelated motions and physico-chemical processes, it is necessary to use the thermodynamic and kinetic principles of physics and chemistry.

The setting-up of such additional relationships involves the introduction of a series of concepts and characteristic numerical quantities. Typical examples are the concepts of temperature, entropy, internal energy, physical constants that determine physical and chemical properties, concentrations of the various components in mixtures, etc.

In constructing theoretical models of material media, each small particle can be thought of as an elementary physico-chemical system for which the motion and the physical and chemical state are characterized by a certain finite number of quantities given by numbers, i.e., the defining parameters.

For certain classes of problems examined, the elementary properties and parameters characterizing small parts of the system, both from the practical and theoretical points of view, are introduced either on the basis of certain experiments or with the help of a series of hypotheses. In general, these experimental and theoretical methods are closely interwoven with one another. In many cases, a problem dealing with certain complicated processes is still open and is the subject of investigations; for example, models of visco-plastic solids, nonequilibrium phenomena associated with radiation in gases at high temperatures, and many other problems.

In constructing the various models in continuum mechanics, it is possible to be guided by and to use the concepts and results of statistical physics.

The characteristics and the basic laws can be introduced on the basis of statistical observations by considering large sets of interacting molecules, atoms, ions, electrons, and other elementary particles.

For certain conditions and processes, under certain additional simple assumptions within the framework of the classical or quantum theory of microscopic interactions and properties of large sets of particles, the macroscopic characteristics of the state, and processes and the basic statistical laws pertaining to macroscopic averages can be determined by the theoretical method.

In macroscopic theories, the elementary physically small particles of the medium can be considered as thermodynamic systems for which the mechanical concepts concerning position, motion, and the physical concepts concerning internal state are defined.

Thus, for a physically infinitesimal particle, systems of numbers can be introduced which describe the properties and characterize a given state of the particle. Questions which arise in solving various types of theoretical or practical problems must be formulated as questions as to the numerical values of, or the functional relations between, quantities that are defined as characteristics of mechanical or, in general, physico-chemical states.

The problem of the system of defining characteristics is often difficult, and requires an analysis of the mechanism of the processes that are basic in the given problem. In many cases, the problem of clarifying the internal mechanism of the interaction is the subject of investigation.

Apart from setting up systems of defining characteristics, it is also necessary to establish the basic laws regulating the mechanical and physico-chemical interactions and processes.

From the point of view of practical applications, in setting up these defining characteristics, it is expedient to consider effects which are generally speaking equally significant in the applicable approximate scheme.

The formation of a system of defining parameters is related to the setting up of the problem; for this, it is always necessary to use schematic descriptions, hypotheses, and reduced experimental data.

A system of defining parameters is always easy to obtain if there is a closed system of equations. The converse is not true, because exhaustive information about the series of quantities defining the state is still by no means sufficient for the actual formulation of a closed system of the equations of motion.

It is necessary to distinguish between the system of defining parameters in a particular given problem and the system of parameters defining the state of the medium. *In the first case, we have a set of parameters that defines a unique phenomenon by means of a system of equations and supplementary boundary and other conditions. In the second case, we have the characteristics of a state for which we must establish a set of equations that are valid for all possible processes and each of which is related to the supplementary external conditions.*

In the formulation of the external conditions, other parameters can be introduced which need not be included in the system of parameters defining the state of the medium.

On the other hand, in practice not all the parameters *characterizing the state* are included in the list of defining parameters. In this case, it is necessary to include only those defining parameters which are essential to the solution of the problem. This also allows for the fact that the system of equations exists, although it might be still unknown. One must bear in mind that the desired results can be obtained experimentally both when the closed system of equations is known and when it is unknown.

The definition of the concept of the macroscopic state and the formulation of the corresponding characteristics of the state, can, generally speaking, be accomplished by using statistical physics.

The fixing of a system of parameters defining the physical and mechanical state of an element of the medium is important, and logically it is the initial stage in determining the model of a continuous medium. In practice, the complete determination of the system of defining parameters can coincide with the final stage of study and formulation of the model.

Later we shall examine more general questions of constructing continuum models, in which it is assumed that an infinitesimal particle is simply a local concept characterizing the kinematic and internal physico-chemical properties and processes in a given particle. This assumption does not exclude processes in which an integral interaction between the given small particle and the finite masses in the system in question takes place. For example, one can consider the finite mass of an ideal gas made up of moving neutral and charged particles that attract each other by the forces of Newtonian gravitation and by interacting electromagnetic forces in accordance with the laws of Coulomb and Lorentz. The total external gravitational and electromagnetic forces acting on a hypothetical individual particle are determined by the position, distribution, and motion of the mass in finite volumes. However, the internal state of a given infinitesimal particle, even when there is no thermodynamic equilibrium, can often be characterized by quantities which are defined in a local sense.

Below, we shall develop more advanced models for the mechanics of a continuous medium, beginning with the general concepts formulated above.

Thus, we can assume that any model of an infinitesimal particle of a material medium will have a finite system of characteristics given by the numbers

$$\mu_1, \mu_2, \ldots, \mu_n, \qquad k_1, k_2, \ldots, k_m. \tag{6.1}$$

Some of these are mechanical quantities, for example, space coordinates, velocity, density, the characteristics of the deformation, the rotation of a particle, etc.; others are chemical or physical quantities, for example, temperature, physical parameters of the structure, and the composition and peculiarities of the substance, the coefficients of thermal conductivity and viscosity, etc.

We assume that the quantities μ_i can be variable and that the k_j have constant values – the physical constants. In many cases, it is necessary to introduce physical characteristics that maintain constant values in the classes of problems in question.

By definition, for a fixed small particle, the quantities (6.1) form a basis; they can be given independently and in known ranges arbitrarily. The quantities (6.1) are also determined by the condition that all the characteristics of the states and motions in the various problems can be studied as quantities which depend on the basis. This follows from their definition, or from the fundamental finite or differential laws, which form a closed system of relationships for the infinitesimal particles. In specific problems, for the solution of the differential laws, it is necessary to make use of supplementary boundary, initial, and other conditions. The conditions in turn can depend on certain additional parameters which do not appear in system (6.1). In particular cases, the systems of defining parameters are examined for the bodies of finite or infinite volumes in terms of which the problem is stated.

It can happen that no unique solution exists for the particular form in which a problem is stated. The solutions can form a discrete sequence or can depend continuously on several parameters.

For the system as a whole, the parameters appearing in the solution have to be linked up with the system of defining parameters. In order to pick out the proper solution, additional data on the external conditions are needed. The physical hypotheses and principles for the system as a whole, or for its individual particles, must also be known. In some cases, such additional principles can be deduced from the general laws of thermodynamics equally applicable to small particles or to the entire system.

For a fixed model, the set of values (6.1) can be different because it is possible to take different variables and parameters as the independent quantities.

The variation of the basis parameters in the time function $\mu_i(t)$, conditioned by the interaction of a particular particle with other particles and bodies, defines a process characterized by the form of the functions $\mu_i(t)$.

In the general case, the dependence of certain quantities on the defining parameters μ_i may be given by differential relationships of the type

$$d\chi = \sum_\alpha \mathscr{A}_\alpha(\mu_1, \mu_2, \dots, \mu_n, k_1, k_2, \dots, k_m)\, d\mu_\alpha, \tag{6.2}$$

where χ is the quantity to be determined and the $\mathscr{A}_\alpha$ are some functions of the base parameters (6.1).

If the differential relationship (6.2) is not integrable (a nonholonomic relationship), the finite quantity χ depends functionally on μ_i, or, in other words, on the process path by which the given values μ_i are attained when they are changed from certain fixed initial values of μ_{io}.

It is obvious that quantities similar to χ which are functionally dependent on the history of the process can also be introduced for an elastic body, for example, by the equation

$$d\chi = \frac{d\mathscr{A}^i}{f(\mathscr{I}_1, \mathscr{I}_2, \mathscr{I}_3)},$$

where $d\mathscr{A}^i$ is the elementary work of the internal forces and $f(\mathscr{I}_1, \mathscr{I}_2, \mathscr{I}_3)$ is some function of the invariants of the stress tensor. Of course, in the general theory of elasticity, quantities of this type need not be used.

We note, however, that this is quite normal in many practical variational problems in the theory of elasticity in which operations involving functionals are used.

The independence of the variable parameters μ_i consists, by definition, in the fact that virtual variations in $\delta\mu_i$ for a given system in a given state can be considered in a certain region as arbitrary infinitesimal quantities and, specifically, as linearly independent quantities. Each possible system of values $\delta\mu_i$ corresponds to some system of external conditions which in a known sense can be thought of as supplementary relationships.

The separation of admissible states and processes is an integral part of the process of determining a physical system and the defining basis. In specific problems, not all the admissible states and processes are or can be actually brought about.

The formulation of the question under consideration as to the defining basis is typical in the physics of elementary objects. It is obvious that in certain cases the possibility of fixing a finite defining basis can be related to the choice of the number of variable parameters, and functional relationships may have to be used in order to reduce this number.

For example, in the investigation of gas-dynamic processes governed by different laws of heat flow, the connection between the density and pressure is a functional relationship.

If we introduce temperature as a new supplementary variable, the connection between temperature, density, and pressure for a small particle is always universal, independent of the process.

The characteristics of the state (6.1) can correspond to the cases in which not only mechanical, but also thermodynamic equilibrium is absent and can be used to describe reversible as well as irreversible processes.

The variation of the basis parameters in the time function, conditioned by the interaction of a given particle with other particles and bodies, defines a sequence of positions and states. External effects can cause a particle of fixed mass to undergo various processes. A process in which at any two instants of time, t_0 and t, all the parameters of the defining basis and therefore all the characteristic essential quantities are the same, is called a closed cycle, or simply a cycle. A given particle can go through cycles of many kinds.

For every process, one can consider the work of the *external macroscopic forces* applied to the points in the volume and on the boundaries of an isolated individual infinitesimal particle. For an infinitesimal variation in the parameters of system (6.1), this work is given by the expression

$$d\mathscr{A}^e = \mathscr{M}_1\, d\mu_1 + \mathscr{M}_2\, d\mu_2 + \mathscr{M}_3\, d\mu_3 + \cdots + \mathscr{M}_n\, d\mu_n, \tag{6.3}$$

in which some of the coefficients $\mathscr{M}_i$ that are dependent on the defining parameters can always be zero. The quantities $\mathscr{M}_i$ can be described as generalized forces.

The quantity $d\mathscr{A}^e$ can be considered as the mechanical energy transmitted to a given particle by the other bodies.

In general, the differential expression for $d\mathscr{A}^e$ is not a total differential. The total work of the external forces over a finite path is obtained by integrating the totality of elementary works (6.3), and is quite dependent on the form of the process; in particular, the work of the external forces for a closed cycle can be different from zero.

Apart from the work $d\mathscr{A}^e$, a given particle dm can acquire energy in other forms, in particular, thermal energy. The general additional influx of energy, *which is not due to the work* of the external macroscopic forces, will be denoted by dQ^*. In the general case, $dQ^* \neq dQ$, where dQ is the influx of thermal energy.†

The value of the influx of energy dQ^* as well as the work of the external forces can be expressed in terms of the increments of the defining parameters $d\mu_i$ by a formula of the form

$$dQ^* = Q_1\, d\mu_1 + Q_2\, d\mu_2 + \cdots + Q_n\, d\mu_n. \tag{6.4}$$

The differential expression (6.4) is generally not a total differential of any function.

Formulas (6.3) and (6.4) give expressions for the external influences $d\mathscr{A}^e$ and dQ^* on the particle in terms of the parameters μ_i, defining the state of the particle, and in terms of their increments $d\mu_i$, corresponding to some elementary process.

In the general case, it is necessary to know the state and the elementary

† In particular, the difference $dQ^* - dQ$ can be nonzero if the influx of electromagnetic energy or diffusion is taken into consideration.

process to which the particle in question is subjected before equations (6.3) and (6.4) can be formulated.

If the model of the medium, and consequently the enumeration of all the defining variable parameters μ_i is known, then for a known state (i.e., for given μ_i and for a known elementary process determined by the system of increments $d\mu_i$) we must consider the representation of $d\mathscr{A}^e$ and dQ^* by formulas (6.3) and (6.4) as a consequence of the concepts of the state and the processes that were introduced above in a local sense.

In order to solve problems on the determination of the state of a particle and the corresponding processes, the quantities $d\mathscr{A}^e$ and dQ^*, must be expressed mathematically in terms of quantities defining the interaction between the given particle and the external bodies. Not only the parameters μ_i which define the state of a given particle, but also other parameters which define the states of the external bodies, or the distributions of certain characteristic quantities throughout the mass or volume of the interacting particles, can serve as such quantities.

The integral

$$\int_{\mu_{0i}}^{\mu_i} dQ^*$$

depends on the path of the integration and is generally nonzero for a closed cycle. The coefficients $\mathscr{M}_i$ and Q_i in (6.3) and (6.4) for a small particle can be assumed small and proportional to the mass of the particle $dm = \rho\, d\tau$.

The total influx of energy $U^* dm$ into a particle for a finite change in the state of the particle is given by the linear integral

$$U^* dm = \int_{\mu_{0i}}^{\mu_i} (d\mathscr{A}^e + dQ^*) = \int_{\mu_{0i}}^{\mu_i} \{(\mathscr{M}_1 + Q_1)\, d\mu_1 + \cdots + (\mathscr{M}_n + Q_n)\, d\mu_n\}\,. \quad (6.5)$$

According to the law of conservation of energy, the total influx of energy into the particle for any closed cycle (both reversible and irreversible) is zero. Thus it follows that the quantity U^* depends only on μ_i and k_j and does not depend on the path of the integration for the integral in (6.5). The function of the parameters of the state U^* is completely defined by the integral (6.5).

Since the original state μ_{0i} can be chosen quite arbitrarily, the function U^* is defined accurately on the basis of the law of conservation of energy only up to an additive constant: this additive constant can be determined with the aid of supplementary physical hypotheses.

The function $U^*(\mu_1, \mu_2, \ldots, \mu_n, k_1, k_2, \ldots, k_m)$ is called the total energy of a particle computed for a unit mass. By integrating (6.5) throughout the mass (volume) and separating out the energy coming in from the outside, it is possible to determine the total energy of any finite part of the body in question.

The total energy of a small particle can be written as the sum

$$U^* \, dm = \frac{dm\mathbf{v}^2}{2} + U \, dm \,, \tag{6.6}$$

in which the first term is the kinetic energy and the second is the internal energy. The kinetic energy corresponding to a unit mass for a small particle and any process is simply equal to half the square of its velocity, which generally has to be considered as one of the parameters μ_i. The internal energy calculated for a unit mass can, for a small particle, be represented in the form of some function of the defining parameters

$$U(\mu_1, \mu_2, \ldots, \mu_n, k_1, k_2, \ldots, k_m) \,. \tag{6.7}$$

We shall further suppose that for the *finite* thermodynamic systems that we are examining, the internal energy can be represented as the sum

$$U_m + V^i \,, \tag{6.8}$$

where $dV^i = -\,d\mathscr{A}^i_M$, and for a small mass dm we take $U_m = Udm$ because V^i/dm is an infinitesimal quantity.

In constructing theoretical models for a given medium, the form of the function (6.7), which is the same for all processes in the problems under consideration, can be found by experiment or by using additional hypotheses. In certain cases, in the construction of ideal media, the form of the function (6.7) can be introduced into the definition of the corresponding model of the material medium.

The concept of the internal energy, like the law of the conservation of energy, is valid both for reversible and irreversible processes. For a given model of a material medium, in describing irreversible processes, the number of variable defining parameters may be larger than in the case of reversible processes.

If the classes of phenomena which play essential roles in the questions under study are extended, it will be necessary to widen the concepts of a thermodynamic system and of internal energy and to introduce additional defining parameters. For example, this would occur in shifting from the study of the motion of inert gases to the study of the flow of gases that is accompanied by chemical processes, dissociation, ionization, or nuclear reactions. The emission or absorption of energy in chemical or nuclear reactions can be considered as a change in the internal energy which is determined by the corresponding composition of the substance.

In certain cases, the internal energy can be considered as the sum of the kinetic and potential energies, which are determined by the random thermal motion and interaction of the small particles of which the body is composed, and for which, within the framework of the mechanics of continuous media, the corresponding continuum models are built.

The basic equation for the conservation of energy – the first law of thermodynamics – can be written in the form

$$dE + dU_m + dV^i = d\mathscr{A}^e + dQ^* ; \tag{6.9}$$

the left-hand side is the sum of the increments in the kinetic and internal energies of the mass of the thermodynamic system under consideration. The basic equation (6.9), accompanied by corresponding definition of its terms, is applicable both to a small particle and to a finite volume. If (6.9) is integrated along the path of the process, a relationship for finite changes will be obtained. The energy equation (6.9) does not contain the work of the internal forces, and it is formulated on the basis of the change dE in the kinetic energy of macroscopic motion.

From the kinetic energy equation (5.1), on the basis of (6.8) and from (6.9), we obtain the equation of the heat influx:

$$dQ^* = dU_m + d\mathscr{A}^i . \tag{6.10}$$

For an infinitesimal particle, in accordance with (5.4), we obtain the equation

$$dQ^* = dU_m - \frac{1}{\rho} p^{\alpha\beta}\, d\varepsilon_{\alpha\beta}\, dm ,$$

where

$$dU_m = d(U \cdot dm) ,$$

which is suitable for examining the internal thermodynamic processes, because this equation does not contain the energy of the macroscopic motion or the work of the external forces.

Equation (6.10) is called the equation of heat influx. The work of the surface stresses and the external influx of energy dQ^* (the influx of energy in addition to the work of the external forces), which must be given separately, appear in this equation.

In the presence of dynamic equations, the equation of heat influx (6.10), which is equivalent to the law of conservation of energy (6.9), can be considered as a fundamental universal thermodynamic scalar equation, which supplements the equations of mechanics established above.

If $d\mathscr{A}^i{}_{\mathscr{M}} = 0$ and if the kinetic energy is constant, in particular, for a stationary medium in equilibrium, it follows from equation (5.1) that

$d\mathscr{A}^i = -d\mathscr{A}^e$. Therefore, in this case, the $d\mathscr{A}^i$ in equation (6.10) may be replaced by $-d\mathscr{A}^e$, the negative of the work of the external forces. However, in general, we must remember that the work of the internal surface forces appears in (6.10), but the work of the external forces does not.

7. Basic principles and consequences of the second law of thermodynamics

The basic thermodynamic concept characterizing the state of physical bodies is that of temperature. The original concept of the temperature of a body is directly related to the sensations of our everyday experience. The temperature is the basic characteristic determining the transfer of thermal energy between bodies. Experiment shows that the thermal energy flows from a body at a high temperature into one at a lower temperature. The basic condition for the thermal equilibrium of a body in which there is no heat transmission from one part of the body to another is that the temperature be constant throughout the volume of the body.

Temperature may be characterized by numbers and measured by thermometers – devices in which certain physical effects determined by the temperature are indicated.

The concept of temperature is universal and is the basic physical characteristic of all bodies made up of elementary particles (atoms, molecules, etc.) moving and interacting with one another. Temperature can be regarded as the statistical mean energy per one degree of freedom in the random thermal motion of a given set of particles. The process of temperature equalization depends on the statistical law concerned with the overall uniform distribution of energy in the state of equilibrium of the particles constituting the body per number of degrees of freedom. The difference in average energy for different particles or in a given particle for various degrees of freedom entails, as a result of the interaction between particles, the transfer of the energy of the microscopic thermal motion which leads to an equalization of the mean energies.

In clearly defined nonequilibrium processes, the concept of temperature loses its meaning when there is no statistical equalization of energy between the different degrees of freedom for a physically small particle. For example, in certain cases, when an abrupt change occurs in the state of the particle, one may speak of several temperatures, e.g., the temperature of the vibrational motions of molecules or the temperature of the translational degrees of freedom of the molecules. Under conditions of thermodynamic equilibrium in small volumes of a body, the temperature is uniquely defined.

Experiment shows that in many practical problems one can often suppose that thermodynamic equilibrium does exist in small volumes of the system. In applications, nonequilibrium and irreversibility frequently take place only because of the absence of equilibrium in large volumes of a body when temperature and the other thermodynamic characteristics such as the concentration of the chemical components of mixtures, etc., are inhomogeneously distributed among the particles.

For many nonequilibrium processes, the so-called Onsager principle holds. This states that all the microscopic interactions between the elementary particles are reversible and that irreversibility appears only because of the statistical laws for the equalization of the average macroscopic characteristics for large collections of elementary particles.

The concepts of absolute temperature and entropy can be introduced as macroscopic characteristics by using the second law of thermodynamics. The second law of thermodynamics can be formulated in the following way: it is impossible to produce perpetual motion of the second type, i.e., a machine, which, in accordance with the first law, would convert the thermal energy taken from a source of lowest temperature into mechanical energy.

This empirical premise suffices in order to prove [19] that for any thermodynamic system there exists a function of the state of entropy which, in many cases, has additive properties*

$$S_m = \int_m S(\mu_1, \mu_2, \dots, \mu_n, k_1, k_2, \dots, k_m)\, dm\,.$$

For a small particle, in the case of reversible processes, the entropy is defined with an accuracy up to an additive constant by the equation

$$dS\, dm = dS_m = \frac{dQ}{T}, \tag{7.1}$$

where T is the absolute temperature and dQ is the external flow of heat into the particle.†

Equation (7.1) defines the absolute temperature T and entropy S simultaneously.

The existence of the entropy indicated in equation (7.1) is equivalent to the condition that for a given particle and any reversible closed cycle, the

---

* It is further assumed that the entropy of a finite body can be obtained as a sum of the entropies of all the small parts of the body.

† In formulating the first law, the quantity dQ^* could have included the general external transfer of energy without the work of the external forces. In the equation of the second law, dQ equals the external influx of thermal energy. Henceforth, we shall consider only those cases where $dQ = dQ^*$.

equation

$$\oint \frac{dQ}{T} = \oint \left[\frac{Q_1\, d\mu_1 + Q_2\, d\mu_2 + \cdots + Q_n\, d\mu_n}{T} \right] = 0 \tag{7.2}$$

holds. As a consequence of this condition, the differential dQ/T is a total differential and T^{-1} serves as an integrating factor, which, according to the second law (7.2) always exists for the differential expression dQ, and which, very significantly, is identical for any two thermodynamic systems in equilibrium and interacting with each other by means of contact. This last condition is important for a unique determination of the integrating factor.

As in the case of temperature, entropy can be introduced statistically. Entropy is thought of as the probability of the corresponding macroscopic state.

In statistical physics, entropy is defined by the following formula given by Boltzmann:

$$S = \boldsymbol{k} \ln \mathscr{P}, \tag{7.3}$$

where $\boldsymbol{k}$ is Boltzmann's constant, and $\mathscr{P}$ is a measure of the probability of the state in question, which can be defined as the number of possible microscopic states corresponding to a given macroscopic state.

Because actually attainable states correspond to the greatest probability, it follows from (7.3) that as an isolated system approaches equilibrium, its entropy increases. It is also obvious that if a thermally isolated system is brought to a state of equilibrium from a state of nonequilibrium, the entropy will increase.

Equation (7.1) is defined and valid only for reversible processes. In particular, from (7.1) it follows that for reversible (and therefore in the state of thermodynamic equilibrium) adiabatic processes defined by the condition $dQ = 0$, i.e., in the absence of heat influx, the entropy in a particle is constant.

If the process is irreversible, then from the second law of thermodynamics instead of equation (7.1), we have the inequality

$$dS_m > \frac{dQ}{T} = \frac{dU_m + d\mathscr{A}^i}{T}, \tag{7.4}$$

and, in particular, for irreversible adiabatic processes the entropy increases.

In contrast to the concept of temperature, it is possible to define the entropy (like the internal energy) for thermodynamically unstable states. This follows, for example, from the statistical formula (7.3).

We shall now consider irreversible processes in which the state of a given small particle is characterized by a defined absolute temperature T.

In this case, according to the second law of thermodynamics [9, 19], for an elementary process equation (7.1) must be replaced by the equation

$$T\,dS_m = dQ + dQ', \qquad \text{where} \qquad dQ' > 0. \tag{7.5}$$

The positive quantity dQ' is called the uncompensated heat. For reversible processes in a given particle, $dQ' = 0$.

The condition $dQ' = 0$ is necessary for the reversibility of a process in a particle. In the presence of a temperature gradient and of interaction between neighboring particles, the condition $dQ' = 0$ is not sufficient for reversibility of processes.

In order to describe irreversible processes, the data on the value of the noncompensated heat dQ' must be used.

On the basis of equations (6.10) and (7.5) defining the first and second laws of thermodynamics, it is possible to write

$$dQ' = T\,dS_m - dU_m - d\mathscr{A}^i. \tag{7.6}$$

If the model of a continuous medium is known, then the entropy S_m, the internal energy U_m, and the work of the internal forces are known for a given state of the particle and for a given elementary process. In this case, the equations (6.9), (6.10), and (7.6) can be used for determining the values of dQ, $d\mathscr{A}^e$, and dQ' in the function of the defining parameters and their increments. These data can also be used for determining the same quantities in the function of the quantities characterizing the interaction of the various particles of the medium and the particles of a given medium with other bodies.

Equations (6.9), (6.10), and (7.6) represent universal macroscopic relationships which are applicable to any process in any continuum.

Obviously, these relationships are analogous to the universal dynamic equations (4.7) and (4.8).

For models of material continuous media, equations (4.7) and (4.8) can be considered as consequences of certain definitions and of the general universal equations (6.9), (6.10), and (7.6). This also follows from the fact that for a given model with given $d\mathscr{A}^e$ and dQ, the equation of the law of the conservation of energy, which expresses the first law of thermodynamics, can, after the use of the second law, be examined and used for investigations and for obtaining closed systems of equations in exactly the same manner as the principle of possible displacements is used in mechanics.

In particular, it is possible to obtain the universal dynamic equations of mechanics [35, 88] from the universal equations of thermodynamics by such a method.

By utilizing the states of equilibrium and motion, Newton's equation (4.4) furnishes the fundamental concept in defining the operation of weighing. This operation consists of equating the known forces to the unknown ones and, in this manner, results in establishing the laws of reciprocity of forces on the basis of observations and experiments.

The first and second laws of thermodynamics must be used in a similar way. On one hand, they must be used as a basis in solving the problem of constructing the model of the properties of the continuum, i.e., in establishing the properties of the internal energy U_m and the noncompensated heat dQ (here, it is convenient to regard entropy as the defining parameter and the temperature and internal stresses as the defining quantities) on the basis of hypotheses and experimental observations. On the other hand, when U_m and dQ' are given, these laws must be used in defining the properties of the elementary work $d\mathscr{A}^e$ and the external influx of heat dQ in direct dependence on the parameters which define the states and the conditions of interaction of the various elements of the bodies.

It is obvious that for these operations, it is necessary in certain cases to use the equations of the mass balances.*

Each of the problems mentioned above is related to fundamental questions as to the properties of a given medium and the laws of interaction of the elements of a given medium among themselves or with external bodies. The solution of these problems, applicable for defined bodies and physico-chemical phenomena, is always directly or indirectly related to the data from experiments and observations, and it constitutes the problem of macroscopic thermodynamics.

In the theory of real bodies, it is possible to study and determine the internal energy, noncompensated heat, temperature, and entropy as well as their relationship with and dependence on other parameters by means of methods of statistical physics, using certain simple schemes and assumptions as to the properties and structure of the body and the nature of interaction of the particles constituting the body.

The laws defining the compensated heat are nothing else but the laws of dissipation of energy, which lead to an increase in entropy due to the internal irreversible effects. Typical examples of irreversible processes are the phenomena of diffusion, viscosity, residual plastic deformations, etc.

---

* In constructing certain models, one may impose supplementary nonholonomic relations of both kinematic and physical nature on the determining parameters [37].

The study of the laws describing irreversible phenomena is based in many cases on the following fundamental assumptions.

1. Every state of a particle in a coordinate system that translates together with the center of gravity of the particle can be considered as a state of thermodynamic equilibrium or can be regarded as some other state of equilibrium, corresponding to the given state of the particle by having the same values of the defining parameters which determine uniquely the internal energy and entropy.

2. Any two equilibrium states of a small particle can be mentally connected by some ideal reversible process in which the change in internal energy and entropy is the same as in the irreversible process.

It is obvious that in an irreversible process and the corresponding reversible process, the external influx of heat and the work of the internal forces are generally different.

If an irreversible process corresponds to an infinitesimal element of length of the path in the space of the defining parameters, it is not permissible, in general, to predicate that a reversible path connecting closely located equilibrium states does not contain finite deviations of the defining parameters from the values corresponding to the neighboring state in question.

With these assumptions, the increase in entropy and the noncompensated heat can be computed by using the following formulas:

$$dQ = dU_m + d\mathscr{A}^i_{\text{irrev}}, \qquad T\,dS_m = dQ_{\text{rev}} = dQ + dQ' = dU_m + d\mathscr{A}^i_{\text{rev}}. \quad (7.7)$$

It follows that

$$dQ' = dQ_{\text{rev}} - dQ = d\mathscr{A}^i_{\text{rev}} - d\mathscr{A}^i_{\text{irrev}} > 0. \quad (7.8)$$

Thus, in this case, the compensated heat is equal to the difference in the work of the internal forces in the reversible and irreversible processes for the same change in entropy and internal energy and for a given identical change in that part of the parameters which defines the equilibrium states of the medium.

Diffusion is an important example of an irreversible process leading to the blending of different substances. Together with the irreversible process of diffusion, we can find, in the case of gases [9], reversible processes leading to mixing or to the separation of the mixture into its component parts. In this way, the quantity dQ' for the diffusion of gases can be determined.

For reversible processes, the differential equation of the law of conservation of energy can, when we take into account the second law of thermodynamics ($Q = T\,dS_m$), be used to derive various equations expressing the different thermodynamic laws connected with equilibrium processes. These equations and the corresponding conclusions can be considered as a direct generalization of the equation of mechanics, which, for systems with multiple degrees of freedom, expresses the principle of possible displacements and its implications in ideally connected mechanical systems.

For reversible processes, the equation of heat influx of the form (7.7) can be written in open form:

$$\delta S_m = \frac{1}{T}\left[\left(\frac{\partial U_m}{\partial \mu_1} + \mathscr{P}_1\right)\delta\mu_1 + \left(\frac{\partial U_m}{\partial \mu_2} + \mathscr{P}_2\right)\delta\mu_2 + \cdots + \left(\frac{\partial U_m}{\partial \mu_n} + \mathscr{P}_n\right)\delta\mu_n\right] \tag{7.9}$$

where the $\mathscr{P}_i$ are the coefficients in the differential form:

$$\delta\mathscr{A}^i_{\text{rev}} = \mathscr{P}_1\,\delta\mu_1 + \mathscr{P}_2\,\delta\mu_2 + \cdots + \mathscr{P}_n\,\delta\mu_n. \tag{7.10}$$

The condition that the left-hand side of (7.9) be a total differential leads to the following equations, which are satisfied as a consequence of the second law of thermodynamics:

$$\frac{\partial \mathscr{P}_j}{\partial \mu_i} - \frac{\partial \mathscr{P}_i}{\partial \mu_j} = \frac{1}{T}\left\{\left[\frac{\partial T}{\partial \mu_i}\frac{\partial U_m}{\partial \mu_j} - \frac{\partial T}{\partial \mu_j}\frac{\partial U_m}{\partial \mu_i}\right] + \frac{\partial T}{\partial \mu_i}\mathscr{P}_j - \frac{\partial T}{\partial \mu_j}\mathscr{P}_i\right\}$$
$$(i,j = 1,2,3,\ldots,n). \tag{7.11}$$

When establishing the equalities (7.11), it is accepted that the determining parameters $\mu_1, \mu_2, \ldots, \mu_n$ are not connected with any nonholonomic relationships and, in particular, with differential relationships of the type $d\mu_K/dt = \mu_i$. We can consider the models of the mediums with nonholonomic relationships in which reversible processes can take place. The corresponding corollaries are from the first and second laws of thermodynamcs, and in such cases can also be obtained by taking certain complications into account.

Equation (7.11) imposes significant limitations on the type of dependence of the coefficients of form (7.10) on the parameters of state μ_i. Moreover, these relationships establish the connection between the coefficients $\mathscr{P}_i$ and the internal energy of the system.

For reversible processes, the functional relationships of the internal energy U_m and the coefficients $\mathscr{P}_i$ in the parameter function $\mu_1, \mu_2, \ldots, \mu_n, k_1, k_2, \ldots, k_m$ appear in the definition of the thermodynamic properties of the model of the medium. These relationships must satisfy the conditions (7.11).

The functions $\mathscr{P}_i(\mu_1, \mu_2, \ldots, \mu_n, k_1, k_2, \ldots, k_m)$ are called the equations of the state of the medium.

In order to describe irreversible processes, it is necessary to use data on the quantity dQ' and the elementary work of the internal forces $d\mathscr{A}^i_{\text{irrev}}$ [35].

In case the parameters essentially connected with irreversibility appear among the defining parameters, then, in order to obtain laws governing the variation of these parameters and new values for $\mathscr{P}_{i\,\text{irrev}}$, it is necessary to use new supplementary laws for the $\mathscr{P}_{i\,\text{irrev}}$ and to establish kinetic equations characterizing the nonequilibrium processes for the supplementary parameters.

8. Ideal liquids and gases

In the mechanics of a continuum, gases and liquids are called ideal if the internal stresses are orthogonal to the element of area over which they are being examined, i.e.,

$$\boldsymbol{p}_n \| \boldsymbol{n} \quad p_{nn} \lesseqgtr 0 \qquad \text{or} \qquad p_{n\tau} = 0 .$$

The corresponding processes in liquids and gases can be reversible or irreversible.

From this definition, it follows that for an ideal medium, the stress tensor is spherical.

In fact, by definition and on the strength of (4.10), in any cartesian orthogonal system we have the equations

$$\boldsymbol{p}_n = p_{nn} \cos(\widehat{nx'})\,\boldsymbol{\mathit{Э}}_1 + p_{nn} \cos(\widehat{nx^2})\,\boldsymbol{\mathit{Э}}_2 + p_{nn} \cos(\widehat{nx^3})\,\boldsymbol{\mathit{Э}}_3 ,$$

and from the definition of an ideal medium, we have

$$\boldsymbol{p}_n = p^{11} \cos(\widehat{nx'})\,\boldsymbol{\mathit{Э}}_1 + p^{22} \cos(\widehat{nx^2})\,\boldsymbol{\mathit{Э}}_2 + p^{33} \cos(\widehat{nx^3})\,\boldsymbol{\mathit{Э}}_3 .$$

From this it follows that

$$p_{nn} = p^{11} = p^{22} = p^{33} = -p$$

or

$$\boldsymbol{P} = -p \cdot \boldsymbol{G} . \tag{8.1}$$

The quantity p may be called the pressure.* For compression, $p > 0$; however, stress states in which there is stretching in all directions are possible in which $p < 0$. In the case when $p = 0$, there exist no internal surface stresses. In this way, the internal surface interactions in an ideal medium are defined by a spherical tensor and, consequently, are fully defined by a scalar p, which is equal to the pressure in the interior of the medium.

---

* Normally, for irreversible processes, it is convenient to represent the quantity p as the sum $p' + p''$, where p' is the pressure in the corresponding reversible process. We may call the quantity p' the pressure in the irreversible process.

The general equations for an ideal medium acquire the following form: The continuity equation preserves its own form:

$$\frac{1}{\rho}\frac{d\rho}{dt} + \operatorname{div} \mathbf{v} = 0. \tag{8.2}$$

The dynamic equations are simplified and take the form

$$\rho \frac{d\mathbf{v}}{dt} = \rho \boldsymbol{F} - \operatorname{grad} p. \tag{8.3}$$

Equations (8.3) are called Euler's equations. The equation for the influx of heat is also simplified and is of the form

$$T\,dS \geq dq = dU + p d\frac{1}{\rho}, \tag{8.4}$$

where $dS = dS_m/dm$, $dq = dQ/dm$, $dU = d\,U_m/dm$; here, we took into account equation (8.2) and the following formulas for $d\mathscr{A}^i$, valid in an ideal medium:

$$d\mathscr{A}^i = -\frac{p^{\alpha\beta}\,d\varepsilon_{\alpha\beta}}{\rho}\,dm = \frac{p}{\rho}\operatorname{div}\mathbf{v}\,dt\,dm = p\,d\frac{1}{\rho}\,dm. \tag{8.5}$$

The systems of equations (8.2), (8.3), and (8.4) are closed systems if the internal energy U per unit of mass and the external heat influx dq/dt per unit of mass and unit of time are known functions of p and ρ. In many cases these quantities are conditioned by the value of the density and the distribution of temperature T throughout the volume occupied by the ideal medium.

For ideal liquids or gases in reversible processes, we may, in a number of cases, assume that the internal state of a small particle is completely characterized by two independent variable parameters if no qualitative transformation is involved. Apart from the variable parameters defining the state of the particle, the properties of the medium depend also, and generally, on certain physical constants with and without dimensions which characterize the properties of the medium independently of the states of the separate particles given by the variable quantities.

It is possible and convenient to choose different quantities to act as independent variable parameters describing the internal state for the various processes. In particular, if the state is characterized by the values of p and ρ, then the following functional relationships occur:

$$T = T(p, \rho), \qquad U = U(p, \rho), \qquad S = S(p, \rho).$$

Since T, U, S, p, and ρ are dimensional quantities, the functions T, U, and S generally contain dimensional physical constants which have to be added to the parameters defining the properties of the medium.

The set of the three functions T, U, and S of p and ρ forms the equations of state for the medium. For different media, these functions can be different, and their form has to be determined experimentally or with the aid of the theoretical hypotheses of statistical physics. However, independently of the particular characteristics of the substance in question, the first and second laws of thermodynamics establish the following two relations between the three quantities T, U, and S.

1. The formula for the calculation of entropy:

$$dS = \frac{1}{T}\left(\frac{\partial U}{\partial p}\right)_\rho dp + \frac{1}{T}\left[\left(\frac{\partial U}{\partial \rho}\right)_p - \frac{p}{\rho^2}\right] d\rho . \tag{8.6a}$$

2. The condition of integrability of (8.6a):

$$\frac{\partial T}{\partial \rho}\frac{\partial U}{\partial p} = \frac{\partial T}{\partial p}\frac{\partial U}{\partial \rho} - \frac{p}{\rho^2}\frac{\partial T}{\partial p} + \frac{T}{\rho^2} . \tag{8.6b}$$

Thus, giving the internal energy U as a function of p and ρ does not completely define the thermodynamic properties of the medium, because, for a fixed function $U(p, \rho)$, according to equation (8.6), the equation of state $T(p, \rho)$, and correspondingly according to equation (8.6a), the entropy $S(p, \rho)$ can have a considerable amount of freedom.

In the case of adiabatic processes with $dq = 0$ or processes with heat influx in which the quantity dq/dt is known as a function of the pressure p and the density ρ and, possibly, as a function of the coordinates and time, the system of equations (8.2), (8.3), and (8.4) will be closed. In case the boundary conditions are formulated independently of the form of functions $T(p, \rho)$ and $S(p, \rho)$, the mechanical processes in which thermal effects are accounted for will be similarly described in terms of the variables p and ρ for media whose equations of state differ, i.e., for equations of state in which the functions $T(p, \rho)$ and $S(p, \rho)$ will not be uniquely determined by equations (8.6a) and (8.6b).

With a different choice of independent variable parameters, it will be convenient to write the equations of state for reversible processes by introducing the thermodynamic potentials on the basis of the equation of heat influx (8.4) in the following fashion:

1. For variable ρ and S, we have

$$dU = T\,dS + \frac{p}{\rho^2}\,d\rho .$$

The equations of state are

$$U = U(\rho, S), \qquad T = \left(\frac{\partial U}{\partial S}\right)_\rho, \qquad p = \rho^2\left(\frac{\partial U}{\partial \rho}\right)_S. \tag{8.7}$$

2. For variable p and S, we have

$$d\left(U + \frac{p}{\rho}\right) = T\,dS + \frac{1}{\rho}\,dp.$$

The equations of state are

$$U + \frac{p}{\rho} = i = i(p, S), \qquad T = \left(\frac{\partial i}{\partial S}\right)_p, \qquad \frac{1}{\rho} = \left(\frac{\partial i}{\partial p}\right)_S. \tag{8.8}$$

The function of state $i = U + p/\rho$ is called the enthalpy (heat content). It is not difficult to see that the addition of an additive constant to internal energy U or to the enthalpy i will not change the form of the other two relationships.

3. For variable ρ and T, we have

$$d(U - TS) = -S\,dT + \frac{p}{\rho^2}\,d\rho.$$

The equations of state are

$$U - TS = \mathscr{F} = \mathscr{F}(\rho, T), \qquad -S = \left(\frac{\partial \mathscr{F}}{\partial T}\right)_\rho, \qquad \frac{p}{\rho^2} = \left(\frac{\partial \mathscr{F}}{\partial \rho}\right)_T. \tag{8.9}$$

The function of state $\mathscr{F} = U - TS$ is called the free energy.

4. For variable p and T, we have

$$d\left(U - TS + \frac{p}{\rho}\right) = -S\,dT + \frac{1}{\rho}\,dp.$$

The equations of state are

$$U - TS + \frac{p}{\rho} = \psi = \psi(p, T), \qquad -S = \left(\frac{\partial \psi}{\partial T}\right)_p, \qquad \frac{1}{\rho} = \left(\frac{\partial \psi}{\partial p}\right)_T. \tag{8.10}$$

The function of state $\psi = U - TS + p/\rho$ is called the thermodynamic potential.

If the internal energy and entropy are defined with an accuracy up to an additive constant, then the free energy $\mathscr{F}$ and the thermodynamic potential ψ are defined with an accuracy up to a linear function of the temperature.

It is obvious that in the four cases considered above, the introduction of the indicated potentials permits the problem to reduce from the definition of three characteristic functions to the definition of only one corresponding potential.

For the pairs of variables p and ρ, or T and S, no corresponding potentials are in existence.

The thermodynamic and mechanical properties of an ideal compressible two-parameter medium are completely defined by prescribing one of the functions: $U(\rho, S)$, $i(p, S)$, $\mathscr{F}(\rho, T)$, or $\psi(p, T)$.

As was shown above, prescribing the function $U(p, \rho)$ is sufficient for the solution of certain classes of mechanical problems; however, prescribing this function is not sufficient for a complete definition of the medium.

In order to establish the form of thermodynamic functions characterizing a medium and also to establish the equations of state, one can, together with the mechanical measurements, use data obtained from calorimetric measurements. In particular, the specific heat of a unit mass of the substance is of great importance. The specific heat is defined as the amount of heat required to raise the temperature of a unit mass of substance by one degree celsius. In a two-parameter medium, the specific heat depends greatly on the variation of both the variable parameters. The specific heat is uniquely determined only when the process accompanied by an increase in temperature is completely defined.

The specific heats of a compressible medium at constant pressure and at constant volume c_p and c_v, respectively, play an important role. The specific heats c_p and c_v are defined by

$$c_p = \left(\frac{dq}{dT}\right)_p = \left(\frac{\partial i}{\partial T}\right)_p = \left(\frac{\partial U}{\partial T}\right)_p - \frac{p}{\rho^2}\left(\frac{\partial \rho}{\partial T}\right)_p$$

$$= \left(\frac{\partial U}{\partial \rho}\right)_T\left(\frac{\partial \rho}{\partial T}\right)_p + \left(\frac{\partial U}{\partial T}\right)_\rho - \frac{p}{\rho^2}\left(\frac{\partial \rho}{\partial T}\right)_p \tag{8.11}$$

and

$$c_v = \left(\frac{dq}{dT}\right)_\rho = \left(\frac{\partial U}{\partial T}\right)_\rho = \left(\frac{\partial i}{\partial p}\right)_T\left(\frac{\partial p}{\partial T}\right)_\rho + \left(\frac{\partial i}{\partial T}\right)_p - \frac{1}{\rho}\left(\frac{\partial p}{\partial T}\right)_\rho. \tag{8.12}$$

The difference $c_p - c_v$ is given from formulas (8.11) and (8.12) by the equation

$$c_p - c_v = \left[\left(\frac{\partial U}{\partial \rho}\right)_T - \frac{p}{\rho^2}\right]\left(\frac{\partial \rho}{\partial T}\right)_p = -\left[\left(\frac{\partial i}{\partial p}\right)_T - \frac{1}{\rho}\right]\left(\frac{\partial p}{\partial T}\right)_\rho. \tag{8.13a}$$

From this equation and equation (8.4), it follows that

$$c_p = c_v = -\frac{T}{\rho^2}\left(\frac{\partial p}{\partial T}\right)_\rho\left(\frac{\partial \rho}{\partial T}\right)_p, \tag{8.13b}$$

which, on the basis of the equation $(\partial p/\partial T) = -(\partial p/\partial \rho)_T(\partial \rho/\partial T)_p$ following from the formulas $dp = (\partial p/\partial T)_\rho\, dT + (\partial p/\partial \rho)_T\, d\rho$, reduces to the form

$$c_p - c_v = \frac{T}{\rho^2}\left(\frac{\partial p}{\partial \rho}\right)_T \left(\frac{\partial \rho}{\partial T}\right)_p^2 . \qquad (8.13c)$$

Equations (8.13) are valid for arbitrary two-parameter media of the type under consideration. By using experimental data on the coefficients of specific heats c_p and c_v, or the measured values of the coefficients of thermal change of density at constant pressure $(\partial \rho/\partial T)_p = k_\rho$, or the coefficients of change of pressure at constant volume $(\partial p/\partial T)_\rho = k_p$, it is possible to determine the derivatives of the internal energy and the enthalpy from the equations

$$\left(\frac{\partial U}{\partial \rho}\right)_T = \frac{c_p - c_v}{k_\rho} + \frac{p}{\rho^2} = -\frac{1}{\rho^2}\left[T\left(\frac{\partial p}{\partial T}\right)_\rho - p\right], \quad \left(\frac{\partial U}{\partial T}\right)_\rho = c_v \qquad (8.14)$$

and

$$\left(\frac{\partial i}{\partial T}\right)_p = c_p, \quad \left(\frac{\partial i}{\partial p}\right)_T = -\frac{c_p - c_v}{k_p} + \frac{1}{\rho} = \frac{1}{\rho^2}\left[\mathrm{T}\left(\frac{\partial \rho}{\partial T}\right)_p + \rho\right]. \qquad (8.15)$$

The right-hand sides of (8.14) and (8.15) are determined conveniently by experiment. The conditions of integrability of (8.14) and (8.15) are automatically satisfied as a consequence of the first and second laws of thermodynamics. These conditions have the form

$$-\frac{T}{\rho^2}\left(\frac{\partial^2 p}{\partial T^2}\right)_\rho = \left(\frac{\partial c_v}{\partial \rho}\right)_T \qquad (8.16)$$

and

$$\left(\frac{\partial c_p}{\partial p}\right)_T = -T\left(\frac{\partial^2 (1/\rho)}{\partial T^2}\right)_p . \qquad (8.17)$$

The conditions in (8.16) and (8.17) can be used to reduce the number of the experiments and to verify the results of the experiments.

We shall now consider several examples of ideal media and their thermodynamic properties.

1. As a very simple example of an ideal medium, we can consider an incompressible fluid. The condition for incompressibility for each particle has the form

$$\rho = \rho_0 = \text{const.}$$

In the case of a nonhomogeneous fluid, ρ_0 depends on the Lagrangian coordinates ξ^1, ξ^2, ξ^3, and for a homogeneous fluid ρ_0 is the same for all the particles.

For an ideal incompressible fluid, the system of four scalar equations (8.2) and (8.3) forms a closed system for the determination of the pressure p and velocity vector $\mathbf{v}$.

The equation of heat influx can be considered as an equation of transmission of heat in a flowing liquid. For an ideal incompressible fluid, the work of the internal surface forces is always equal to zero.

If the fluid is ideal and incompressible, the equation of the heat influx for a reversible process has the form

$$T\,dS = dU\,. \tag{8.18}$$

It therefore follows that $S = f(U)$ and consequently $U = U(T)$ and $S = S(T)$. In this case, the entropy and the internal energy are defined in terms of the specific heat $c_v(T)$ according to the formulas

$$U = \int c_v\,dT \qquad \text{and} \qquad S = \int \frac{c_v\,dT}{T}\,. \tag{8.19}$$

2. As a second important example, we consider an ideal gas governed by the equation of state

$$p = \rho \boldsymbol{R} T\,, \tag{8.20}$$

which is called the Clapeyron equation and in which the constant $\boldsymbol{R}$ is called the gas constant. In many cases, and usually for the motions of air in the atmosphere or gases in gas-operated machinery, one can assume that the Clapeyron equation holds. The gas constant has the dimensions

$$[\boldsymbol{R}] = \mathrm{m}^2/\mathrm{sec}^2\cdot\mathrm{degree}$$

and is different for different gases. The kinetic theory of gases and experiment show that the gas constant is given by the formula

$$\boldsymbol{R} = \frac{\boldsymbol{R}_a}{M} = \frac{\boldsymbol{k}}{m^*}, \tag{8.21}$$

where $\boldsymbol{R}_a$ and $\boldsymbol{k}$ are absolute constants, $\boldsymbol{R}_a = 8.3144 \times 10^7$ ergs/mole·degree and $\boldsymbol{k} = 1.38 \times 10^{-16}$ ergs/degree. The constant $\boldsymbol{k}$ is called Boltzmann's constant, M is the mean molar mass, and m^* is the mean molecular mass in grams. For air, $\boldsymbol{R} = 28.7042\ \mathrm{m}^2/\mathrm{sec}^2\cdot\mathrm{deg}$. On the basis of (8.20) and (8.4), it follows that

$$dU = T\,d(S + \boldsymbol{R}\ln\rho)\,. \tag{8.22}$$

From equation (8.22), it follows that for gases obeying the Clapeyron equation (8.20), the internal energy and the combination $S + \boldsymbol{R}\ln\rho$ can depend only on temperature and, consequently, do not depend on density.

It is obvious that an analogous conclusion for the internal energy and the combination $S + \int \boldsymbol{R}(dp/p)$ is true also in the case when the equation of state (8.20) applies, in which, however, in contrast with the Clapeyron equation, $\boldsymbol{R}$ can be any function of the density ρ.

If $\boldsymbol{R} = \text{const}$, (8.20) and (8.13) lead to Meyer's formula

$$c_p - c_v = \boldsymbol{R}. \tag{8.23}$$

From (8.22), by setting $dU = c_v(T)\,dT$, we obtain the formula for the entropy

$$S = \int \frac{c_v\,dT}{T} - \boldsymbol{R} \ln \rho. \tag{8.24}$$

If equation (8.20) holds and the function $U(T)$ is known, we will obtain the function $S(T, \rho)$ from (8.24), and from the definitions (8.8), (8.9), and (8.10), we obtain formulas for the thermodynamic functions i, $\mathscr{F}$, and ψ.

Thus, for a homogeneous particle of a perfect gas ($\boldsymbol{R} = \text{const}$) with mass m, we have the formulas*

$$\begin{aligned}
U_m &= m\left(U^0 + \int_{T_0}^{T} c_v\,dT\right),\\
S_m &= m\left(S^0 + \int_{T_0}^{T} \frac{c_p\,dT}{T} - \boldsymbol{R}\ln\frac{p}{p_0}\right),\\
i_m &= m\left(i^0 + \int_{T_0}^{T} c_p\,dT\right),\\
\mathscr{F}_m &= m\left(U^0 - TS^0 + \int_{T_0}^{T} c_v\,dT - T\int_{T_0}^{T} \frac{c_v}{T}\,dT - \boldsymbol{R}T\ln\frac{\rho_0}{\rho}\right),\\
\psi_m &= m\left(i^0 - TS^0 + \int_{T_0}^{T} c_p\,dT - T\int_{T_0}^{T} \frac{c_p}{T}\,dT + \boldsymbol{R}T\ln\frac{p}{p_0}\right).
\end{aligned} \tag{8.25}$$

In these formulas, the specific heats $c_v(T)$, $c_p(T)$ are with respect to a unit of mass. The constants U^0, S^0, and i^0 are the values of the quantities U, S, and i at temperature T_0, pressure p_0, and density ρ_0. In many cases, for

---

* We shall henceforth use the term "perfect gas" because the equation of state (8.20) and the functions of state (8.25) can hold for a viscous medium which is not ideal from the point of view of the internal stresses.

different gases under consideration, the quantities U^0, S^0, i^0, c_p, c_v, and $\boldsymbol{R}$ can be considered as inversely proportional to the polar mass M.

It is obvious that the equation of state (8.20) follows from formula (8.25) for $\mathscr{F} = \mathscr{F}_m/m$ and from formula (8.9).

Formulas (8.25) become particularly simple in the important practical case when the specific heat c_v can be assumed constant, i.e., when c_v does not depend on temperature. In this case, it follows from (8.23) that the specific heat c_p must also be constant.

If $c_v = \text{const}$, we have from (8.25) the formulas

$$U = c_v T + \text{const}, \qquad i = c_p T + \text{const},$$

$$S = c_v \ln \frac{T}{\rho^{\gamma-1}} + \text{const} = c_v \ln \frac{p}{\rho^\gamma} + \text{const},$$

or (8.25′)

$$p = \rho^\gamma e^{S + \text{const}/c_v},$$

where the abstract constant $\gamma = c_p/c_v$ is called the Poisson coefficient.

The relationships among S, T, and ρ or S, ρ, and p can be considered for any process as an equation of state analogous to the equation of state (8.20).

The equation of state (8.20) does not agree with reality in the case of highly compressed gases, in which the density is very great. Also, this equation is not valid for states which are close to the point of condensation of a gas to a liquid, nor is it valid for liquid states.

Moreover, it may be noted that at very low temperatures, close to absolute zero, the equation of state (8.20) and the formulas (8.25) no longer satisfy the general thermodynamic laws (the second law, Nernst's theorem, and its corollaries) which describe the behavior of substances near absolute zero.

3. Let us now consider an ideal gas that satisfies the van der Waals equation of state:

$$p = \frac{\rho \boldsymbol{R} T}{1 - b\rho} - a\rho^2, \tag{8.26}$$

where $\boldsymbol{R}$, b, and a are positive physical constants. Equation (8.26) is, in fact, a more precise version of Clapeyron's equation. This equation describes processes close to the condensation point of gases and also describes the actual relationships for certain ranges of the liquid phase. The denominator $1 - b\rho = 1 - \rho/\rho^*$ leads to a sharp increase in pressure at high densities ρ approaching ρ^*; the extra term $-a\rho^2$ also is significant only at high densities. This term is associated with the forces of repulsion between molecules which exist only at high densities when the molecules are close to each other.

From equation (8.26) and formulas (8.14), it follows that

$$\left(\frac{\partial U}{\partial \rho}\right)_T = -a \quad \text{and} \quad \left(\frac{\partial U}{\partial T}\right)_\rho = c_v(T). \tag{8.27}$$

It is quite obvious from the first equation (8.27) that the specific heat c_v for a van der Waals medium depends only on temperature.

The function $c_v(T)$ is determined by the properties of the medium and the form of this function is an additional concept to the equation of state (8.26) defining the medium.

From (8.27) it follows that the internal energy for a van der Waals gas is given by the formula

$$U = \int_{T_0}^{T} c_v(T)\,dT - a\rho + \text{const} = \Phi\left[\frac{1}{\rho}(p + a\rho^2)(1 - b\rho)\right] - a\rho. \tag{8.28}$$

The function $\Phi\,(T)$ is defined in an obvious manner in terms of the function $c_v(T)$.

From (8.4) and (8.26), we obtain the formula for the calculation of the entropy of a van der Waals medium:

$$dS = \frac{dU}{T} + \frac{p}{T}d\frac{1}{\rho} = \frac{c_v(T)\,dT}{T} + \frac{R d(1/\rho)}{1/\rho - b},$$

and thence

$$S = \int_{T_0}^{T} \frac{c_v\,dT}{T} + R\ln\left(\frac{1-\rho b}{\rho}\right) + \text{const}. \tag{8.29}$$

It is obvious that for a van der Waals gas, the formulas for the thermodynamic potentials i, $\mathscr{F}$, and ψ follow immediately from their definition according to formulas (8.8), (8.9), and (8.10) and from (8.26), (8.28), and (8.29).

Consider now the general case when the internal energy is given by a formula of the form

$$U = f(\rho) + \phi(S). \tag{8.30}$$

From (8.7), we obtain

$$T = \phi'(S) \quad \text{and} \quad p = \rho^2 f'(\rho). \tag{8.31}$$

Consequently, in this case, the pressure for any process depends only on the density, and the temperature depends only on the entropy.

The finite relationships (8.31) completely replace the equation of heat influx.

Obviously, from formulas (8.30) and (8.31), we obtain

$$\begin{aligned} i &= f_1(p) + \phi(S), \\ \mathscr{F} &= f(\rho) + \omega(T), \\ \psi &= f_1(p) + \omega(T). \end{aligned} \tag{8.32}$$

It is easy to see that the fulfillment of one of the formulas (8.32) implies the fulfillment of all the remaining formulas of (8.32) and (8.30).

It is also clear that if the pressure p, for the particles of some medium and for all possible reversible processes, depends only on the density ρ, the temperature can depend only on the entropy, and that formulas (8.30) and (8.32) must be valid for the thermodynamic potentials.

9. The simplest ideal processes

The equation of heat influx in the general form (6.10) or in the special form (8.4) given for an ideal continuum contains the external heat influx. The expression dq denotes the quantity of external heat that is flowing into a unit of mass for an elementary change of state.

In certain cases, the equation of the heat influx can be used for determination of the required or attained influx of heat if the motion and the sequence of the states of the continuum are given or known.

In problems involving the determination of motions and states of a medium, it is necessary to know the laws defining the external transfer of heat. The influx or emission of thermal energy can take place by means of a variety of physical phenomena.

The most important mechanisms of the physical transfer of heat are summarized below.

1. Thermal conductivity is the process of equalization of the mean thermal energy between the parts of the medium which are in direct contact. It is the result of collisions and mechanical interactions occurring in the thermal motion between the molecules, atoms, electrons, etc., of which the medium is composed.

The emission of heat, which is affected by the thermal conductivity, is closely related to the macroscopic nonuniform distribution of temperature throughout the volume of the body.

2. The radiation or absorption of heat is a phenomenon connected with changes in the possible states of the elementary particles (molecules, atoms, electrons, etc.) of which the medium is composed.

3. The liberation of heat is conditioned by electrical dissipative processes; in particular, the Joule heat is emitted inside a body in the presence of an electric current.

4. Sometimes it is possible with the aid of a supplementary condition to assign to the external influx of heat dQ a certain portion of the increase in the internal energy dU and of the work of the internal forces $d\mathcal{A}^i$ by transposing these terms over to the left-hand side of equation (6.6).

For example, the change in the internal energy due to chemical transformations or phase transitions arising from the emission or absorption of heat can be replaced by the external influx of heat, and one need consider only the change in the internal energy due to the temperature, the mechanical parameters, and possibly changing properties of the medium.

The solution of specific problems by use of the equation of heat influx, in which the physical laws for heat influx are taken into account, are, as a rule, very difficult from a mathematical point of view. In applications, one frequently makes use of additional assumptions. In particular, the following ideal processes are in general use.

1. Processes in which there is no external influx of heat or heat exchange between neighboring particles, i.e.,

$$dQ = 0. \tag{9.1}$$

Such an ideal process is called adiabatic.

For reversible adiabatic processes, we have

$$dQ = T\,dS_m = 0 \qquad (S = \text{const}), \tag{9.2}$$

i.e., the entropy in the particles of the medium is constant.

It is obvious that the constant value can differ from point to point of the medium.

If the process is adiabatic and irreversible, then

$$T\,dS_m = dQ' > 0, \tag{9.3}$$

i.e., the entropy increases for each particle.

In the case of an ideal compressible medium, according to (8.4), the condition for adiabaticity takes the form

$$dU + p\,d\frac{1}{\rho} = 0. \tag{9.4}$$

This relationship is true both for reversible and irreversible adiabatic processes.

For reversible adiabatic processes, the integral of equation (9.4) yields one relationship between the parameters defining a thermodynamic state.

In this case, the condition (9.4) is equivalent to equation (9.2), which is an integral of equation (9.4).

In particular, if the medium is described by two parameters, the differential equation (9.4) defines the relationship between the pressure and the density

$$p = f(\rho, C), \tag{9.5}$$

where C for a given particle is a constant of integration which can, in the reversible case, be taken as the entropy S_0, or can be set $C = \phi(S_0)$.

If Clapeyron's equation is valid and the specific heat c_v is constant, then on the basis of (8.25) and (9.2), we obtain

$$p = C\rho^\gamma = e^{S/c_v}p^\gamma. \tag{9.6}$$

If the process is adiabatic but irreversible, then equation (9.2) and its corollaries for S = const will not be fulfilled.

The concept of adiabatic processes is connected with the examination of thermally isolated bodies, or with rapid-flow (but sometimes reversible) processes in which heat exchange does not have time to attain any degree of significance.

2. A second limiting example is an ideal process in which the heat exchange due to heat conduction or radiation is an extremely intensive process, and the changes of state take place very slowly in comparison with the process of equalization of temperature as a consequence of the heat exchange.

In such a way, the concept of an isothermal process in which the temperature is the same for all parts of the system can be introduced.

One may speak of isothermal processes when the temperature of all parts of the medium is the same and remains constant with respect to time.

It is also possible to examine those isothermal processes in which the temperature of all parts of the medium is the same but can change during the course of time according to some law which can be defined independently by some equation for the system on the whole.

In the first case, the equation of the process is of the form

$$T = \text{const}. \tag{9.7}$$

In the second case, we have

$$\operatorname{grad} T = 0 \qquad \text{or} \qquad T = f(t), \tag{9.8}$$

where $f(t)$ is some function of time.

Equations (9.7) and (9.8) together with the equation of state of the medium replace the equation of heat influx. This substitution, generally speaking, greatly simplifies the problem of the motion of the medium.

It is obvious that for a two-parameter ideal medium, the assumption of isothermality implies a connection between the density and pressure, which by (8.9) can be given by the formula

$$p = \rho^2 \left(\frac{\partial \mathscr{F}}{\partial \rho} \right)_T, \tag{9.9}$$

where $\mathscr{F}(\rho, T)$ is the free energy. In formula (9.9), the temperature appears either as a constant parameter or as a known function of the time t.

3. In the case of a two-parameter continuous medium, we may take for a relationship defining a process some direct connection between the density and the pressure instead of the equation of heat inflow.

If the connection is the same for all the particles, then such a process is called barotropic.

In particular, a process is called polytropic if the following equation is satisfied:

$$p = c\rho^n. \tag{9.10}$$

Here n is a constant called the index of polytropy, and c is an arbitrary constant.

With the aid of the equation of heat influx it is easy, for a given relationship $p = f(\rho)$, to determine the amount of external heat influx that is necessary for this relationship to exist.

If the gas is perfect and the process polytropic, then from equations (8.4) and (8.2) for $n > 1$, we find that

$$dq = dU + c\rho^n d\frac{1}{\rho} = c_v\, dT - \frac{d\boldsymbol{R}T}{n-1}. \tag{9.11}$$

On the basis of Meyer's relationship $\boldsymbol{R} = c_p - c_v$ for constant $\boldsymbol{R}$, we obtain from (9.11) the following simple formula for the influx of heat:

$$dq = c_v \left(\frac{n-\gamma}{n-1} \right) dT = c^* \, dT. \tag{9.12}$$

It therefore follows that, if $n > \gamma > 1$, then with an increase in temperature ($dq > 0$) a heat source is obtained. If $1 < n < \gamma$, then $dq < 0$ for $dT > 0$ and, consequently, an increase in temperature is accompanied by a heat sink. These properties characterize the physical motion of the index of polytropy n.

Let us now examine the amount of influx of heat, assuming that the heat exchange is determined by the thermal conductivity alone.

The basic law of the transmission of heat due to a nonuniform distribution of temperature within the medium can be formulated in the following way.

A flow of heat dQ across an element of area $d\sigma$ during a time dt in the direction defined by the normal $\boldsymbol{n}$ is represented by the expression

$$dQ = -\lambda \frac{\partial T}{\partial n} d\sigma\, dt, \tag{9.13}$$

where λ is the coefficient of thermal conductivity, dependent, generally speaking, on parameters characterizing the state of the medium at the point under consideration.

On the basis of (9.13), the influx of heat due to thermal conductivity, through a closed surface Σ ($\boldsymbol{n}$ is the outer normal), i.e., the boundary of the volume $d\sigma$ of the small particle, is given by the expression

$$dQ = \int_{\Sigma} \lambda \frac{\partial T}{\partial n} d\sigma\, dt = \operatorname{div}(\lambda \operatorname{grad} T)\, d\tau\, dt. \tag{9.14}$$

Consequently, in this case, the equation for the influx of heat (6.10) takes the form

$$\frac{dQ}{dm} = dq = \frac{1}{\rho} \operatorname{div}(\lambda \operatorname{grad} T)\, dt = dU + d\mathscr{A}^{i} \cdot \frac{1}{dm}. \tag{9.15}$$

Equation (9.15) represents a generalization of the equation of thermal conductivity in a stationary body to the case of the motion of an arbitrary continuum.

In a general case, equation (9.15) is a complicated nonlinear partial differential equation.

In order to calculate the entropy per unit mass when transmission of heat due to thermal conductivity takes place, we use the equation

$$T \frac{dS}{dt} = \frac{1}{\rho} \operatorname{div}(\lambda \operatorname{grad} T) + \frac{dQ'}{dm}. \tag{9.16}$$

If the irreversibility is caused only by thermal conductivity ($dQ' = 0$), the entropy can either increase or decrease for the separate particles. The expression $\operatorname{div}(\lambda \operatorname{grad} T)$ can be positive or negative. However, for a thermally isolated body, the derivative of the entropy is always positive for the entire body, because of the irreversible processes of thermal condition.

In fact, after multiplying (9.16) by $dm = \rho\, d\tau$ and integrating, we obtain

$$\frac{d}{dt} \int_{m} S\, dm = \int_{V} \frac{\operatorname{div}(\lambda \operatorname{grad} T)}{T} d\tau = \int_{V} \frac{\lambda}{T} (\operatorname{grad} T)^2\, d\tau, \tag{9.17}$$

and since from the condition of thermal isolation on the boundary Σ of the volume of the body, $\partial T/\partial n = 0$, we have,

$$\int_V \operatorname{div} \frac{\lambda \operatorname{grad} T}{T} d\tau = \int_\Sigma \lambda \frac{1}{T} \frac{\partial T}{\partial n} d\sigma = 0 .$$

Formula (9.17) shows that the condition of increase in entropy is connected with the positiveness of the coefficient of thermal conductivity λ, which in actuality is always the case as a consequence of the second law of thermodynamics.

10. Special examples of ideal compressible media

In specific problems, the physical properties of the media can exert a very real influence on the mechanical effects through the properties of the equations of state, which are different for different media and therefore for different models of material bodies.

In many cases, physical models are constructed by the analysis of experimental data and establishing of empirical formulas.

An empirical relationship can always be chosen with a certain degree of freedom. We can always vary the values of the characteristics of the processes and the form of the functional connections within the limits of accuracy of the experiments and the initial data. This freedom can always be used to some advantage from the mathematical point of view. Such an advantage is not limited to the simplicity of the formulas or to external visual clarity. In particular, we may demand that the equations of motion admit certain types of solutions which will be convenient for qualitative or quantitative analysis or for an effective description of the phenomena under consideration. Sometimes these requirements of mathematical nature have a particular form which is related to the formulation of a particular problem. If these mathematical requirements can be satisfied within the framework of the statement of the problem and the empirical data, it is obvious that taking advantage of such possibilities is helpful and physically quite justified. For example, for the existence of the important class of self-similar solutions of the equations of motion, it is sufficient to require that no more than two dimensionally independent physical constants appear in these equations when the characteristics of motion and of the state appearing in these equations are measured in terms of mechanical units [32].

The appearance of dimensional constants in the previously established system of equations of motion of the continuum is possible only if we have additional physical data about the stress tensor, the internal energy, the heat influx, and the possible additional equations that are necessary to describe the various types of physico-chemical processes accompanying the motion of the medium (chemical reactions, phase changes, plastic deformations, etc.).

Consider the case of an ideal two-parameter continuous medium. We take the pressure p and the density ρ as the quantities defining the state of a particle. The internal energy, the temperature, the entropy, the free energy, etc., can be considered as functions of p and ρ.

The dimensions of certain of the dependent quantities, for example, the temperature, can be considered independent of the dimensions of the pressure p and the density ρ. It is obvious that the equation of state

$$\mathscr{F}(p, \rho, T) = 0 \tag{10.1}$$

must contain physical dimensional constants.

Let us use a system of units in which the independent units are the gram-mass, the centimeter, the second, the calorie, and the degree. Thus for the dimensions of pressure, density, and temperature, we have

$$[p] = \text{gm/cm}\cdot\text{sec}^2, \qquad [\rho] = \text{gm/cm}^3, \qquad [T] = \text{degrees}.$$

In mechanical phenomena that are accompanied by thermal effects, it will be necessary to introduce as a physical constant the mechanical equivalent of heat J:

$$[J] = \text{cal}\cdot\text{sec}^2/\text{gm}\cdot\text{cm}^2,$$

in the chosen system of units.

The quantities p, ρ, T, and J have independent dimensions; therefore, in the equation of state (10.1), there must appear physical constants other than these quantities.

Let us suppose that only the physical constants c_1, c_2, c_3, ..., having the same dimensions as the specific heat, appear in the equation of state, i.e.,

$$[c_1] = [c_2] = [c_3] = \cdots = \text{cal/degree}.$$

On the basis of the general theory of dimensional analysis, from the assumption that the quantities

$$p, \rho, T, J, c_1, c_2, c_3, \ldots \tag{10.2}$$

are functionally related but are independent of the choice of the system of units, it follows that

$$p = Jc_1 f\left(\frac{c_2}{c_1}, \frac{c_3}{c_1}, \cdots\right)\rho T, \tag{10.3}$$

where $Jc_1 f = R$ and R is a dimensional constant: $[R] = \text{cm}^2/\text{sec}^2\cdot\text{degree}$.

Equation (10.3) represents the Clapeyron equation. Thus, the Clapeyron equation can be regarded as a corollary of the unique hypothesis that the characteristic constants of the medium and the parameters determining its state [the system (10.2)] are connected by a functional relationship. The form of this functional connection (10.3) is obtained as a consequence of the assumption of its existence.

If the physical properties of a medium, in addition to the constants $c_1, c_2, c_3, \ldots$, depend also on the constants $\rho^*, \rho_1, \rho_2, \ldots$, which have the dimensions of density, then consideration of the dimensions leads to an equation of state of the form

$$p = \rho \boldsymbol{R} T \cdot f\left(\frac{\rho}{\rho^*}\right). \tag{10.4}$$

In the study of the variable states and the motion of a fixed medium, the abstract physical constants $c_2/c_1, c_3/c_1, \ldots, \rho_1/\rho^*, \rho_2/\rho^*, \ldots$, on which the function $f(\rho/\rho^*)$ may depend parametrically, need not be indicated. If, besides the constant $\boldsymbol{R}$, the medium is characterized by certain physical constants whose dimensions are dependent on the dimensions of $\boldsymbol{R}$ and those of some constant Q, whose dimensional form is given by

$$[Q] = [p^\lambda][\rho^\mu],$$

it is obvious that the equation of state of such a medium can be written in the form

$$\boldsymbol{R} T = \frac{p}{\rho} f\left(\frac{p^\lambda \rho^\mu}{Q}\right), \tag{10.5}$$

where $f(x)$ is in general an arbitrary function of its argument.

In the most general case, the equation of state of an arbitrary two-component medium can always be represented in the form

$$\boldsymbol{R} T = \frac{p}{\rho} f\left(\frac{p}{p^*}, \frac{\rho}{\rho^*}\right), \tag{10.6}$$

where p^* and ρ^* are constants with the dimensions of pressure and density, respectively.

If the equation of state of a medium is written in the form (10.6), we can express the parameters $\boldsymbol{R}$, p^*, and ρ^*, with whose aid the dimensionless function $f(p/p^*, \rho/\rho^*)$ of two dimensionless variable parameters is written, in terms of the physical parameters characterizing the medium.

The various physical constants which appear in the equation of state can also appear in the equation of heat influx and can influence the solution of the system of equations of motion.

If the equation of the heat influx is replaced by the simplified condition of absence of the temperature gradient (intensive heat exchange), i.e., if

$$\operatorname{grad} T = 0, \tag{10.7}$$

then, provided the Clapeyron equation is satisfied, we obtain the equation

$$\operatorname{grad} \frac{p}{\rho} = 0, \tag{10.8}$$

which does not contain dimensional constants.

The equation of state (10.4) or (10.5) leads to the equations

$$\operatorname{grad}\left[\frac{p}{\rho} f\left(\frac{\rho}{\rho^*}\right)\right] = 0,$$

and

$$\operatorname{grad}\left[\frac{p}{\rho} f\left(\frac{p^\lambda \rho^\mu}{Q}\right)\right] = 0, \tag{10.9}$$

containing only the dimensional physical constants ρ^* or Q.

In the most general case, we will obtain the equation

$$\operatorname{grad}\left[\frac{p}{\rho} f\left(\frac{p}{p^*}, \frac{\rho}{\rho^*}\right)\right] = 0, \tag{10.10}$$

which, generally speaking, contains two physical dimensional constants p^* and ρ^*.

In the study of adiabatic motions of an ideal two-parameter continuum whose state is fixed by the values of p and ρ, dimensional constants can appear in the condition of adiabaticity, which, for reversible processes, can be written in the form

$$\frac{dS}{dt} = 0 \qquad \text{and} \qquad dU + p d\frac{1}{\rho} = 0. \tag{10.11}$$

In the most general case, the dependence of the internal energy on p and ρ can be expressed by

$$U = \frac{p}{\rho} f\left(\frac{p}{p^*}, \frac{\rho}{\rho^*}\right).$$

Therefore, generally speaking, the adiabatic equation will contain the two essentially different physical constants p^* and ρ^*.

If the internal energy is represented in the form

$$U = \frac{p}{\rho} f\left(\frac{p^\lambda \rho^\mu}{Q}\right) + \omega\left[S\left(\frac{p}{p^*}, \frac{\rho}{\rho^*}, R, \ldots\right), A, B, \ldots\right], \tag{10.12}$$

where $\omega(S)$ is an arbitrary function of the entropy containing various constants p^*, ρ^*, $\boldsymbol{R}$, ..., A, B, ..., then the adiabatic equation can depend essentially on the physical constant Q alone.

For a gas satisfying Clapeyron's equation, the function f reduces to an abstract constant. In this case, the adiabatic equation and, consequently, the entire system of equations of motion, will contain no dimensional constants at all.

One can show that the reverse assumption is also true: if the adiabatic equation contains only one essential dimensional constant Q, then the internal energy must be represented in the form (10.12) [41].

If the form of the equation of state or the form of the dependence of the internal energy on p and ρ is fixed, then, according to § 8, this imposes certain restrictions on the form of the other functions characterizing the physical properties of the medium. However, this does not completely define these functions.

Fixing of the equation $F(p, \rho, T) = 0$ or of just the properties of the internal energy $U(p, \rho)$ is not sufficient for a complete description of the medium. The arbitrariness that remains in the other functional relations describing the medium is easily removed by means of the equation and formulas given in § 8.

In particular, if the expression for adiabaticity contains no dimensional constants or only one essential dimensional constant Q, then the physical properties of the medium can depend on other dimensional physical constants.

Various cases have been established above in which the equations of motion contain no dimensional constants or contain only one physically essential dimensional constant. In the general case, for adiabatic and isothermal motions, the equations of motion depend only on the two dimensional constants p^* and ρ^*; therefore there always exist self-similar solutions dependent on the two physical constants with independent dimensions, *viz.*, the pressure p^* and the density ρ^*.

If the equations of motion contain only one dimensional constant Q, then there exist self-similar solutions depending on the constant Q and also on another dimensional constant Q_1, whose dimensions are expressed in mechanical units independently of the dimensions of Q.

If the equations of motion do not contain physical dimensional constants, as for example is true of the cases considered above when the medium obeys the Clapeyron equation, the self-similar solutions exist and depend on two different constants with independent dimensions.

The solutions of certain specific problems are self-similar provided that the equations admit such solutions and, moreover, if the additional conditions, such as the initial and boundary conditions or the conditions that exist at the discontinuities (if any exist inside the medium), do not contain supplementary dimensional constants whose dimensions are independent of the constants on which the self-similar solutions depend.

One can also consider particular cases when it is possible to satisfy supplementary conditions which are not self-similar with the aid of self-similar solutions of the equations of motion.

If problems are stated in a manner that admits self-similar solutions, the qualitative analysis of the solutions and the procurement of them in an effective form is, in certain cases, greatly simplified. In establishing empirical formulas describing the properties of the medium, one can, in some cases, be guided by the above considerations with regard to the form which these empirical formulas must have in order to formulate the problem so that a self-similar solution can be obtained.

In employing analytical methods of solution, the particular form of the arbitrary functions that appear in the formulas describing the physical properties of the medium is of considerable mathematical significance.

11. The equations of motion for gaseous mixtures with physico-chemical interactions among the components

Let us consider a model of a material medium made up of various components. The different components can be gases or groups of elementary particles of varied chemical or physical nature which are significant in the phenomena that are being studied; they can be molecules or atoms of the various elements, ions, electrons, etc. In certain cases, molecules of a single substance excited to different energy levels can be considered as belonging to different components of the given medium, which can be viewed as a mixture. For example, molecules of a single substance but at different levels of energy of the vibrational degrees of freedom or atoms at different degrees of ionization can be considered as particles belonging to different components.

In this section we shall consider, within the framework of macroscopic theory, the equations of the balances of masses (taking into account diffusion and chemical reactions) and other basic equations describing reversible processes in ideal media, particularly, reversible chemical reactions in a perfect gas.

Questions concerning irreversible phenomena in ideal media will be dealt with only in the most general form.

The mechanics and thermodynamics of gaseous mixtures, solutions, and other compound material media, are the subject of major areas of physical chemistry. A detailed exposition of the corresponding theories of reversible and irreversible processes which take into account electromagnetic phenomena and describes the presently known data can be found in specialized books [7,9,56,81].

We shall henceforth suppose that in describing the effects, one can use statistical averages and that each of the components and the mixture as a whole can be replaced by material continua filling the same volume of space simultaneously and continually and having the corresponding properties and interactions.

Let us consider some physically infinitesimal volume V and let $m_1, m_2, \ldots, m_q$ be the masses of the constituent components that are situated at a given instant of time t within this volume.

The densities of the components in a mixture are given by the formulas

$$\rho_1 - \frac{m_1}{V}, \qquad \rho_2 = \frac{m_2}{V}, \ldots, \qquad \rho_q = \frac{m_q}{V}. \tag{11.1}$$

According to the basic physical property of additivity of masses for systems of bodies, the mass and the density of the mixture as a whole can be defined by the relationships

$$m = m_1 + m_2 + \cdots + m_q, \qquad \rho = \frac{m}{V}. \tag{11.2}$$

The densities $\rho_1, \rho_2, \ldots, \rho_q$ can be considered as additional parameters characterizing the properties of the mixture of the overall continuum.

Below we shall set up the mechanical and thermodynamic equations which will allow us to describe the motion and the state of a mixture as a continuous material medium with composite physical and chemical properties.

As an initial step we can introduce, for each component of the mixture considered as a material continuum, its own velocity field $\mathbf{v}_1, \mathbf{v}_2, \ldots, \mathbf{v}_q$ and its movable Lagrangian volumes $V_1, V_2, \ldots, V_q$ which are made up of fixed particles. If diffusion occurs, the Lagrangian volumes for the different components move with respect to one another. If these Lagrangian volumes occupy at the instant t the same volume V in space, then at a successive instants of time these volumes separate because of the difference in the velocity fields $\mathbf{v}_1, \mathbf{v}_2, \ldots, \mathbf{v}_q$. The moving volumes of the different components which are coincident at time t will be different at other instants of time. The diffusion effect can be considered as a mutual penetration and motion of the Lagrangian volumes of the various components.

The velocity $\mathbf{v}$ of points in the continuum, which models the mixture as a whole, is defined by the formula

$$\rho\mathbf{v} = \rho_1\mathbf{v}_1 + \rho_2\mathbf{v}_2 + \cdots + \rho_q\mathbf{v}_q .$$

Let dm_i^1/dt be the change in a unit of time of the mass of the m_ith component in the volume V_i moving with the particles of the component with field velocity $\mathbf{v}_i$, and let dm_i/dt be the change in a unit of time of the ith component in the volume V moving with the velocity field $\mathbf{v}$ of the overall continuum.

The derivative dm_i^1/dt can be different from zero because of the conversion of the particles of the ith component of the medium into particles of the other components. The derivative dm_i/dt can be different from zero both because of the mutual conversion of the particles and because of diffusion.

On the basis of the transformation (3.3), these derivatives can be written as

$$\frac{dm_i^1}{dt} = \int\limits_V \left(\frac{\partial\rho_i}{\partial t} + \operatorname{div}\rho_i\mathbf{v}_i\right)d\tau = \left(\frac{\partial\rho_i}{\partial t} + \operatorname{div}\rho_i\mathbf{v}_i\right)V,$$

$$\frac{dm_i}{dt} = \int\limits_V \left(\frac{\partial\rho_i}{\partial t} + \operatorname{div}\rho_i\mathbf{v}\right)d\tau = \left(\frac{\partial\rho_i}{\partial t} + \operatorname{div}\rho_i\mathbf{v}\right)V,$$

or

$$\frac{dm_i}{dt} = \frac{dm_i^1}{dt} - V\operatorname{div}\mathfrak{J}_i \qquad (i = 1, 2, \ldots, q). \tag{11.3}$$

From this, we have the equations for the densities ρ_i:

$$\frac{\partial\rho_i}{\partial t} + \operatorname{div}\rho_i\mathbf{v} = \frac{1}{V}\frac{dm_i^1}{dt} - \operatorname{div}\mathfrak{J}_i \qquad (i = 1, 2, \ldots, q). \tag{11.4}$$

In these equations, the vectors $\mathfrak{J}_i$ of the diffusion flows are introduced in accordance with the formulas

$$\mathfrak{J}_i = \rho_i(\mathbf{v}_i - \mathbf{v}). \tag{11.5}$$

In order to express the vectors $\mathfrak{J}_i$ as functions of the parameters characterizing the states and their distributions throughout the volume of the mixture, it is necessary to use experimental data or the results of the kinetic theory of matter. The vectors $\mathfrak{J}_i$ can be different from zero because of the nonhomogeneous distribution of the concentrations and of temperature, the presence of electric currents, etc. Instead of the velocities $\mathbf{v}_i$, one can always consider only the diffusion vectors $\mathfrak{J}_i$, which, by assumption, can be regarded as quantities definable in terms of other parameters of state, using certain known formulas expressing the physical laws of diffusion.

In a given mixture, conversions of the particles can occur as a result of chemical reactions or physical interactions between the components of the mixture. Suppose that in a given volume, r reactions take place, each of which, generally speaking, has an effect on the change in the mass of the ith component.

The chemico-physical equation of the mass balances can be written in the following form:

$$\frac{dm_i^1}{dt} = M_i \sum_{\alpha=1}^{r} \nu_{i\alpha} v_\alpha \qquad (i = 1, 2, \ldots, q), \tag{11.6}$$

where the M_i are the molar masses and the $\nu_{i\alpha}$ are the stochiometric coefficients, negative for the components entering into the reaction and positive for the products of the reaction when the reaction goes in the positively assigned direction. The coefficients $\nu_{i\alpha}$ define the portions of the mass allotted to the corresponding components entering into the reaction. The quantity v_α characterizes the speed of the reaction with number α; $v_\alpha > 0$ if the reaction goes in the positive direction. Equation (11.6) can also be written in the form

$$\frac{dn_i^1}{dt} = \sum_{\alpha=1}^{r} \nu_{i\alpha} v_\alpha .$$

Here, n_i^1 is the number of moles in a moving volume V_i, and dn_i^1/dt is the change in the number of moles in V_i in a unit of time. The quantities v_α can be assumed to be proportional to the volume V or to the overall mass m contained in this volume. These quantities depend only on the number of the reaction α and are the same for the different components participating in this reaction. For a small volume, the quantities

$$v_\alpha = m w_\alpha$$

are small and the quantity w_α can be finite.

If the reaction with number α takes place, then $w_\alpha \neq 0$, and in the opposite case, $w_\alpha = 0$.

The principle of conservation of mass for r conversion reactions produces the r equations

$$\sum_{i=1}^{q} M_i \nu_{i\alpha} = 0 \qquad (\alpha = 1, 2, \ldots, r). \tag{11.7}$$

From (11.4), (11.5), and (11.7), one obtains the equation for the principle of conservation of the total mass m for all internal processes accompanied by motions

$$\frac{\partial \rho}{\partial t} + \operatorname{div} \rho \mathbf{v} = 0 .$$

If no diffusion takes place ($\mathbf{v} = \mathbf{v}_i$ and $\mathfrak{J}_i = 0$), then, for a moving Lagrangian volume V which is the same for all the components, the quantities m_i and w_α can be considered as characteristics of the fixed masses which are functions of time, and m can be taken as constant. In this case, (11.6) can be integrated, after which we obtain

$$m_i - m_{i0} = m M_i \sum_{\alpha=1}^{q} \nu_{i\alpha} \xi_\alpha$$

and (11.8)

$$\rho_i = \rho \left[\frac{m_{i0}}{m} + M_i \sum_{\alpha=1}^{r} \nu_{i\alpha} \xi_\alpha \right].$$

The ratios m_{i0}/m describe the concentrations of the components of mixtures corresponding to the state $\xi_\alpha = 0$. The parameter ξ_α, defined by the equation $w_\alpha = d\xi_\alpha/dt$, characterizes the portion of the reacting masses relative to the total mass of the particle participating in the reaction with number α.

On the basis of the chemical equation for the balance of masses (11.6), the continuity equation for the ith component can be rewritten in the form

$$\frac{\partial \rho_i}{\partial t} + \operatorname{div} \rho_i \mathbf{v} = \rho M_i \sum_{\alpha=1}^{r} \nu_{i\alpha} w_\alpha - \operatorname{div} \mathfrak{J}_i \qquad (i = 1, 2, \ldots, q). \tag{11.9}$$

Equations (11.9) represent the general diffusion equations which can be applied in the examination of any motion of arbitrary mixtures when the constituent components and the chemical reactions can be considered as continuously distributed throughout the space.

In equations (11.9), the quantities w_α must be determined from additional physico-chemical laws. For irreversible (nonequilibrium) processes, it is convenient to refer to the dependence of velocities w_α on the parameters determining the state and composition of the mixture as equations of the kinetics of chemical reactions or physical processes, when it is a matter of a redistribution of the components that is not connected with a change in the basic nature of the particles of which the components are made up. If the densities ρ_i are defined by other relationships in terms of the parameters $\omega_1, \omega_2, \ldots$, and because $m_i = \rho_i m/\rho$, equations (11.6) can serve to determine the velocities of the reaction $v_\alpha = m w_\alpha$ in terms of the parameters $\omega_1, \omega_2, \ldots$.

All the preceding formulas in this section were obtained by considering only the laws of conservation of mass, and therefore the concepts introduced and the equations obtained are applicable to the examination of any medium – gaseous, liquid, or solid.

Let us now examine the equations of state and the equations describing the physico-chemical processes – the phase transitions or chemical reactions in ideal material media (we further assume that the internal forces of interaction lead to stresses, i.e., that they are pressures) made up of q components which differ among themselves in phase or chemical properties.

Thus, we assumed that for a given composition of the medium, the internal properties of the various small particles or of one and the same small particle in different states are determined by the system of parameters

$$S_m, \rho, m_1, m_2, \dots, m_q,$$

and, in particular, the internal energy is defined by a formula of the form

$$U_m = U_m(S_m, \rho, m_1, m_2, \dots, m_q). \tag{11.10}$$

On the basis of the equations for the first and second laws of thermodynamics, for a given particle with mass $m = m_1 + m_2 + \cdots + m_q$ we can write

$$T\,dS_m = dQ + dQ' = dU_m + pd\frac{1}{\rho}\cdot m + dQ',$$

where $dQ' \geq 0$ is the uncompensated heat. From this, we have

$$dU_m = T\,dS_m - mpd\frac{1}{\rho} - dQ', \tag{11.11}$$

and moreover, a change in the internal energy U_m can be written as

$$dU_m = \frac{\partial U_m}{\partial S_m} dS_m + \frac{\partial U_m}{\partial (1/\rho)} d\frac{1}{\rho} + \sum_{k=1}^{q} \frac{\partial U_m}{\partial m_k} dm_k. \tag{11.12}$$

In this equation, the differentials dS_m, $d(1/\rho)$, dm_1, dm_2, ..., dm_q can be independent and generally arbitrary. In equation (11.11), the system of differentials defines the element of the process. For a given particle, equation (11.11) can be examined for different sets of elementary processes in which some conditions or other are imposed on these increments. In particular, for chemical reactions or phase transitions, the increments dm_1, dm_2, ..., dm_q can be connected by the equations of the balance of mass (11.6), in which the r quantities $v_\alpha\, dt = m\, d\xi_\alpha$ can be considered linearly independent. The number r is equal to the number of independent chemical reactions and phase transitions.* One may also examine the relationships included in the equations $S_m = \text{const}$, $\rho = \text{const}$, etc.

* The question of the number of independent reactions or phase transitions (Gibbs' phase rule) is examined in physical chemistry courses. For example, see references [55] and [56].

For a given particle, by adding or removing the corresponding conditions, the increments dS_m and $d(1/\rho)$ on the one hand and $dm_1, dm_2, \ldots, dm_q$ on the other can always be considered as linearly independent.

Together with the system of defining parameters $S_m, \rho, m_1, m_2, \ldots, m_q$, let us examine other systems and the thermodynamic functions corresponding to them. We shall include the pressure p and the temperature T as independent variables in the system of defining parameters. We set

$$i_m = U_m + \frac{p}{\rho} m, \qquad i_m = i_m(S_m, p, m_1, m_2, \ldots, m_q), \tag{11.13}$$

$$\mathscr{F}_m = U_m - T S_m, \qquad \mathscr{F}_m = \mathscr{F}_m(T, \rho, m_1, m_2, \ldots, m_q), \tag{11.14}$$

$$\psi_m = U_m - T S_m + \frac{p}{\rho} m, \qquad \psi_m = \psi_m(T, p, m_1, m_2, \ldots, m_q). \tag{11.15}$$

From (11.11) and from (11.13) to (11.15), with $m = \text{const}$, we can write

$$di_m = T\,dS_m + \frac{m}{\rho} dp - dQ',$$

where (11.16)

$$di_m = \frac{\partial i_m}{\partial S_m} dS_m + \frac{\partial i_m}{\partial p} dp + \sum_k \frac{\partial i_m}{\partial m_k} dm_k,$$

$$d\mathscr{F}_m = -S_m\,dT - mp\,d\frac{1}{\rho} - dQ',$$

where (11.17)

$$d\mathscr{F}_m = \frac{\partial \mathscr{F}_m}{\partial T} dT + \frac{\partial \mathscr{F}_m}{\partial (1/\rho)} d\frac{1}{\rho} + \sum_k \frac{\partial \mathscr{F}_m}{\partial m_k} dm_k,$$

and

$$d\psi_m = -S_m\,dT + \frac{m}{\rho} dp - dQ',$$

where (11.18)

$$d\psi_m = \frac{\partial \psi_m}{\partial T} dT + \frac{\partial \psi_m}{\partial p} dp + \sum_k \frac{\partial \psi_m}{\partial m_k} dm_k.$$

The above considerations apply to both reversible and irreversible processes.

We first consider reversible processes.

For reversible phenomena, we have

$$dQ' = 0.$$

From this we obtain

$$\frac{\partial U_m}{\partial S_m} = T, \qquad \frac{\partial U_m}{\partial(1/\rho)} = -mp, \qquad \frac{\partial i_m}{\partial S_m} = T, \qquad \frac{\partial i_m}{\partial p} = \frac{m}{\rho}, \tag{11.19}$$

$$\frac{\partial \mathcal{F}_m}{\partial T} = -S_m, \qquad \frac{\partial \mathcal{F}_m}{\partial(1/\rho)} = -mp, \qquad \frac{\partial \psi_m}{\partial T} = -S_m, \qquad \frac{\partial \psi_m}{\partial p} = \frac{m}{\rho},$$

which coincide respectively with the formulas (8.7) through (8.10) for

$$U = \frac{U_m}{m}, \qquad S = \frac{S_m}{m}, \qquad i = \frac{i_m}{m}, \qquad \mathcal{F} = \frac{\mathcal{F}_m}{m}, \qquad \psi = \frac{\psi_m}{m}.$$

Besides the equations of state (11.19), in the presence of reversible physicochemical transformations, we obtain another r equilibrium equations by using (11.11) and (11.8):

$$\sum_{k=1}^{q} \frac{\partial U_m}{\partial m_k} dm_k = \sum_{\alpha=1}^{r} \left(\frac{\partial U_m}{\partial \xi_\alpha}\right)_{S_m,\rho} d\xi_\alpha = 0, \qquad \frac{\partial U_m}{\partial \xi_\alpha} = 0 \qquad (\alpha = 1, 2, \ldots, r), \tag{11.20}$$

which, on the basis of (11.16), (11.17), and (11.18), can be written in the following variant forms:

$$\sum_{k=1}^{q} \frac{\partial i_m}{\partial m_k} dm_k = \sum_{\alpha=1}^{r} \left(\frac{\partial i_m}{\partial \xi_\alpha}\right)_{S_m,p} d\xi_\alpha = 0, \qquad \frac{\partial i_m}{\partial \xi_\alpha} = 0 \qquad (\alpha = 1, 2, \ldots, r), \tag{11.21}$$

$$\sum_{k=1}^{q} \frac{\partial \mathcal{F}_m}{\partial m_k} dm_k = \sum_{\alpha=1}^{r} \left(\frac{\partial \mathcal{F}_m}{\partial \xi_\alpha}\right)_{T,\rho} d\xi_\alpha = 0, \qquad \frac{\partial \mathcal{F}_m}{\partial \xi_\alpha} = 0 \qquad (\alpha = 1, 2, \ldots, r), \tag{11.22}$$

and

$$\sum_{k=1}^{q} \frac{\partial \psi_m}{\partial m_k} dm_k = \sum_{\alpha=1}^{r} \left(\frac{\partial \psi_m}{\partial \xi_\alpha}\right)_{T,p} d\xi_\alpha = 0, \qquad \frac{\partial \psi_m}{\partial \xi_\alpha} = 0 \qquad (\alpha = 1, 2, \ldots, r). \tag{11.23}$$

These equations can be used to determine $\xi_1, \xi_2, \ldots, \xi_r$ and, using (11.18), $m_1, m_2, \ldots, m_q$ in terms of the initial composition of the medium and in terms of p and T or ρ and T or S_m and p or S_m and ρ.

For reversible equilibrium processes, the derivatives $d\xi_\alpha/dt$, and consequently dm_k/dt, are expressed in terms of the derivatives dp/dt, dT/dt, which in turn are determined by the dynamic equations and the equations for the flow of heat.

For the actual composition of any of the systems of equations (11.20) through (11.23), it is necessary to prescribe or determine from experiment one of the functions (11.10), (11.13), (11.14), or (11.15).

We often take as a basic assumption that the thermodynamic functions S_m, U_m, i_m, $\mathscr{F}_m$, and ψ_m, with constants ρ, T, and p, will increase by a factor n where all the masses and dimensions of the body also increase by a factor n.

From this, it follows in particular that

$$\psi_m(T, p, nm_1, nm_2, \dots, nm_q) = n\psi_m(T, p, m_1, m_2, \dots, m_q). \quad (11.24)$$

On the basis of Euler's theorem, it follows from (11.24) that

$$\psi_m = \sum_{k=1}^{q} m_k \left(\frac{\partial \psi_m}{\partial m_k}\right)_{T,p} = \sum_{k=1}^{q} m_k \mu_k. \quad (11.25)$$

The quantities $\mu_k = (\partial\psi_m/\partial m_k)_{T,p}$ are called the chemical potentials. Equation (11.24) indicates that the chemical potentials μ_k are homogeneous dimensionless functions of the components of masses m_k:

$$\mu_k = \mu_k\left(p, T, \frac{m_1}{m}, \frac{m_2}{m}, \dots, \frac{m_q}{m}\right).$$

From this,

$$\sum_{i=1}^{q} m_i \left(\frac{\partial \mu_k}{\partial m_i}\right)_{p,T} = 0 \quad \text{and} \quad \sum_{i=1}^{q} m_i \left(\frac{\partial \mu_i}{\partial m_k}\right)_{p,T} = 0,$$

because

$$\frac{\partial \mu_k}{\partial m_i} = \frac{\partial \mu_i}{\partial m_k} = \frac{\partial^2 \psi_m}{\partial m_i \partial m_k}.$$

The determination of the chemical potentials is one of the most important problems of statistical physics and experimental work in physical chemistry.

When the properties (11.24) hold, the formula for the potential ψ_m and the equilibrium equation (11.23) can be written in the form

$$\psi_m = \sum_{k=1}^{q} m_k \mu_k \quad \text{and} \quad \sum_{k=1}^{q} \mu_k \, dm_k = 0.$$

For a reversible transformation on the basis of (11.18) the equilibrium equation becomes

$$\sum_{k,\alpha} M_k \mu_k \nu_{k\alpha} \cdot d\xi_\alpha = 0,$$

which separates into r equations, where r is equal to the number of independent transformations-reactions:

$$\sum_k M_k \mu_k \nu_{k\alpha} = 0 \qquad (\alpha = 1, 2, \ldots, r). \tag{11.26}$$

In the case of equilibrium of two phases, when the molecules of each phase are the same, we have $r = 1$, $k = 1, 2$, $\nu_1 = +1$, $\nu_2 = -1$, and $M_1 = M_2$. Hence, equation (11.26) reduces to

$$\mu_1 = \mu_2 .$$

Obviously, in the case of three-phase equilibrium, two equations must be satisfied simultaneously:

$$\mu_1 = \mu_2 \qquad \text{and} \qquad \mu_2 = \mu_3 .$$

The conditions that have been obtained for phase equilibrium will now be applied to solids, liquids, and gases. In particular we consider the phase equilibrium of the contact area, but in this case, possible surface effects are not taken into consideration.

We shall consider as examples reversible chemical reactions such as dissociation and recombination in a moving mixture of perfect gases.

In this case, the equation of state and the equations defining the composition and all the thermodynamic properties of the mixture can be obtained from the following expression for the thermodynamic potential:

$$\psi_m = \sum_{k=1}^{q} \psi_{mk}(p_k, T), \tag{11.27}$$

where ψ_{mk} is the thermodynamic potential corresponding to the kth component defined by formula (8.25):

$$\psi_{mk} = m_k \left(i_k^0 - TS_k^0 + \int_{T_0}^{T} c_{pk}\, dT - T \int_{T_0}^{T} \frac{c_{pk}}{T}\, dT + \boldsymbol{R}_k T \ln \frac{p_k}{p_{0k}} \right) = m_k \mu_k . \tag{11.28}$$

Since in equilibrium the temperature T for all the components is the same, the partial pressure p_k is related to the temperature and density ρ_k of the kth component by the Clapeyron equation

$$p_k = \rho_k \boldsymbol{R}_k T, \tag{11.29}$$

while the total pressure in the mixture is given by Dalton's law

$$p = p_1 + p_2 + \cdots + p_q = \sum_{k=1}^{q} \rho_k \boldsymbol{R}_k T = \rho \boldsymbol{R} T, \tag{11.30}$$

where

$$\boldsymbol{R} = \frac{m_1}{m} \boldsymbol{R}_1 + \frac{m_2}{m} \boldsymbol{R}_2 + \cdots + \frac{m_q}{m} \boldsymbol{R}_q . \tag{11.31}$$

From (11.29), (11.30), and (8.21) it follows that

$$p_k = p\frac{R_k m_k}{\sum_{i=1}^{q} R_i m_i} = p\cdot\frac{n_k}{n_1 + n_2 + \cdots + n_q}, \tag{11.32}$$

where n_k is the number of moles in the kth component for a given particle with mass m, since $R_k = R_a(1/M_k)$, and R_a is a universal constant.

Using these formulas, we obtain

$$\mu_k = i_k^0 - TS_k^0 + \int_{T_0}^{T} c_{pk}\,dT - T\int_{T_0}^{T} \frac{c_{pk}}{T}\,dT + R_k T \ln\frac{p}{p_{0k}} + R_k T \ln\frac{n_k}{n_1 + n_2 + \cdots + n_q}. \tag{11.33}$$

From formulas (11.27) and (11.28), it is easy to derive relationships for the internal energy and the entropy of the gas mixture. These relationships have the form

$$U_m = \sum_{k=1}^{q} U_{mk}(T) \quad \text{and} \quad S_m = \sum_{k=1}^{q} S_{mk}(p_k, T), \tag{11.34}$$

where U_{mk} and $S_{mk}(p_k, T)$ are defined by the formulas (8.25) for each of the components of the mixture.

Conversely, formula (11.27) can be obtained from (11.34) and Dalton's law (11.30). These in turn are based on experimental data or statistical deductions based on the assumption that the gas is sufficiently rarefied. In this case, the internal energy, within the accuracy of the additive constant, is equal to the kinetic energy of the random molecular motion. The internal energy of each of the constituent gases is independent of the presence of other gases, and it is therefore obvious that the internal energy of each of the constituent components of the mixture depends only on temperature and is proportional to the mass of the gas, and that the total internal energy of the mixture is equal to the sum of the energies of the constituent gases.

We can define the entropy of a mixture by assuming that it is equal to the sum of the entropies of the constituent parts. For this we use an adiabatic reversible process involving a set of partitions, each of which can be penetrated only by one of the components of the substance. Because of this separation, we obtain q equal volumes with the same temperature T and pressures equal to the partial pressure p_k. The total entropy of these q subdivided volumes is represented as the sum (11.34).

In the absence of diffusion it is possible to have an equilibrium state for the different separated constituent parts with the same p and T but with different volumes corresponding to masses m_k. For this state, the entropy is written in the form of the sum

$$S_{m0} = \sum_{k=1}^{q} S_{mk}(p, T).$$

It is easy to show that

$$S_m = \sum_k S_{mk}(p_k, T) > S_{m0} = \sum_k S_{mk}(p, T),$$

since the difference

$$S_m - S_{m0} = -\sum_{k=1}^{q} m_k R_k \ln \frac{n_k}{n_1 + n_2 + \cdots + n_q} > 0.$$

The difference $S_m - S_{m0}$ can be thought of as an increase in entropy due to the internal mixing process which occurs as a result of diffusion.

On the basis of (11.28), equations (11.26) can be written in the form

$$p_1^{\nu_{1\alpha}} \cdot p_2^{\nu_{2\alpha}} \cdots p_q^{\nu_{q\alpha}} = k_1^{\nu_{1\alpha}} \cdot k_2^{\nu_{2\alpha}} \cdots k_q^{\nu_{q\alpha}} \qquad (\alpha = 1, 2, \ldots, r), \tag{11.35}$$

where

$$k_i(T) = p_{0i} \exp \frac{1}{R_i T}\left[S_i^0 T + T\int_{T_0}^{T} \frac{c_{pi}\, dT}{T} - U_i^0 - R_i T_0 - \int_{T_0}^{T} c_{pi}\, dT\right]. \tag{11.36}$$

If the specific heats c_p and c_v are constant, the quantities k_i are given by the formulas

$$k_i(T) = p_{0i}\left(\frac{T}{T_0}\right)^{\gamma_i/\gamma_i - 1} A_i e^{U_i^*/R_i T},$$

where (11.37)

$$\gamma_i = \frac{c_{pi}}{c_{vi}}, \qquad A_i = e^{S_i^0 - c_{pi}/R_i}, \qquad U_i^* = U_i^0 - c_{vi} T_0.$$

Equations (11.35) express the law of mass action or the Guldberg-Waage law.

The Guldberg-Waage equations define the composition of a mixture for reversible chemical reactions.

Indeed, let us set $\nu'_{i\alpha} = \nu_{i\alpha} > 0$ and $\nu''_{j\alpha} = -\nu_{j\alpha} > 0$. Using equations (11.29) and taking into account (8.21), (11.35) can be written in the form

$$(R_\alpha T)^{\nu''_\alpha} \prod_j \left(\frac{\rho_j}{M_j k_j}\right)^{\nu''_{j\alpha}} - (R_\alpha T)^{\nu'_\alpha} \prod_i \left(\frac{\rho_i}{M_i k_i}\right)^{\nu'_{i\alpha}} = 0, \tag{11.38}$$

where

$$\nu''_\alpha = \sum_j \nu''_{j\alpha} \quad \text{and} \quad \nu'_\alpha = \sum_i \nu'_{i\alpha} \qquad (\alpha = 1, 2, \ldots, r).$$

We now use the formula (11.8) and replace the densities ρ_i and ρ_j in equation (11.38) by the summed density ρ and the quantities ξ_α. As a result we shall obtain r equations for the determination of $\xi_1, \xi_2, \ldots, \xi_r$ in terms of the complete density ρ of the mixture, temperature T, and in terms of constant parameters characterizing the composition and properties of the components of the mixture.

Thus, for reversible chemical reactions (dissociation and recombination) or for physical transformations, the mixture can be thought of as a two-parameter medium, the state of which is defined by the given density ρ and temperature T, and the composition of which is defined by equation (11.8) and the Guldberg-Waage law.

This method used for the study of reversible processes in mixtures can be applied to ionized gases; electrons and the ions or molecules excited in different ways can be regarded as separate components. The degree of ionization is characterized by the corresponding parameters ξ_α. In this case, the equation (11.38) defines the degree of ionization, and is called Saha's equation when applicable to this phenomenon.

In order to obtain a closed system of equations describing the motion and the physico-chemical reversible processes in a mixture, apart from the equation of state and the Guldberg-Waage equation defining the composition of the mixture, it is necessary to use the continuity equation, the Euler dynamic equation, and the equation of the second law of thermodynamics:

$$T\,dS_m = dQ\,,$$

where dQ is the external input of heat which must be given as supplementary information.

We will now consider briefly certain general assumptions concerned with irreversible processes in gaseous mixtures.

In the case of irreversible phenomena, equations (11.20) through (11.23) and their corollaries are generally not fulfilled.

The equilibrium of a physical system is unstable if a spontaneous deviation from the equilibrium state can occur as a result of some irreversible process.

Bearing this in mind, we shall consider the stability conditions for thermodynamic equilibrium in an ideal medium in the form of a mixture of several components.

For reversible processes we can consider the equilibrium state corresponding to a fixed value of one of the pairs of variables U_m, ρ; S_m, ρ; S_m, p; T, ρ; T, p. In the vicinity of these states, irreversible processes can occur in general, and the remaining determining parameters which characterize the composition of the mixture vary in these processes.

The spontaneous development of such irreversible processes can be excluded by stipulating the following conditions.

For U_m = const and ρ = const from (11.11), we have

$$T\,dS_m = dQ' \geq 0. \tag{11.39}$$

If in equilibrium the entropy S_m has a maximum, then for any deviation from equilibrium, we have $\delta S_m < 0$, which is incompatible with (11.39); therefore, the condition for a maximum entropy for constant internal energy and density (volume) guarantees the stability indicated above.

For S_m = const and ρ = const, we have from (11.11)

$$dU_m = -\,dQ' \leq 0.$$

If in a state of equilibrium the internal energy U_m has a minimum, then $\delta U_m > 0$; therefore, the stability conditions for constants S_m and ρ are the conditions for minimum internal energy.

In an analogous manner, for S_m = const and p = const we obtain from (11.16)

$$di_m = -\,dQ' \leq 0,$$

and therefore the minimum enthalpy condition yields the sufficient condition of stability for constant S_m and p.

The corresponding sufficient condition for T = const and ρ = const based on equation (11.14) and the equation

$$d\mathscr{F}_m = -\,dQ' \leq 0$$

is reduced to the condition for minimum free energy $\mathscr{F}_m$.

Finally, for T = const and p = const, on the basis of (11.15), we obtain

$$d\psi_m = -\,dQ' \leq 0,$$

and therefore in this case the condition for minimum thermodynamic potential ψ_m guarantees stable equilibrium.

In general, the quantity dQ' can be defined according to one of the formulas (11.11), (11.16), (11.17), or (11.18) if the thermodynamic properties of the system are known and if the process, i.e., the law of variation of the defining parameters, is also known. Thus, by using various theoretical and experimental data for the study of the various processes, it is possible to establish the laws which allow the quantity dQ' to be determined as a function of magnitudes and increments of defining parameters for a given class of phenomena.

The method of determining dQ' from the thermodynamic laws is completely analogous to the method of determining the force acting on a point mass by the basic equation: $\mathscr{F} = m\boldsymbol{a}$.

Together with the problem of determining dQ' and $\mathscr{F}$ for given processes and given laws of motion, there arises the important problem of establishing the general physical laws for the determination of dQ' and $\mathscr{F}$, which laws are applicable in various processes and motions.

In general, for an ideal mixture, on the basis of (11.18) we may write

$$dQ' = \alpha\, dT + \beta\, dp + \sum_k Q_k\, dm_k = -\, d\psi_m - S_m\, dT + \frac{m}{\rho}\, dp. \tag{11.40}$$

This equation is valid for various possible processes. If we assume that α, β, and Q_k depend only on T, p, and m_k, and that the increments dT, dp, on the one hand, and dm_k, on the other, can be considered as being linearly independent, from (11.40) we will obtain

$$\begin{aligned} -\,\alpha &= \frac{\partial \psi_m}{\partial T} + S_m\,, \\ -\,\beta &= \frac{\partial \psi_m}{\partial p} - \frac{m}{\rho}\,. \end{aligned} \tag{11.41}$$

If α and β are different from zero, we will find that the corresponding formulas (11.19) are valid for reversible processes, but not for irreversible processes, and in the latter case they must be replaced by the formulas (11.41).

However, if for irreversible processes we can assume, on the basis of experimental data or additional hypotheses, that

$$\alpha = \beta = 0, \tag{11.42}$$

then (11.41) will be the equivalent to the corresponding formulas in (11.19). It is also easy to see that if $\alpha = \beta = 0$, all the formulas (11.19) can be applied to irreversible processes. Indeed, from (11.15) and (11.41) for $\alpha = \beta = 0$, we have

$$\sum_{k=1}^{q} \left(\frac{\partial \psi_m}{\partial m_k}\right)_{p,T} dm_k = \sum_{k=1}^{q} \left(\frac{\partial U_m}{\partial m_k}\right)_{\rho,S_m} dm_k + \left[\left(\frac{\partial U_m}{\partial S}\right)_{m_k,\rho} - T\right] dS_m + \left[\frac{\partial U_m}{\partial (1/\rho)} + mp\right] d\frac{1}{\rho}.$$

Since the possible variations in the parameters m_k, ρ, and S_m are independent, it follows that

$$\frac{\partial U_m}{\partial S} = T, \qquad \frac{\partial U}{\partial (1/\rho)} = -mp,$$

$$\sum_{k=1}^{q} \left(\frac{\partial \psi_m}{\partial m_k}\right)_{p,T} dm_k = \sum_{k=1}^{q} \left(\frac{\partial U_m}{\partial m_k}\right)_{\rho,S_m} dm_k.$$

By an analogous method, we can show that the remaining formulas (11.19) are valid.

Thus, if $\alpha = \beta = 0$, then for irreversible processes in a mixture, the following equations are valid: *

$$dQ' = -\sum_{k=1}^{q} \left(\frac{\partial \psi_m}{\partial m_k}\right)_{\rho,T} dm_k = -\sum_{k=1}^{q} \left(\frac{\partial U_m}{\partial m_k}\right)_{\rho,S_m} dm_k$$

$$= -\sum_{k=1}^{q} \left(\frac{\partial i_m}{\partial m_k}\right) dm_k = -\sum_{k=1}^{q} \left(\frac{\partial \mathcal{F}_m}{\partial m_k}\right) dm_k. \tag{11.43}$$

Equations (11.43) may serve to determine dQ' when the medium and the processes are known.†

On the other hand, formulas (11.43) can be used to establish kinetic equations for irreversible processes, analogously to equations (11.20) to (11.23); these equations replace equations (11.20) to (11.23), and in particular, replace the Guldberg-Waage equations established for reversible processes.

In order to obtain the kinetic equations, additional laws for the definition of dQ' must be used. In macroscopic theory, these additional laws can be obtained or verified from previous investigations using (11.43), or by drawing upon the data obtained by the use of this equation.

---

* Equation (11.43) is obtained from (11.42) and the finite relationships (11.13), (11,14), and (11,15), which are independent of the equation of the balance of mass. If the differentials $dm_1, dm_2, \ldots, dm_q$ are arbitrary and independent of one another, we obtain

$$\mu_k = \left(\frac{\partial \psi_m}{\partial m_k}\right)_{p,\,T} = \left(\frac{\partial U_m}{\partial m_k}\right)_{\rho,\,S_m} = \left(\frac{\partial i_m}{\partial m_k}\right)_{p,\,S_m} = \left(\frac{\partial \mathcal{F}_m}{\partial m_k}\right)_{\rho,\,T}. \tag{11.44}$$

† If $dQ^* - dQ = d\mathcal{A}^* \neq 0$, then on the left-hand side of (11.43), instead of dQ', one should have the difference $dQ' - d\mathcal{A}^*$. In the presence of diffusion, $d\mathcal{A}^* \neq 0$.

We have considered above the reversible and irreversible processes which may take place in an infinitesimal particle. In many cases, the physical processes for sets of interacting particles are irreversible, whereas the processes in each particle taken separately are reversible.

For example, the thermal interaction between two particles of a solid with temperatures T_1 and $T_2 > T_1$, isolated from all external influences, is an irreversible effect.

In this case, the transfer of a quantity of heat $dQ > 0$ from a particle with temperature T_2 to a particle with temperature T_1 causes an increase in the total entropy, which is given by the formula

$$dS = dS_1 + dS_2 = \frac{dQ}{T_1} - \frac{dQ}{T_2} = dQ\frac{T_2 - T_1}{T_1 \cdot T_2} > 0 . \tag{11.44}$$

Each of the processes in an individual particle, which consists, in one case, of emission of heat and a decrease in energy, and, in the other case, of absorption of heat and an increase in energy, can be considered as reversible. However, the process of heat transfer between two particles with different temperatures taken as a whole is irreversible.

Thus the irreversibility of the processes in a set of interacting particles is due both to their interaction (e.g., thermal conductivity) and due to the internal irreversible processes in each small particle.

In order to obtain the reversibility conditions and the kinetic equations for the interaction of a set of particles undergoing an irreversible process, we consider a small element of the medium, occupying volume V and bounded by surface Σ, as a multiple particle system. The full entropy increment of this volume element denoted by dS_m will be divided into the increment d_eS_m due to external flow of entropy through the moving boundary (the vector velocity is $\mathbf{v}$) of element Σ produced by thermal and diffusion currents, and the increment d_iS_m due to internal irreversible effects.

We have

$$dS_m = d_eS_m + d_iS_m . \tag{11.45}$$

The reversibility condition is

$$d_iS_m = 0 .$$

The irreversibility condition is

$$d_iS_m > 0 .$$

We have already shown that the determination of the kinetic equations for irreversible processes for an isolated particle may be reduced to the problem of determining the uncompensated heat dQ'.

In the more general case, the determination of the macroscopic kinetic equations for irreversible processes for arrays of interacting particles may be reduced to the determination of the magnitude of the irreversible part of the entropy increment $d_i S_m$.

Let us consider a continuous material medium. Let $\boldsymbol{q}$ be the vector flow of energy through the volume occupied by the medium. From the definition of $\boldsymbol{q}$, it follows that the general flow of energy dQ^* in time dt through an arbitrary volume V bounded by surface Σ is given by

$$dQ^* = -\int_\Sigma (\boldsymbol{q}, \boldsymbol{n})\, d\sigma\, dt,$$

where $\boldsymbol{n}$ is a unit vector directed along the external normal to surface Σ.

For an infinitesimal volume V, dQ^* can be written as

$$dQ^* = -V\,dt\,\mathrm{div}\,\boldsymbol{q} = -VT\left[\mathrm{div}\frac{\boldsymbol{q}\,dt}{T} + \frac{\boldsymbol{q}\,\mathrm{grad}\,T}{T^2}dt\right], \tag{11.46}$$

in which the second term on the right-hand side is different from zero only if grad $T \neq 0$.

It is not difficult to see that the expression

$$-V\,\mathrm{div}\frac{\boldsymbol{q}\,dt}{T} = -\int_\Sigma \left(\frac{\boldsymbol{q}\,dt}{T}, \boldsymbol{n}\right) d\sigma$$

represents the entropy transfer in time dt through the volume bounded by surface Σ. This transfer is due to the increase in entropy of the mass enclosed by Σ, which is caused by an exchange of entropy from particles outside the volume V to a given particle within the volume.

In the general case, the external flow of entropy through the movable surface Σ is not due only to the flow of energy, but also to an entropy transfer from the mass either by diffusion or because of the relative motions of the components which are related to the variation in the velocities of the components of the mixture with respect to the points of the movable surface Σ.

For the total entropy flow toward the given liquid volume bounded by surface Σ moving with a velocity field $\mathbf{v}$, we can write the formula

$$d_e S_m = -\int_\Sigma (\boldsymbol{\omega}\cdot\boldsymbol{n})\, d\sigma\, dt = -V\,dt\,\mathrm{div}\,\boldsymbol{\omega}, \tag{11.47}$$

where $\boldsymbol{\omega}$ is a vector of entropy flow. For the vector $\boldsymbol{\omega}$ in the case of a mixture consisting of q components having properties indicated above, with diffusion taken into account, we can write

$$\boldsymbol{\omega} = \frac{\boldsymbol{q}}{T} + \sum_{k=1}^{q} S_k \cdot \mathfrak{J}_k, \tag{11.48}$$

where $S_k(p, T, m_1, m_2, \ldots, m_q)$ is an entropy referred to a unit mass for the kth component in the given mixture with energy U_m and volume V (density ρ), and $\mathfrak{J}_k$ are the vectors of diffusion currents defined by the equation (11.5).

To calculate d_iS_m, we can use the formula

$$T\,dS_m = T\,d_eS_m + T\,d_iS_m = dQ + dQ' = dQ^* + dQ' - d\mathscr{A}^*. \qquad (11.49)$$

Hence, from (11.46), (11.47), and (11.48), for a small particle with volume V, we obtain

$$d_iS_m = -V\,dt\frac{\boldsymbol{q}\,\mathrm{grad}\,T}{T^2} + V\,dt\,\mathrm{div}\left(\sum_{k=1}^{q} S_k\,\mathfrak{J}_k\right) + \frac{dQ' - d\mathscr{A}^*}{T}.$$

From (11.49), (11.43), and (11.44), and setting $dQ^* \neq dQ$, the entropy increment is given by

$$T\,dS_m = dU_m + mp\,d\frac{1}{\rho} - \sum_{k=1}^{q} \mu_k\,dm_k. \qquad (11.50)$$

This is called Gibbs' formula.

From this formula, it follows that

$$\left(\frac{\partial S_m}{\partial m_k}\right)_{U_m,\rho} = S_k = -\frac{\mu_k}{T}. \qquad (11.51)$$

On the basis of (11.3), (11.6), (11.51), and (11.43), for the increment d_iS_m, we have

$$\frac{1}{m}\frac{d_iS_m}{dt} = -\frac{\mathrm{grad}\,T}{\rho T^2}\,\boldsymbol{q} - \frac{1}{\rho}\sum_k \mathrm{grad}\left(\frac{\mu_k}{T}\right)\mathfrak{J}_k = \sum_{k,\alpha}\frac{\mu_k M_k v_{k\alpha}}{T}\,w_\alpha. \qquad (11.52)$$

Formula (11.52) serves as a basis for finding the kinetic equations in phenomenological theories. Formula (11.52) can be written in the form

$$\rho\frac{d_iS}{dt} = \frac{1}{T}\sum_\gamma X_\gamma \Omega_\gamma, \qquad (11.53)$$

where Ω_γ are the components of the generalized flows, and X_γ are the generalized forces:

$$\Omega_1 = q_x, \quad \Omega_2 = q_y, \quad \Omega_3 = q_z, \quad \Omega_4 = J_{1x}, \quad \Omega_5 = J_{1y},$$

$$\Omega_6 = J_{1z}, \ldots, \quad \Omega_{3q+4} = \rho w_1, \quad \Omega_{3q+5} = \rho w_2, \ldots,$$

$$X_1 = -\frac{1}{T}\frac{\partial T}{\partial x}, \quad X_2 = -\frac{1}{T}\frac{\partial T}{\partial y}, \quad X_3 = -\frac{1}{T}\frac{\partial T}{\partial z},$$

$$X_4 = -T\frac{\partial}{\partial x}\left(\frac{\mu_1}{T}\right), \ldots, \quad X_{3q+4} = -\sum_k \mu_k M_k v_{k1}, \ldots.$$

The problem of setting up the kinetic equations in some cases is solved by formulating the functional relationships

$$\Omega_\gamma = \Omega_\gamma(p, T, m_1, m_2, \ldots, m_q; X_1, X_2, \ldots).$$

For the investigation of irreversible processes differing only slightly from reversible equilibrium processes, it is assumed in many cases that these functions are linear, i.e.,

$$\Omega_\gamma = \sum_\beta L_{\gamma\beta} X_\beta, \tag{11.54}$$

where the matrix of the coefficients $L_{\gamma\beta}$ is made up of some functions of the parameters of the state.

The Onsager principle for processes of thermal conductivity, diffusion, and chemical reactions considered above is included in the equations

$$L_{\gamma\beta} = L_{\beta\gamma}, \tag{11.55}$$

which for small deviations from equilibrium can be obtained by using the methods of statistical physics and by assuming that the microscopic physico-chemical reactions between the elementary particles of the medium (molecules, atoms) are reversible.

The phenomenological coefficients $L_{\gamma\beta}$ are expressed directly in terms of the coefficients of the thermal conductivity, diffusion, thermal diffusion, etc. The relationships (11.54) can be considered as generalizations of the elementary laws of individual phenomena of thermal conductivity or diffusion into more complex processes in which heat transfer, diffusion, and chemical reactions are taking place in the medium simultaneously.

From the second law of thermodynamics it follows that the quadratic form

$$\sum_{\gamma,\beta} L_{\gamma\beta} X_\gamma X_\beta = T\rho \frac{d_i S}{dt} > 0$$

is positive definite.

We will not present in detail the theory of the properties of the coefficients $L_{\gamma\beta}$, some of which are zero, nor the theory which considers the effects on the components of a mixture of the unequal forces calculated for a unit corresponding masses m_k (for example, resistive forces due to the relative motion of the components, or electromagnetic forces). These theories are discussed in other books[7, 9, 56, 81].

In concluding this section, we note that in several cases it is not possible to obtain adequate descriptions of irreversible processes of chemical reactions using linear relationships of the form (11.54).

12. Viscous liquids and gases

From the mechanical and thermodynamic points of view, models of material continua can be established for liquids or gases, if, in a state of rest, it is only the pressure which produces internal stresses. Moreover, for any process, the internal energy and entropy of liquids and gases can be represented by the functions

$$\rho, T, \mu_1, \mu_2, \dots \qquad \text{or} \qquad p, T, \mu_1, \mu_2, \dots,$$

where μ_1, μ_2 are constant or variable parameters of a physico-chemical nature, characterizing the properties and composition of the substance and the internal physical-mechanical processes.

Thus for liquids and gases, we have

$$\begin{aligned} U &= U(\rho, T, \mu_1, \mu_2, \dots), \\ S &= S(\rho, T, \mu_1, \mu_2, \dots), \\ U - TS = \mathscr{F} &= \mathscr{F}(\rho, T, \mu_1, \mu_2, \dots). \end{aligned} \tag{12.1}$$

We assume that for any motion during any process, the pressure p within the liquid or gas will be given by the equation

$$p = -\left(\frac{\partial \mathscr{F}}{\partial(1/\rho)}\right)_{T,\mu_1,\mu_2,\dots} = \rho^2 \frac{\partial \mathscr{F}}{\partial \rho}. \tag{12.2}$$

At rest, and in the presence of thermodynamic equilibrium, we can deduce from formulas (8.1) and (8.8), that the internal stress tensor within liquids and gases will be written in the form

$$\boldsymbol{P} = -p\boldsymbol{G}, \qquad p^{ij} = -pg^{ij}. \tag{12.3}$$

If equation (12.3) also applies for motion, the liquid or gas will be ideal in a mechanical and thermodynamic sense.

A liquid or a gas is termed viscous if, during motion, the internal stresses are related by the equation

$$\boldsymbol{P} = -p\boldsymbol{G} + \mathfrak{T}, \qquad p^{ij} = -pg^{ij} + \tau^{ij}, \tag{12.4}$$

where tensor $\mathfrak{T}$, which is different from zero, is called the viscous stress tensor.

In specific models of viscous media introduced in order to describe the motions of real liquids and gases, the tensor $\mathfrak{T}$ will not be spherical for an arbitrary motion. It therefore follows that the definition of a mechanically ideal continuum for a liquid or gas, given in § 8 as a medium with a spherical stress tensor, is exactly the same as the definitions included in formulas (12.2) and (12.3) for media characterized by many parameters ρ, T, $\mu_1, \mu_2, \dots$.

The equation of heat flow (6.10) for liquids and gases can be written in the form

$$dQ = dU_m + p\,d\frac{1}{\rho}\,dm - \frac{1}{\rho}\tau^{\alpha\beta}e_{\alpha\beta}\,dt\,dm\,. \tag{12.5}$$

From the hypothesis that the increment dU_m is reversible for a viscous medium, it follows that the elementary work of the internal forces due to the viscosity

$$d\Phi = -\frac{1}{\rho}\tau^{\alpha\beta}e_{\alpha\beta}\,dt\,dm = -\,dQ' \tag{12.6}$$

is related to the irreversibility of the process. For a change in entropy, the following formula is valid:

$$T\,dS = dQ + dQ' = dQ + \frac{1}{\rho}\tau^{\alpha\beta}e_{\alpha\beta}\,dt\,dm\,. \tag{12.7}$$

The construction of concrete models of viscous liquids and gases and the formulation of a closed system of equations of motion are related to properties of the viscous stress tensor $\mathfrak{T}$.

We make the fundamental assumption, established on the basis of experiments and the kinetic theory of liquids and gases, that a tensor relationship of the following form exists:

$$\mathfrak{T} = f(\mathfrak{E}, \omega_1, \omega_2, \dots, \boldsymbol{A}_1, \boldsymbol{A}_2, \dots), \tag{12.8}$$

where $\mathfrak{E}$ is the tensor of rates of deformations defined by the formulas (6.8) and (6.9) of Chapter II, $\omega_1, \omega_2, \dots$, are scalars, and $\boldsymbol{A}_1, \boldsymbol{A}_2, \dots$ are the tensor characteristics of the state.

If the parametric physical tensors $\boldsymbol{A}_1, \boldsymbol{A}_2, \dots$ are absent, then the viscous liquid is isotropic.

On the basis of formula (5.17) of Chapter I, the tensor equation (12.8) for an isotropic medium can be written in the form

$$\mathfrak{T} = k_0\boldsymbol{G} + k_1\mathfrak{E} + k_2\mathfrak{E}^2, \tag{12.9}$$

where k_0, k_1, k_2 are functions of the invariants $\mathcal{J}_1^e, \mathcal{J}_2^e, \mathcal{J}_3^e$ of tensor $\mathfrak{E}$ and of the scalars $\omega_1, \omega_2, \dots$.

Newton's law for the relationship between the stress tensor P and the tensor of rates of deformation $\mathfrak{E}$ is a particular case of formula (12.9), in which the relationship between the components of these tensors is linear and homogeneous.

For viscous stresses, this law is represented by the formulas

$$\mathfrak{T} = \lambda\mathcal{J}_1\boldsymbol{G} + \mu\mathfrak{E} \qquad \text{or} \qquad {}^{ij} = \lambda\,\mathrm{div}\,\boldsymbol{v}\,g^{ij} + \mu e^{ij}, \tag{12.10}$$

where μ and $\zeta = \lambda - \frac{2}{3}\mu$ are the viscosity coefficients, which in general are functions of scalar parameters defining the thermodynamic state of the particles of the liquid or gas.

If we introduce a scalar function $\Psi(\mathscr{I}_1^e, \overset{*}{\mathscr{I}}{}_2^e)$ defined by the formula

$$\Psi = \tfrac{1}{2}[\lambda(\mathscr{I}_1^e)^2 + \mu \overset{*}{\mathscr{I}}{}_2^e] = \tfrac{1}{2}\{\zeta(\mathscr{I}_1^e)^2 + \mu[\tfrac{2}{3}(\mathscr{I}_1^e)^2 + \overset{*}{\mathscr{I}}{}_2^e]\}$$
$$= \tfrac{1}{2}[\lambda g^{\alpha\beta} e_{\alpha\beta} g^{\gamma\delta} e_{\gamma\delta} + \mu g^{\alpha\beta} g^{\gamma\delta} e_{\beta\delta} e_{\alpha\gamma}], \qquad (12.11)$$

then formula (12.10) can be written in the form

$$\tau^{ij} = \frac{\partial \Psi}{\partial e_{ij}}. \qquad (12.12)$$

The function Ψ is a homogeneous quadratic form of the components of the tensor of rates of deformation; the work of the internal viscous forces (12.6) can be written in terms of Ψ as

$$dQ' = -\,d\Phi = \frac{2}{\rho}\Psi\, dm\, dt. \qquad (12.13)$$

Formulas (12.10) and (12.12), valid for linear homogeneous functions, can be generalized for the case of nonlinear relationships, when the relationships (12.12) are satisfied in the case of some more general form of function Ψ of components of a tensor of rates of deformation. Such a generalization is possible in the case of both isotropic and anisotropic media. For an isotropic medium, this gives a particular form of equation (12.9) when a potential exists (see § 7, Chapter I).

If the external flow of heat is zero, then it follows from (12.7) and (12.13) that

$$\frac{dS}{dt} = \frac{2}{\rho}\Psi\, dm. \qquad (12.14)$$

From this and the second principle we have $\Psi \geq 0$. This condition, on the basis of formulas (12.11), means that the coefficients ζ and μ, which characterize the viscosity properties for any medium, cannot be negative.

It is obvious that the processes of dissipation of energy, leading to an increase in entropy at the expense of the stresses, can occur only when there is motion and deformation in which the tensor of the rates of deformation is different from zero.

13. Turbulent motion in continua

In many moving liquids and gases, the velocity field and other physical quantities for each particle, and at each point of space, undergo complicated oscillations about some mean value. Such a motion is called a turbulent one.

Experiment and theory show that in liquids with high Reynolds numbers (i.e., in liquids at high velocities and large scales), the regular laminar motion becomes unstable and turbulent, and the particles of the liquid describe complicated swirling trajectories.

A detailed study of the spatial and time distributions of the instantaneous values of the characteristics of the motion is extremely difficult, and along with this, in many cases, from the practical point of view, a detailed description of such fluctuating unstable motions is not needed.

In the turbulent motion of liquids and gases, it is useful to introduce the averaged values of velocities, density, pressure, the mean values of pulsations for various magnitudes, etc., which vary continuously with respect to space and time.

In this way, it is possible to construct new continuum models in which one can define the various mechanical and physical characteristics, and think of them as the mean values of the corresponding characteristics of fluctuating motions in a continuum with a known mechanical and physical nature.

The development of the theory of turbulent motion and the formulation of generally different continuum models for the determination of averaged processes for certain classes of turbulent motion in a given medium with fixed properties is related to the analysis of averaging methods and the problem of establishing the system of functional relationships and mean-value equations.

Until now the theoretical analysis of turbulent motions has been carried out for only a few incompressible liquids and ideal gases, in which the true fluctuating motions obey the Navier-Stokes equation.

In certain cases, the theory of turbulent motions of liquids and gases has been formulated by taking electromagnetic effects into account.

In order to determine the mean values of the various quantities in pulsating flows, it is necessary to consider the experimental methods for measuring mean values and to use the practically important properties of such mean values in the class of mechanical problems under consideration.

In practice, the method of averaging with respect to time at fixed points in space is fundamental. For turbulent motions stabilized on the average, the interval of time over which one takes the average can, in theory, be infinite. If the turbulent motion on the average does change with time (non-stationary turbulent motion), the period over which the averaging is carried out should be sufficiently large in comparison with the periods of individual pulsations and must be small in comparison with the time for a perceptible change in the mean of the quantities.

It is also possible to introduce the mean of a quantity over some volume which is sufficiently large compared with the dimensions of a region of perceptibly different pulsations, and small compared with the dimensions of a volume in which the mean of the quantity changes significantly.

In several cases, the means with respect to time and volume indicated above coincide. Such a coincidence is a basic factor in hypotheses and in certain cases of mean-value theorems.

The methods and concepts of the theory of probability can be used in the study of turbulent motion. In this case, the instantaneous values of the mechanical characteristics can be considered as random quantities, and their means are defined as mathematical probabilities.

Using supplementary hypotheses of a physical nature, which as investigation will show are necessary for the construction of models of averaged turbulent motions, the development of the turbulence theory can be carried out without a detailed description of how the means are obtained. The method of finding the average, however, must have the following general features.

Let a be the instantaneous value of some characteristic turbulent motion of the medium, the mean value of the quantity being represented by the same letter with a bar above it.

The value of a can be written in the form

$$a = \bar{a} + a' . \tag{13.1}$$

The quantity a' is called the pulsating component and by definition its mean value is zero:

$$\bar{a}' = 0 . \tag{13.2}$$

From the definition of the mean it follows that

$$\bar{\bar{a}} = \bar{a} . \tag{13.3}$$

Let b be another quantity of the same type as a. Then we have

$$\overline{a + b} = \bar{a} + \bar{b} \tag{13.4}$$

and

$$\overline{ab} = \bar{a} \cdot \quad + \overline{a'b'} . \tag{13.5}$$

Consequently, $\overline{\bar{a}b'} = \overline{\bar{b}a'} = 0$. From (13.5) it follows in particular that $\bar{a}^2 = (\bar{a})^2 + \bar{a}'^2$.

Moreover, the operation of differentiation with respect to time and coordinates must be transposable with the operation of averaging:

$$\overline{\frac{\partial a}{\partial t}} = \frac{\partial \bar{a}}{\partial t} \quad \text{and} \quad \overline{\frac{\partial a}{\partial x}} = \frac{\partial \bar{a}}{\partial x} . \tag{13.6}$$

If the mean is defined as the mathematical probability, the properties indicated above will be precisely fulfilled. If the mean is taken with respect to time, the nonstationary properties of the motion (13.3) and (13.5) are only approximately fulfilled.*

The mean-value equations of motion can be obtained by averaging the equations of motions for magnitudes which describe the instantaneous state of the motion.

Let us consider the averaged equations for an incompressible liquid using an example of application of the Navier-Stokes equation.

With the aid of the continuity equation

$$\sum_{k=1}^{3} \frac{\partial u_k}{\partial x^k} = 0, \tag{13.7}$$

these equations in a cartesian coordinate system can be written as

$$\frac{\partial u_i}{\partial t} + \sum_{k=1}^{3} \frac{\partial u_i u_k}{\partial x^k} = -\frac{1}{\rho}\frac{\partial p}{\partial x^i} + \nu \Delta u_i \qquad (i = 1, 2, 3). \tag{13.8}$$

Applying the averaging operation to (13.7) and (13.8), we obtain

$$\sum_{k=1}^{3} \frac{\partial \bar{u}_k}{\partial x^k} = 0$$

and

$$\frac{\partial \bar{u}_i}{\partial t} + \sum_{k} \frac{\partial \overline{u_i u_k}}{\partial x^k} + \frac{\partial \overline{u_i' u_k'}}{\partial x^k} = -\frac{1}{\rho}\frac{\partial \bar{p}}{\partial x^i} + \nu \Delta \bar{u}_i \qquad (i = 1, 2, 3). \tag{13.9}$$

For the study of real motions, equations (13.7) and (13.8) form a complete system of equations (the number of equations equals the number of unknowns). The system of equations for the mean values, called the Reynolds equations, is not complete because it contains a new unknown symmetrical tensor,

$$\tau_{ik} = \overline{u_i' u_k'},$$

which is obtained by averaging the nonlinear terms.

Thus, in order to obtain the averaged turbulent motions of incompressible liquids, the hydraulic equation, which is adequate for studying the real

---

* A. A. Isaacson "The Determination of Turbulence," *Zh. Russk. Fiz. Khem. Obshchestva*, Vol. XLII, No. 3, 1910.

motion, is not sufficient. It is therefore clear that the detailed theoretical description of turbulent motion is possible only by the use of certain additional hypotheses, the validity of which in the final analysis can be established only experimentally.

In practice, it is found that a hypothesis of such a type is applicable only to distinct particular classes of motion.

At the present time it is impossible to construct a model of a single ideal continuum and to derive a universal system of equations suitable for the description of arbitrary averaged turbulent motions, even in the case of only incompressible liquids.

For the investigation of turbulent motions, it is useful to introduce the so-called moment relationships, representing the mean values of various arbitrary quantities taken at various points of the volume and at different moments of time. For example,

$$\Delta(x_1, x_2, x_3, x_1', x_2', x_3', x_1'', x_2'', x_3'', t, t', t'') = \overline{u_i(x_1, x_2, x_3, t)\, u_k(x_1', x_2', x_3', t')\, p(x_1'', x_2'', x_3'', t'')}. \qquad (13.10)$$

Such quantities, generally speaking, depend on the coordinates of all the points and the corresponding moments of time.

With the help of the equations for the instantaneous characteristics, we can obtain equations for various types of moment relationships. However, without the use of additional essential hypotheses, it is also impossible to obtain a complete system of equations with a finite number of unknowns.

The discovery of additional hypotheses for the moment relationships with certain special types of motion allows a theoretical analysis to be developed and valuable conclusions to be drawn on the averaged turbulent motion.*

14. A model of an elastic body

The fundamental concept of mechanics most widely used in engineering is the concept of an elastic medium which is generally regarded as a solid body. Below we shall show that an ideal liquid or gas can also be considered as an elastic body. The theory of elasticity is the basis for design calculations dealing with the strength of all types of structures, for machines and various pieces of equipment, both those on the drawing board and those already built.

The fundamental idea in elastic theory is the hypothesis of the reversibility

* Treatment of the corresponding theories can be found in the books by D. Batchelor [3] and L. I. Sedov [32].

of the processes. The original model is in the form of a deformed solid considered as a material continuum, for whose small particles the internal energy, free energy, entropy, and other thermodynamic properties can be regarded as functions of the tensor of deformation, temperature, and of the physically constant or variable parameters which characterize the thermal and mechanical properties and the state of the substance. The parameters which characterize the medium can be tensors.

In many practical cases, temperature effects are insignificant, and the components of the deformation tensor are of fundamental importance. However, in the following discussion, we shall consider the model of an elastic body, taking into account both temperature effects and additional physical and chemical phenomena, because this does not really make the general theory any more difficult, and it also allows the thermodynamic laws and concept of entropy to be used more fully.

We will consider below the theory of elasticity for finite deformations. The corresponding simplifications for small deformations will be obvious.

Consider a medium in which the internal energy U and the free energy $\mathcal{F} = U - TS$ calculated for a unit mass, are represented as functions of the following types:

$$U = U(\mathring{g}_{ij}, \varepsilon_{ij}, S, \mu_1, \mu_2, \ldots, \mu_n, \xi^1, \xi^2, \xi^3),$$

or

$$\mathcal{F} = \mathcal{F}(\mathring{g}_{ij}, \varepsilon_{ij}, T, \mu_1, \mu_2, \ldots, \mu_n, \xi^1, \xi^2, \xi^3). \tag{14.1}$$

Here, $\mathring{g}_{ij}$ stands for the covariant components of the fundamental tensor $\mathring{G}$, which defines the square of the line element in the original state:

$$ds_0^2 = \mathring{g}_{\alpha\beta}\, d\xi^\alpha\, d\xi^\beta,$$

$$\mathring{G} = \mathring{g}_{\alpha\beta}\mathring{\mathfrak{I}}^\alpha \mathring{\mathfrak{I}}^\beta = \mathring{g}^{\alpha\beta}\mathring{\mathfrak{I}}_\alpha \mathring{\mathfrak{I}}_\beta = \delta^{\alpha\cdot}_{\cdot\beta}\mathring{\mathfrak{I}}_\alpha \mathring{\mathfrak{I}}^\beta,$$

where ξ^1, ξ^2, ξ^3 are the Lagrangian coordinates of the particles of the medium. If these coordinates do not appear in the formula (14.1) explicitly, then the body is called homogeneous.

The covariant components of the finite deformation tensors $\mathring{\mathscr{E}}$ and $\hat{\mathscr{E}}$ are denoted by (see § 4, Chapter II)

$$\varepsilon_{ij} = \tfrac{1}{2}(\hat{g}_{ij} - \mathring{g}_{ij}),$$

$$\mathring{\mathscr{E}} = \varepsilon_{\alpha\beta}\mathring{\mathfrak{I}}^\alpha \mathring{\mathfrak{I}}^\beta, \qquad \hat{\mathscr{E}} = \varepsilon_{\alpha\beta}\hat{\mathfrak{I}}^\alpha \hat{\mathfrak{I}}^\beta = \varepsilon'_{\alpha\beta}\mathfrak{I}^\alpha \mathfrak{I}^\beta. \tag{14.2}$$

We shall recall that the stationary basis $\mathfrak{I}_i$ corresponds to a coordinate system $Ox^1x^2x^3$ which is defined as a reference system, and it is with respect to this system that displacements or movements of the points of the continuum take place.

In the deformed state, an element ds corresponds to ds_0, and is defined by the formula $ds^2 = \hat{g}_{\alpha\beta} d\xi^\alpha d\xi^\beta$.

Let S and T be the entropy of unit mass and the absolute temperature, and let $\mu_1, \mu_2, \ldots, \mu_n$ be physical and chemical parameters which are defined as independent defining parameters, and which can be constants or variables if the mechanical phenomena are associated with changes in the physico-chemical properties of the medium. The set of certain parameters μ_i can depend on the choice of coordinate system ξ^i and in the basis $\mathring{\mathbf{Э}}_i$ can form tensors. If all the parameters μ_i are scalars, then the body is isotropic. A body can be inhomogeneous but isotropic. In accordance with the assumption, the system of virtual increments $\delta\mu_i \neq 0$ is linearly independent (see § 6).

In § 4 and § 5, the internal stress tensors were introduced and the strain energy for any point of the body per unit of mass is given for any displacement as follows:

$$\mathring{P} = \mathring{p}^{\alpha\beta} \mathring{\mathbf{Э}}_\alpha \mathring{\mathbf{Э}}_\beta, \qquad \hat{P} = \hat{p}^{\alpha\beta} \hat{\mathbf{Э}}_\alpha \hat{\mathbf{Э}}_\beta = p'^{\alpha\beta} \mathbf{Э}_\alpha \mathbf{Э}_\beta,$$

and (14.3)

$$\delta \mathscr{A}^i = -\frac{p^{\alpha\beta}}{\rho} \delta\varepsilon_{\alpha\beta},$$

where $\mathring{p}^{\alpha\beta} = \hat{p}^{\alpha\beta} = p^{\alpha\beta}$ and $\delta\varepsilon_{\alpha\beta} = e_{\alpha\beta}\delta t$, where $e_{\alpha\beta}$ are the components of the tensor of the rates of deformation. If the bases $\hat{\mathbf{Э}}_\alpha$ and $\mathbf{Э}_\alpha$ coincide at a given moment of time, we have

$$\varepsilon_{\alpha\beta} = \varepsilon'_{\alpha\beta} \qquad \text{and} \qquad p^{\alpha\beta} = p'^{\alpha\beta}.$$

We will now show that in order to obtain a closed system of equations for reversible processes in elastic theory, it is sufficient to know the external heat flow dQ into unit mass and one of the functions U and $\mathscr{F}$ of (14.1).

Indeed the equation of heat flow for reversible processes corresponding to all possible variants δU, δS, $\delta\varepsilon_{\alpha\beta}$, or $\delta\mathscr{F}$, δT, and $\delta\varepsilon_{\alpha\beta}$, leads to the expressions

$$\delta Q = T\delta S \tag{14.4}$$

and

$$\begin{aligned} \delta U &= \frac{\partial U}{\partial S}\delta S + \frac{\partial U}{\partial \varepsilon_{\alpha\beta}}\delta\varepsilon_{\alpha\beta} + \frac{\partial U}{\partial \mu_i}\delta\mu_i = T\delta S + \frac{p^{\alpha\beta}}{\rho}\delta\varepsilon_{\alpha\beta}, \\ \delta \mathscr{F} &= \frac{\partial \mathscr{F}}{\partial T}\delta T + \frac{\partial \mathscr{F}}{\partial \varepsilon_{\alpha\beta}}\delta\varepsilon_{\alpha\beta} + \frac{\partial \mathscr{F}}{\partial \mu_i}\delta\mu_i = -S\delta T + \frac{p^{\alpha\beta}}{\rho}\delta\varepsilon_{\alpha\beta}. \end{aligned} \tag{14.5}$$

If the possible increments in the components of the deformation tensor

$\delta\varepsilon_{\alpha\beta}$ are linearly independent (no geometric relationships similar to the incompressibility conditions, etc., ...), then from (14.5) we have

$$p^{\alpha\beta} = \rho\left(\frac{\partial U}{\partial \varepsilon_{\alpha\beta}}\right)_{S,\mu_i} = \rho\left(\frac{\partial \mathscr{F}}{\partial \varepsilon_{\alpha\beta}}\right)_{T,\mu_i} . \tag{14.6}$$

Consequently, the internal energy and the free energy defined as functions of their arguments can be considered in (14.1) as potentials for the contravariant components of the stress tensors $(1/\rho)\mathring{\boldsymbol{P}}$ and $(1/\rho)\hat{\boldsymbol{P}}$.

For adiabatic processes $S = \text{const}$, and therefore it is convenient to use the formula with the internal energy as a potential; for isothermal processes $T = \text{const}$, and it is therefore convenient to use the equation with the free energy as a potential. However, both these equations are applicable for any reversible process with any heat flow δQ.

In the general case, in the formulas (14.6), the entropy S or the temperature T as well as the values of the variable parameters $\mu_1, \mu_2, \ldots, \mu_m (m \leq n)$ must be determined with the aid of the thermodynamic equations which are defined by (14.5):

$$T = \left(\frac{\partial U}{\partial S}\right)_{\varepsilon_{\alpha\beta},\mu_i}$$

or (14.7)

$$S = -\left(\frac{\partial \mathscr{F}}{\partial T}\right)_{\varepsilon_{\alpha\beta},\mu_i}$$

and

$$\left(\frac{\partial U}{\partial \mu_i}\right)_{\varepsilon_{\alpha\beta},S} = \left(\frac{\partial \mathscr{F}}{\partial \mu_i}\right)_{\varepsilon_{\alpha\beta},T} = 0 \qquad (i = 1, 2, \ldots, m \leq n), \tag{14.8}$$

and with the aid of one of the following equations which result from the expression for the flow of heat (14.4) with (14.7) taken into account:

$$dQ = \left(\frac{\partial U}{\partial S}\right)_{\varepsilon_{\alpha\beta},\mu_i} dS$$

or (14.9)

$$dQ = -Td\left(\frac{\partial \mathscr{F}}{\partial T}\right) = -T\left(\frac{\partial (p_{\alpha\beta}/\rho)}{\partial T} d\varepsilon_{\alpha\beta} + \frac{\partial^2 \mathscr{F}}{\partial T^2} dT\right).$$

The first of the equations (14.7) serves for the determination of temperature using potential U, and the second for the determination of entropy using potential $\mathscr{F}$.

Equation (14.8) can be thought of as an additional finite relationship, defining the laws of change of the parameters $\mu_1, \mu_2, \ldots, \mu_m$ in terms of S and $\varepsilon_{\alpha\beta}$ or T and $\varepsilon_{\alpha\beta}$; these equations are analogous to the Guldberg-Waage equation for the description of reversible chemical reactions, or to Saha's equation for the description of ionization phenomena in gases (see § 11, Chapter III).

Equation (14.9) can be thought of as the equations for the determination of the change in entropy utilizing the potential U or as equations for the determination of the change in temperature utilizing the potential $\mathscr{F}$.

If this process is an adiabatic one, $\delta Q = \delta S = 0$. For an isothermal process, $T = \text{const}$, and the second of the equations (14.9) serves to determine the heat flow.

In elastic theory, special courses, scientific papers, and in practice, one does not encounter equation (14.8), because usually the mechanical phenomena related to physico-chemical changes are not considered in elastic bodies; however, such processes are possible, and equation (14.8) may prove to be necessary.

The continuity equation (3.8), the dynamic equations (4.17), the compatibility equations [see formulas (7.4) of Chapter II], the equations of state (14.6), the equations of the physico-chemical equilibrium (14.8), and the equations of heat flow (14.9) form a completely closed system of thermoelastic equations for any elastic and generally anisotropic media.

The explicit form of these equations is defined by the form of one of the functions (14.1) and by the data on heat flow dQ.

The system of equations (14.6) to (14.9) is established for the general case of finite deformations. In practice, the components of the deformation tensor can often be assumed to be small, and in this case the following approximate formulas are valid for components of the deformation tensor:

$$\varepsilon_{\alpha\beta} = \tfrac{1}{2}(\nabla_\alpha w_\beta + \nabla_\beta w_\alpha),$$

where w_i are the components of the displacement vector [see formula (4.32), Chapter I]. The corresponding theory for small deformations is called the geometrically linear theory.

In geometrically linear problems, one has often to consider, in the expressions for the thermodynamic functions and in the equations of state (14.6), the nonlinear relationships with the components of the deformation tensor defined in a geometrically linear approximation. In this case, the geometrically linear theory is used, but with nonlinear physical and dynamic relationships, in particular, those between the components of the stress and deformation tensors.

It is easy to see that in applying the theory of geometrically small deformations, the density ρ of formulas (14.6) can be taken as a constant, because within the limits of accuracy of this theory, the effects of small changes in density on the components of the stress tensor are negligible.

It is obvious that in the theory of small deformations, the stress tensor has a potential, which is not so in the general case.

In the relationships (14.6) to (14.9), we take as independent variables the systems

$$\varepsilon_{\alpha\beta}, S, \mu_i$$

or (14.10)

$$\varepsilon_{\alpha\beta}, T, \mu_i.$$

On the basis of the equation of state (14.6) it is obvious that the independent variables can be the contravariant components $p^{\alpha\beta}$ of the stress tensor instead of the covariant components $\varepsilon_{\alpha\beta}$ of the deformation tensors. Let us consider the system of variables

$$\sigma^{\alpha\beta}, S, \mu_i$$

or (14.11)

$$\sigma^{\alpha\beta}, T, \mu_i,$$

where

$$\sigma^{\alpha\beta} = \frac{p^{\alpha\beta}}{\rho}.$$

In this case, one may write down a system of equations analogous to the systems (14.6) to (14.9) if we introduce the following potentials: thermal capacity i, and the thermodynamic potential Ψ per unit mass:

$$\begin{aligned} i &= i(\mathring{g}_{\alpha\beta}, \sigma^{\alpha\beta}, S, \mu_1, \mu_2, \dots, \mu_n, \xi^1, \xi^2, \xi^3) = U - \sigma^{\alpha\beta}\varepsilon_{\alpha\beta}, \\ \Psi &= \Psi(\mathring{g}_{\alpha\beta}, \sigma^{\alpha\beta}, T, \mu_1, \mu_2, \dots, \mu_n, \xi^1, \xi^2, \xi^3) = \mathscr{F} - \sigma^{\alpha\beta}\varepsilon_{\alpha\beta}. \end{aligned} \tag{14.12}$$

Indeed, using i and Ψ, the relationships (14.5) can be written in the form

$$\begin{aligned} \delta i &= \frac{\partial i}{\partial S}\delta S + \frac{\partial i}{\partial \sigma^{\alpha\beta}}\delta\sigma^{\alpha\beta} + \frac{\partial i}{\partial \mu_i}\delta\mu_i = T\delta S - \varepsilon_{\alpha\beta}\delta\sigma^{\alpha\beta}, \\ \delta\Psi &= \frac{\partial \Psi}{\partial T}\delta T + \frac{\partial \Psi}{\partial \sigma^{\alpha\beta}}\delta\sigma^{\alpha\beta} + \frac{\partial \Psi}{\partial \mu_i}\delta\mu_i = -S\delta T - \varepsilon_{\alpha\beta}\delta\sigma^{\alpha\beta}. \end{aligned} \tag{14.13}$$

From this it follows that the equations of state (14.6) can take the form

$$\varepsilon_{\alpha\beta} = -\left(\frac{\partial i}{\partial \sigma^{\alpha\beta}}\right)_{S,\mu_i} = -\left(\frac{\partial \Psi}{\partial \sigma^{\alpha\beta}}\right)_{T,\mu_i}. \tag{14.14}$$

Equations (14.7) are replaced by

$$T = \left(\frac{\partial i}{\partial S}\right)_{\sigma^{\alpha\beta},\mu_i} \quad \text{and} \quad S = -\left(\frac{\partial \Psi}{\partial T}\right)_{\sigma^{\alpha\beta},\mu_i}. \tag{14.15}$$

The equations of the physico-chemical processes take the form

$$\left(\frac{\partial i}{\partial \mu_i}\right)_{\sigma^{\alpha\beta},S} = \left(\frac{\partial \Psi}{\partial \mu_i}\right)_{\sigma^{\alpha\beta},T} = 0 \qquad (i = 1, 2, \dots, m). \tag{14.16}$$

The equations of the heat flow (14.9) in terms of the system of variables (14.11) are

$$dQ = \left(\frac{\partial i}{\partial S}\right)_{\sigma^{\alpha\beta},\mu_i} dS$$

or (14.17)

$$dQ = -T d\left(\frac{\partial \Psi}{\partial T}\right) = T\left(\frac{\partial \varepsilon_{\alpha\beta}}{\partial T}\delta\sigma^{\alpha\beta} + \frac{\partial^2 \Psi}{\partial T}dT\right).$$

It is obvious that the complete system of thermoelastic equations in terms of the variables (14.11) is obtained in an explicit form if one of the functions i or Ψ in (14.12) and the heat flow dQ are given.

The equations of state (14.6) in terms of the variables (14.10), or the equations (14.14) in terms of the variables (14.11), can be established by using the covariant components $\varepsilon_{\alpha\beta}$ of tensors $\mathring{\mathscr{E}}$ and $\hat{\mathscr{E}}$ and the contravariant components $p^{\alpha\beta}$ of tensors $\mathring{\boldsymbol{P}}$ and $\hat{\boldsymbol{P}}$.

Let us now consider further groups of formulas in which components of tensors $\mathring{\mathscr{E}}$ and $\mathring{\boldsymbol{P}}$ with different arrangements of indices are used. Because it is assumed that the components of tensor $\mathring{\boldsymbol{G}}$ are referred to a fixed system of coordinates in the space of the initial states, the components $\mathring{g}_{\alpha\beta}$ and $\mathring{g}^{\alpha\beta}$ are constant, and therefore, on the basis of the conclusions of § 7, Chapter I, the following equivalent relationships may be used instead of (14.6):

$$\mathring{p}_{\alpha\cdot}^{\cdot\beta} = \rho\frac{\partial U}{\partial \mathring{\varepsilon}_{\cdot\beta}^{\alpha\cdot}} = \rho\frac{\partial \mathscr{F}}{\partial \mathring{\varepsilon}_{\cdot\beta}^{\alpha\cdot}},$$

$$\mathring{p}_{\alpha\beta} = \rho\frac{\partial U}{\partial \mathring{\varepsilon}^{\alpha\beta}} = \rho\frac{\partial \mathscr{F}}{\partial \mathring{\varepsilon}^{\alpha\beta}}, \tag{14.18}$$

where

$$\mathring{\varepsilon}_{\cdot\beta}^{\alpha\cdot} = \mathring{g}^{\alpha\omega}\varepsilon_{\omega\beta}, \qquad \mathring{\varepsilon}^{\alpha\beta} = \mathring{g}^{\nu\beta}\mathring{\varepsilon}_{\cdot\nu}^{\alpha\cdot},$$

and

$$\mathring{p}_{\alpha\cdot}^{\cdot\beta} = \mathring{g}_{\alpha\omega}p^{\omega\beta}, \qquad \mathring{p}_{\alpha\beta} = \mathring{g}_{\nu\beta}\mathring{p}_{\alpha\cdot}^{\cdot\nu}.$$

In an analogous manner, from the equation (14.14), we have

$$\mathring{\varepsilon}_{\alpha\cdot}^{\cdot\beta} = -\frac{\partial i}{\partial \mathring{\sigma}_{\cdot\beta}^{\alpha\cdot}} = -\frac{\partial \Psi}{\partial \mathring{\sigma}_{\cdot\beta}^{\alpha\cdot}},$$

$$\mathring{\varepsilon}^{\alpha\beta} = -\frac{\partial i}{\partial \mathring{\sigma}_{\alpha\beta}} = -\frac{\partial \Psi}{\partial \mathring{\sigma}_{\alpha\beta}}. \tag{14.19}$$

If the coordinate system in the space of the initial state is an orthogonal cartesian system, then the relationships (14.6) and (14.18), and correspondingly (14.14) and (14.19), coincide.

It is more difficult to solve the analogous problem for the transition to the components of tensors $\hat{\boldsymbol{P}}$ and $\mathscr{E}$ with different arrangements of indices.

The difficulty arises because the covariant and contravariant components $\hat{g}_{\alpha\beta}$ and $\hat{g}^{\alpha\beta}$ of tensor $\hat{\boldsymbol{G}}$ are variable in the particle, and these variations in accordance with formula (14.2) are related to the change of the components $\varepsilon_{\alpha\beta}$ of tensor $\mathscr{E}$.

We note that if the systems of bases $\hat{\mathfrak{I}}_i$ and $\mathfrak{I}_i$ coincide, then from the formulas (6.9) of Chapter II, we obtain

$$d\varepsilon_{ij} = (d\mathring{\varepsilon}_{ij})_{\xi i} = (d\hat{\varepsilon}_{ij})_{\xi i} = e_{ij}\,dt = \tfrac{1}{2}(\nabla_i v_j + \nabla_j v_i)\,dt\,, \qquad (14.20)$$

where v_1, v_2, v_3 are the covariant components of the velocity tensor in basis $\mathfrak{I}^i$ or $\hat{\mathfrak{I}}^i$

Let ε'_{ij} be the covariant components of tensor $\mathscr{E}$ in basis $\mathfrak{I}^i$. From (6.12) of Chapter II we have

$$d\varepsilon'_{ij} = d\varepsilon_{ij} - \varepsilon_{\lambda i}\nabla_j v^\lambda - \varepsilon_{j\lambda}\nabla_i v^\lambda\,, \qquad (14.21)$$

where the differentials $d\varepsilon'_{ij}$ are defined by the formula

$$(d\mathscr{E})_{\xi i} = d\varepsilon'_{ij}\mathfrak{I}^i\mathfrak{I}^j\,.$$

From (14.21) it follows that in the general case the following inequality is valid:

$$p^{\alpha\beta}\,d\varepsilon_{\alpha\beta} \neq p^{\alpha\beta}\,d\varepsilon'_{\alpha\beta}\,.$$

The components of tensor $\mathscr{E}$ with mixed and contravariant indices are defined by the relationships

$$\varepsilon_{\alpha\beta} = \hat{g}_{\alpha\omega}\hat{\varepsilon}^{\omega\cdot}_{\cdot\beta} = (2\varepsilon_{\alpha\omega} + \mathring{g}_{\alpha\omega})\,\hat{\varepsilon}^{\omega\cdot}_{\cdot\beta} \qquad (14.22)$$

and

$$\varepsilon_{\alpha\beta} = \hat{g}_{\alpha\lambda}\hat{g}_{\mu\beta}\hat{\varepsilon}^{\lambda\mu} = (2\varepsilon_{\alpha\lambda} + \mathring{g}_{\alpha\lambda})(2\varepsilon_{\mu\beta} + \mathring{g}_{\mu\beta})\,\hat{\varepsilon}^{\lambda\mu}\,. \qquad (14.23)$$

In the formulas (14.22) and (14.23), the covariant components $\varepsilon_{\alpha\beta}$ have the same values in the bases $\mathring{\mathfrak{I}}^i$ and $\hat{\mathfrak{I}}^i$.

After differentiating (14.22), we obtain

$$d\varepsilon_{\alpha\beta}(\delta^{\beta\cdot}_{\cdot\mu} - 2\hat{\varepsilon}^{\beta\cdot}_{\cdot\mu}) = \hat{g}_{\alpha\omega}\,d\hat{\varepsilon}^{\omega\cdot}_{\cdot\mu}\,,$$

whence

$$d\hat{\varepsilon}^{\lambda\cdot}_{\cdot\mu} = \hat{g}^{\lambda\alpha}\,d\varepsilon_{\alpha\beta}(\delta^{\beta\cdot}_{\cdot\mu} - 2\hat{\varepsilon}^{\beta\cdot}_{\cdot\mu})\,. \qquad (14.24)$$

In an analogous manner, after differentiating (14.23), we find

$$d\hat{\varepsilon}^{\lambda\mu} = \hat{g}^{\lambda\omega}\hat{g}^{\mu\nu}(\delta^{\alpha\cdot}_{\cdot\omega}\delta^{\beta\cdot}_{\cdot\nu} - 2\delta^{\alpha\cdot}_{\cdot\omega}\hat{\varepsilon}^{\beta\cdot}_{\cdot\nu} - 2\delta^{\beta\cdot}_{\cdot\nu}\hat{\varepsilon}^{\alpha\cdot}_{\cdot\omega})\,d\varepsilon_{\alpha\beta}\,. \qquad (14.25)$$

Let us now consider a certain function

$$\Phi(\mathring{g}_{\alpha\beta}, \varepsilon_{\alpha\beta}) = \Phi_1(\mathring{g}_{\alpha\beta}, \hat{\varepsilon}^{\alpha\cdot}_{\cdot\beta}) = \Phi_2(\mathring{g}_{\alpha\beta}, \hat{\varepsilon}^{\alpha\beta}).$$

On the basis of (14.24) and (14.25), we have

$$\Omega^{\alpha\beta} = \frac{\partial\Phi}{\partial\varepsilon_{\alpha\beta}} = \frac{\partial\Phi_1}{\partial\hat{\varepsilon}^{\lambda\cdot}_{\cdot\mu}}\frac{\partial\hat{\varepsilon}^{\lambda\cdot}_{\cdot\mu}}{\partial\varepsilon_{\alpha\beta}} = \frac{\partial\Phi_1}{\partial\hat{\varepsilon}^{\lambda\cdot}_{\cdot\mu}}\hat{g}^{\lambda\alpha}(\delta^{\beta\cdot}_{\cdot\mu} - 2\hat{\varepsilon}^{\beta\cdot}_{\cdot\mu})$$

and

$$\Omega^{\alpha\beta} = \frac{\partial\Phi}{\partial\varepsilon_{\alpha\beta}} = \frac{\partial\Phi_2}{\partial\hat{\varepsilon}^{\lambda\mu}}\frac{\partial\hat{\varepsilon}^{\lambda\mu}}{\partial\varepsilon_{\alpha\beta}} \tag{14.26}$$

$$= \frac{\partial\Phi_2}{\partial\hat{\varepsilon}^{\lambda\mu}}\hat{g}^{\lambda\omega}\hat{g}^{\mu\nu}(\delta^{\alpha\cdot}_{\cdot\omega}\delta^{\beta\cdot}_{\cdot\nu} - 2\delta^{\alpha\cdot}_{\cdot\omega}\hat{\varepsilon}^{\beta\cdot}_{\cdot\nu} - 2\delta^{\beta\cdot}_{\cdot\nu}\hat{\varepsilon}^{\alpha\cdot}_{\cdot\omega}).$$

Using these relationships and lowering the indices of the components using tensor $\hat{g}_{ij}$, the equations of state (14.6) can be written in the form

$$p^{\cdot\beta}_{\omega\cdot} = \rho(\delta^{\beta\cdot}_{\cdot\mu} - 2\varepsilon^{\beta\cdot}_{\cdot\mu})\left(\frac{\partial U}{\partial\varepsilon^{\omega\cdot}_{\cdot\mu}}\right)_S = \rho(\delta^{\beta\cdot}_{\cdot\mu} - 2\varepsilon^{\beta\cdot}_{\cdot\mu})\left(\frac{\partial\mathscr{F}}{\partial\varepsilon^{\omega\cdot}_{\cdot\mu}}\right)_T, \tag{14.27}$$

$$p_{\omega\nu} = \rho\left[\left(\frac{\partial U}{\partial\varepsilon^{\omega\nu}}\right)_S - 2\varepsilon^{\lambda\cdot}_{\cdot\nu}\left(\frac{\partial U}{\partial\varepsilon^{\omega\lambda}}\right)_S - 2\varepsilon^{\lambda\cdot}_{\cdot\omega}\left(\frac{\partial U}{\partial\varepsilon^{\lambda\nu}}\right)_S\right]$$

$$= \rho\left[\left(\frac{\partial\mathscr{F}}{\partial\varepsilon^{\omega\nu}}\right)_T - 2\varepsilon^{\lambda\cdot}_{\cdot\nu}\left(\frac{\partial\mathscr{F}}{\partial\varepsilon^{\omega\lambda}}\right)_T - 2\varepsilon^{\lambda\cdot}_{\cdot\omega}\left(\frac{\partial\mathscr{F}}{\partial\varepsilon^{\lambda\nu}}\right)_T\right]. \tag{14.28}$$

In formulas (14.27), it is understood that the arguments of the functions U and $\mathscr{F}$ are $\mathring{g}_{ij}$, $\varepsilon^{i\cdot}_{\cdot j}$, μ_i, and S or T, respectively, and in the formulas (14.28), the arguments are the following quantities: $\mathring{g}_{ij}$, ε^{ij}, μ_i, and S or T, respectively. If certain sets of parameters μ_i form the components of tensors, then in formulas (14.6), (14.27), and (14.28), it is assumed that these components are taken to the basis $\mathring{\mathbf{Э}}_i$.

Formulas (14.6), (14.27), and (14.28) are valid both in basis $\hat{\mathbf{Э}}_i$ and in basis $\mathbf{Э}_i$, because they have a tensor character, and for any coordinate transformation, in particular for a transformation from a moving Lagrangian coordinate system $\xi^1\xi^2\xi^3$ to a Eulerian one $x^1x^2x^3$, they preserve their form. Because of this, the circumflex symbol on the components of the tensors can be omitted.

In the general case for the elementary strain energy, the following formulas are valid:

$$\delta\mathscr{A}^i = -\frac{1}{\rho}p^{\alpha\beta}\delta\varepsilon_{\alpha\beta} = -\frac{1}{\rho}\mathring{p}^{\cdot\beta}_{\alpha\cdot}\,d\mathring{\varepsilon}^{\alpha\cdot}_{\cdot\beta} = -\frac{1}{\rho}\hat{p}^{\cdot\beta}_{\omega\cdot}q^{\mu\cdot}_{\cdot\beta}\,d\hat{\varepsilon}^{\omega\cdot}_{\cdot\mu},$$

where $g^{\mu\cdot}_{\cdot\beta}$ are matrix elements of the inverse of matrix $\|\delta^{\beta\cdot}_{\cdot\mu} - 2\hat{\varepsilon}^{\beta\cdot}_{\cdot\mu}\|$:

$$\|q^{\mu\cdot}_{\cdot\beta}\| = \|\delta^{\beta\cdot}_{\cdot\mu} - 2\hat{\varepsilon}^{\beta\cdot}_{\cdot\mu}\|^{-1}.$$

On the basis of formulas (14.6), (14.18), and (14.27), it follows that the following equations are fulfilled:

$$\delta\mathscr{A}^i = -\frac{\partial\mathscr{F}}{\partial\varepsilon_{\alpha\beta}}\delta\varepsilon_{\alpha\beta} = -\frac{\partial\mathscr{F}}{\partial\mathring{\varepsilon}^{\alpha\cdot}_{\cdot\beta}}\delta\mathring{\varepsilon}^{\alpha\cdot}_{\cdot\beta} = -\frac{\partial\mathscr{F}}{\partial\hat{\varepsilon}^{\alpha\cdot}_{\cdot\beta}}\delta\hat{\varepsilon}^{\alpha\cdot}_{\cdot\beta} = -(\delta\mathscr{F})_{T,\mu_i} = -(\delta U)_{S,\mu_i}.$$

However, we note that in utilizing the components of the deformation tensor $\varepsilon'_{\alpha\beta}$ and $\varepsilon'^{\alpha\cdot}_{\cdot\beta}$ in the stationary basis of the reference system $\mathit{Э}_i$, in general, by virtue of (14.21), we have the inequality

$$\frac{\partial\mathscr{F}}{\partial\varepsilon_{\alpha\beta}}\delta\varepsilon_{\alpha\beta} \neq \frac{\partial\mathscr{F}}{\partial\varepsilon'_{\alpha\beta}}\delta\varepsilon'_{\alpha\beta} \neq \frac{\partial\mathscr{F}}{\partial\varepsilon'^{\alpha\cdot}_{\cdot\beta}}\delta\varepsilon'^{\alpha\cdot}_{\cdot\beta}.$$

Equations (14.6), (14.8), and other equivalent relationships are formulated on the assumption that for reversible processes, the variations of the components of the deformation tensor $\delta\varepsilon_{\alpha\beta}$, the variations of the physical parameters $\delta\mu_i$ ($i = 1,2, \ldots, m$), and the temperature T or the entropy S are linearly independent. For reversible and linearly independent variations, cases are possible when the region $\mathscr{D}$ over which they vary is not arbitrary. In particular, at the point M defined by $\varepsilon_{\alpha\beta}$, μ_i, T, the permissible region $\mathscr{D}$ can be disposed on one side of some hypersurface which comes to an angular or conical point at M. In this case, the relationships formulated above will be satisfied only in a region $\mathscr{D}$ which is disposed to one side of this surface.

The equations considered above must be supplemented and modified both in the cases of irreversible processes and in the cases of reversible processes, when supplementary relationships are imposed on the enumerated variations. In particular, the number of equations (14.8) or (14.16) is reduced if some of the parameters μ_i are fixed by imposing the corresponding relationships.

If it is assumed that the medium is incompressible, then according to (4.17) of Chapter II the following condition is imposed on the variation of the deformation tensor:

$$g^{\alpha\beta}\delta\varepsilon_{\alpha\beta} = 0. \tag{14.29}$$

For an incompressible medium, the basic equations (14.5) can be rewritten in the form

$$\delta U = T\,\delta S + \frac{p^{\alpha\beta} + pg^{\alpha\beta}}{\rho}\delta\varepsilon_{\alpha\beta},$$
$$\delta\mathscr{F} = -S\,\delta T + \frac{p^{\alpha\beta} + p\hat{g}^{\alpha\beta}}{\rho}\delta\varepsilon_{\alpha\beta}. \tag{14.30}$$

In the relationships (14.30), one can set the coefficients for all the variations equal to zero, and the factor p is defined so that the incompressibility condition (14.29) is satisfied.

Thus, in the presence of relationship (14.29), the expressions (14.26), (14.27), and (14.28) are replaced by

$$p^{\alpha\beta} + pg^{\alpha\beta} = \rho\left(\frac{\partial U}{\partial \varepsilon_{\alpha\beta}}\right)_S = \rho\left(\frac{\partial \mathscr{F}}{\partial \varepsilon_{\alpha\beta}}\right)_T,$$

$$p_{\omega\cdot}^{\cdot\beta} + p\delta_{\omega\cdot}^{\cdot\beta} = \rho\,(\delta^{\beta\cdot}_{\cdot\mu} - 2\varepsilon^{\beta\cdot}_{\cdot\mu})\left(\frac{\partial U}{\partial \varepsilon^{\omega\cdot}_{\cdot\mu}}\right)_S = \rho\,(\delta^{\beta\cdot}_{\cdot\mu} - 2\varepsilon^{\beta\cdot}_{\cdot\mu})\left(\frac{\partial \mathscr{F}}{\partial \varepsilon^{\omega\cdot}_{\cdot\mu}}\right)_T,$$

and (14.31)

$$p_{\omega\nu} + pg_{\omega\nu} = \rho\left[\left(\frac{\partial U}{\partial \varepsilon^{\omega\nu}}\right)_S - 2\varepsilon^{\lambda\cdot}_{\cdot\nu}\left(\frac{\partial U}{\partial \varepsilon^{\omega\lambda}}\right)_S - 2\varepsilon^{\lambda\cdot}_{\cdot\omega}\left(\frac{\partial U}{\partial \varepsilon^{\lambda\nu}}\right)_S\right]$$

$$= \rho\left[\left(\frac{\partial \mathscr{F}}{\partial \varepsilon^{\omega\nu}}\right)_T - 2\varepsilon^{\lambda\cdot}_{\cdot\nu}\left(\frac{\partial \mathscr{F}}{\partial \varepsilon^{\omega\lambda}}\right)_T - 2\varepsilon^{\lambda\cdot}_{\cdot\omega}\left(\frac{\partial \mathscr{F}}{\partial \varepsilon^{\lambda\nu}}\right)_T\right].$$

For reversible processes, it is sufficient to specify one of the functions U or $\mathscr{F}$; this will define the stresses as functions of the deformation and temperature, or entropy.

If all the μ_i are constant and the process is isothermic, then the presence of experimental or theoretical data on the dependence of stress on the deformations for constant temperature T as given by

$$p^{\alpha\beta} = \rho f^{\alpha\beta}(\varepsilon_{ij}, T) = \rho\left(\frac{\partial \mathscr{F}}{\partial \varepsilon_{\alpha\beta}}\right)_{T=\text{const}} \tag{14.32}$$

is sufficient to close the systems of dynamic equations, equations of compatibility, and equtions of continuity.

However, the given functions $f^{\alpha\beta}(\varepsilon_{ij}, T)$, which must satisfy the condition

$$\frac{\partial f^{\alpha\beta}}{\partial \varepsilon_{ij}} = \frac{\partial f^{ij}}{\partial \varepsilon_{\alpha\beta}}, \tag{14.33}$$

are still not sufficient for the determination of the free energy $\mathscr{F}(\varepsilon_{ij}, T)$, the entropy $S(\varepsilon_{ij}, T)$, or the internal energy $U(\varepsilon_{ij}, S)$. It is necessary to know these functions in order to give a complete description of the thermal effects which reveal themselves during nonisothermic processes.

For the specific heat of unit mass $C_{\varepsilon_{\alpha\beta}}(\varepsilon_{\alpha\beta}, T)$, for a given deformation state defined by constant values $\varepsilon_{\alpha\beta}$, we have the equations

$$C_{\varepsilon_{\alpha\beta}} = \left(\frac{dQ}{dT}\right)_{\varepsilon_{\alpha\beta}} = \left(\frac{\partial U}{\partial T}\right)_{\varepsilon_{\alpha\beta}} = T\left(\frac{\partial S}{\partial T}\right)_{\varepsilon_{\alpha\beta}} = -T\left(\frac{\partial^2 \mathscr{F}}{\partial T^2}\right)_{\varepsilon_{\alpha\beta}}.$$

Also taking into account that

$$\left(\frac{\partial S}{\partial \varepsilon_{\alpha\beta}}\right)_T = -\frac{\partial^2 \mathscr{F}}{\partial T\,\partial \varepsilon_{\alpha\beta}} = -\frac{1}{\rho}\frac{\partial p^{\alpha\beta}}{\partial T}$$

and

$$\left(\frac{\partial U}{\partial \varepsilon_{\alpha\beta}}\right)_T = \left(\frac{\partial U}{\partial \varepsilon_{\alpha\beta}}\right)_S + \left(\frac{\partial U}{\partial S}\right)_{\varepsilon_{\alpha\beta}} \left(\frac{\partial S}{\partial \varepsilon_{\alpha\beta}}\right)_T \tag{14.34}$$

$$= \frac{1}{\rho}\left(p^{\alpha\beta} - T\frac{\partial p^{\alpha\beta}}{\partial T}\right) = -\frac{T^2}{\rho}\left[\frac{\partial (p^{\alpha\beta}/T)}{\partial T}\right]_{\varepsilon_{\alpha\beta}}$$

for the total differentials $dS(\varepsilon_{\alpha\beta}, T)$, $dU(\varepsilon_{\alpha\beta}, T)$, and $d\mathscr{F}(\varepsilon_{\alpha\beta}, T)$, we can write

$$dS = -\frac{1}{\rho}\frac{\partial p^{\alpha\beta}}{\partial T}\,d\varepsilon_{\alpha\beta} + \frac{C_{\varepsilon_{\alpha\beta}}}{T}\,dT,$$

$$dU = -\frac{T^2}{\rho}\frac{\partial (p^{\alpha\beta}/T)}{\partial T}\,d\varepsilon_{\alpha\beta} + C_{\varepsilon_{\alpha\beta}}\,dT, \tag{14.35}$$

$$d\mathscr{F} = d(U - TS) = \frac{p^{\alpha\beta}}{\rho}\,d\varepsilon_{\alpha\beta} - S\,dT.$$

Obviously the additional data on the specific heat $C_{\varepsilon_{\alpha\beta}}$ as functions of $\varepsilon_{\alpha\beta}$ and T must satisfy the integrability condition of expressions (14.35). It is not difficult to prove that the integrability conditions for all the formulas (14.35) will be satisfied if along with the equations (14.35) the following equations are fulfilled:

$$\frac{\partial C_{\varepsilon_{\alpha\beta}}}{\partial \varepsilon_{\alpha\beta}} = -T\frac{\partial^2 (p^{\alpha\beta}/\rho)}{\partial T^2}. \tag{14.36}$$

From the continuity equation, it follows that the density depends only on the components of the deformation tensor and consequently not on temperature. Therefore the density in (14.36) can be taken into the derivative with respect to temperature.

In the experimental determination of the thermodynamic functions, relationships (14.33) and (14.36) can be used for the reduction or verification of the experiments.

From (14.35), the entropy can be determined to within the accuracy of the additive constant S_0, the internal energy within the accuracy of the additive constant U_0, and the free energy to within the accuracy of the linear function of temperature $U_0 - S_0T$. It is obvious that the constants U_0 and S_0 are not important in purely thermoelastic problems. They can become important in taking into account physico-mechanical processes defined by parameters μ_i on which these constants may depend.

We shall further express formulas for $\mathscr{F}$ and S in terms of $U(\varepsilon_{\alpha\beta}, T)$, and express a certain arbitrary function only as a function of the components of deformation $S^*(\varepsilon_{\alpha\beta})$. We have

$$S = -\left(\frac{\partial \mathscr{F}}{\partial T}\right)_{\varepsilon_{\alpha\beta}} \quad \text{and} \quad U = \mathscr{F} - T\left(\frac{\partial \mathscr{F}}{\partial T}\right)_{\varepsilon_{\alpha\beta}}.$$

Whence we find

$$\mathscr{F}(\varepsilon_{\alpha\beta}, T) = -\int_{T_0}^{T} \frac{U}{T^2}\, dT - S^*(\varepsilon_{\alpha\beta})\, T + C$$

and

$$S(\varepsilon_{\alpha\beta}, T) = \frac{U}{T} + \int_{T_0}^{T} \frac{U}{T^2}\, dT + S^*(\varepsilon_{\alpha\beta}).$$

The lower limit of integration T_0 can correspond to some arbitrary fixed temperature, and C is a constant of integration. The function $S^*(\varepsilon_{\alpha\beta})$ can easily be determined from the known relationship between the stresses and deformations at temperature T_0.

Indeed we have

$$\left(\frac{p^{\alpha\beta}}{\rho}\right)_{T=T_0} = \left(\frac{\partial \mathscr{F}}{\partial \varepsilon_{\alpha\beta}}\right)_{T_0} = -\,T_0 \frac{\partial S^*(\varepsilon_{\alpha\beta})}{\partial \varepsilon_{\alpha\beta}},$$

whence $S^*(\varepsilon_{\alpha\beta})$ is determined within the accuracy of the additive constant.

We will now consider certain important processes.

Along with the processes mentioned above for constant $\varepsilon_{\alpha\beta}$ corresponding to some unchanged deformation state, we shall consider processes for constant $p^{\alpha\beta}$, that is, for a constant tensor $\hat{\boldsymbol{P}}$ in the particle. (If $p^{\alpha\beta} = \text{const}$, then the components $\hat{p}^{\alpha\cdot}_{\cdot\beta}$, $\hat{p}_{\alpha\beta}$, $p'^{\alpha\cdot}_{\cdot\beta}$ and $p'_{\alpha\beta}$ can be variable.)

We denote the specific heat at constant stress by $C_{p^{\alpha\beta}}$. We have

$$dQ = C_{p^{\alpha\beta}}\, dT = C_{\varepsilon_{\alpha\beta}}\, dT + \left[\left(\frac{\partial U}{\partial \varepsilon_{\alpha\beta}}\right)_T - \frac{p^{\alpha\beta}}{\rho}\right](d\varepsilon_{\alpha\beta})_{p^{\alpha\beta}}.$$

Whence, using (14.34), we obtain

$$C_{p^{\alpha\beta}} - C_{\varepsilon_{\alpha\beta}} = -\frac{T}{\rho}\left(\frac{\partial p^{\alpha\beta}}{\partial T}\right)_{\varepsilon_{\alpha\beta}} \left(\frac{\partial \varepsilon_{\alpha\beta}}{\partial T}\right)_{p^{\alpha\beta}}. \tag{14.37}$$

This formula, established for the general case of an anisotropic medium, is a generalization of formula (8.13b) for an ideally compressible medium.

The relationships between $p_{\alpha\beta}/\rho$, $\varepsilon_{\alpha\beta}$, and T are defined by the formulas (14.6), and are independent of the nature of the process, but the values of $\varepsilon_{\alpha\beta}$ and T at a particular moment of time do depend on the process.

For example, for an isothermic process $T = \text{const}$ and $\Delta S \neq 0$, for an adiabatic process $S = \text{const}$ and $\Delta T \neq 0$, and therefore for the given deformation, the corresponding stresses in the isothermic and the adiabatic cases will be different.

For the corresponding stresses at the same deformation, the following formulas are valid:

$$\left(\frac{p^{\alpha\beta}}{\rho}\right)_{\text{isotherm}} = \frac{\partial \mathscr{F}^0}{\partial \varepsilon_{\alpha\beta}}, \qquad \text{where} \qquad \mathscr{F}^0 = \mathscr{F}(\varepsilon_{\alpha\beta}, T_0),$$

$$\left(\frac{p^{\alpha\beta}}{\rho}\right)_{\text{adiab}} = \frac{\partial \mathscr{F}}{\partial \varepsilon_{\alpha\beta}}, \qquad \text{where} \qquad \mathscr{F} = \mathscr{F}(\varepsilon_{\alpha\beta}, T),$$

where $T \neq T_0$.

The quantity T is defined by the equation

$$S(\varepsilon_{\alpha\beta}, T) = S(\varepsilon_{\alpha\beta}, T_0).$$

Let the deformed state defined by components $\mathring{\varepsilon}_{\alpha\beta}$ correspond to the common origin for the two processes in question.

If $\Delta T = T - T_0$ is small, then the following relationships are valid:

$$\left(\frac{p^{\alpha\beta}}{\rho}\right)_{\text{adiab}} - \left(\frac{p^{\alpha\beta}}{\rho}\right)_{\text{isotherm}} = \frac{\partial^2 \mathscr{F}}{\partial \varepsilon_{\alpha\beta}\, \partial T} \Delta T = \frac{\Delta T}{\rho} \left(\frac{\partial p^{\alpha\beta}}{\partial T}\right)_{\mathring{\varepsilon}_{\alpha\beta}, T_0}. \qquad (14.38)$$

Let us consider the case of a small deformation for adiabatic and isothermal processes about a given finite form of deformation state. From the adiabatic conditions, the small increments ΔT and $d\varepsilon_{\alpha\beta}$ are related by the expression

$$\frac{\partial S}{\partial T} \Delta T + \frac{\partial S}{\partial \varepsilon_{\lambda\mu}} d\varepsilon_{\lambda\mu} = 0.$$

Further, because

$$\left(\frac{\partial S}{\partial T}\right)_{\varepsilon_{\lambda\mu}} = \frac{1}{T}\left(\frac{\partial U}{\partial T}\right)_{\varepsilon_{\lambda\mu}} = \frac{C_{\varepsilon_{\alpha\beta}}}{T}$$

and

$$\frac{\partial S}{\partial \varepsilon_{\lambda\mu}} = -\frac{\partial^2 \mathscr{F}}{\partial T\, \partial \varepsilon_{\lambda\mu}} = -\frac{1}{\rho}\left(\frac{\partial p^{\lambda\mu}}{\partial T}\right)_{\varepsilon_{\alpha\beta}},$$

we obtain the formula

$$p^{\alpha\beta}_{\text{adiab}} - p^{\alpha\beta}_{\text{isotherm}} = \frac{T}{\rho C_{\varepsilon_{\alpha\beta}}} \left(\frac{\partial p^{\alpha\beta}}{\partial T}\right)_{\mathring{\varepsilon}_{ij}} \left(\frac{\partial p^{\lambda\mu}}{\partial T}\right)_{\mathring{\varepsilon}_{ij}} d\varepsilon_{\lambda\mu}. \qquad (14.39)$$

This defines the small difference $p^{\alpha\beta}_{\text{adiab}} - p^{\alpha\beta}_{\text{isotherm}}$ in terms of the small deformation $d\varepsilon_{\lambda\mu}$.

For an elastic medium, the free energy calculated for unit mass depends on the covariant components of the tensors $\mathring{g}_{\alpha\beta}$, $\varepsilon_{\alpha\beta}$, and on the physical properties of the medium, which can be characterized by tensors given for the basis $\mathring{\mathfrak{Э}}_i$ defined in the space of the initial states.

The invariant scalar quantity $\mathscr{F}$ is a function of temperature and of the joint invariants of the deformation tensor and of the tensors characterizing the physical nature of the medium.

The symmetry properties of crystals are defined by a special form of tensor giving the physical properties of the body.

In many cases, the function $\mathscr{F}$ can be a holomorphic function $\Delta T = T - T_0$ and $\varepsilon_{\alpha\beta}$. If, as the initial state corresponding to $\varepsilon_{\alpha\beta} = 0$, we choose an equilibrium state at temperature T_0 with no internal stresses, it is obvious that the series representation of $\mathscr{F}$ in terms of ΔT and $\varepsilon_{\alpha\beta}$ must begin with second-order terms, i.e.,

$$\mathscr{F} = k^{\alpha\beta\gamma\delta}\varepsilon_{\alpha\beta}\varepsilon_{\gamma\delta} + \kappa^{\alpha\beta}\varepsilon_{\alpha\beta}\Delta T + \chi(\Delta T)^2 + \Omega\,, \tag{14.40}$$

where Ω represents terms of smaller order of magnitude.

For small deformations, we can limit ourselves to the first quadratic terms of this series.

Using this, from formulas (14.6) using the approximate substitution of density ρ by a constant value ρ_0 (which produces an error of the smaller order of magnitude), we obtain the general case of Hooke's law when the contravariant components of the stress tensor are linear functions of the covariant components of the deformation tensor.

From these relationships, and "juggling" the indices, one can relate the components of the stress tensors and the deformation tensor with different forms of indices and in various bases. These relationships are approximately linear for small deformations.

If Hooke's law does apply, the properties of special cases of anisotropy* are the symmetry properties of two physical tensors with contravariant components $k^{\alpha\beta\gamma\delta}$ and $\kappa^{\alpha\beta}$.

In the theory developed above, the initial undeformed state was one in which there were no internal stresses. We will now show that any finite form of deformed state of equilibrium with internal stresses different from zero can be chosen as the original state for the calculation of finite deformations and for the determination of the corresponding internal stresses

* Details about the symmetry properties of crystals and expressions for the free energy (14.40) for crystals of various types can be found in L. D. Landau and E. M. Lifshitz [18]

and the new external forces, which become zero in the new initial state.†

Let us consider three bases in the given Lagrangian coordinate system ξ^1, ξ^2, ξ^3: the initial basis $\mathring{\vartheta}_i$, in which there are no stresses; the basis $\overset{*}{\vartheta}_i$, corresponding to equilibrium under external mass forces $\overset{*}{\boldsymbol{F}} = \overset{*}{F}{}^{\alpha}\overset{*}{\vartheta}_\alpha$ with internal stresses $\overset{*}{\boldsymbol{P}} = \overset{*}{p}{}^{\alpha\beta}\overset{*}{\vartheta}_\alpha\overset{*}{\vartheta}_\beta$, while the corresponding finite deformation is defined by the tensor $\overset{*}{\mathscr{E}} = \overset{*}{\varepsilon}_{\alpha\beta}\mathring{\vartheta}^\alpha\mathring{\vartheta}^\beta$; and the basis $\hat{\vartheta}_i$, corresponding to an arbitrary deformed state of the moving medium under external mass forces $\hat{\boldsymbol{F}} = \hat{F}^\alpha\hat{\vartheta}_\alpha$ with internal stresses defined by the tensor $\hat{\boldsymbol{P}} = \hat{p}^{\alpha\beta}\hat{\vartheta}_\alpha\hat{\vartheta}_\beta$.

Let $\hat{\mathscr{E}} = \hat{\varepsilon}_{\alpha\beta}\mathring{\vartheta}^\alpha\mathring{\vartheta}^\beta$ be the deformation tensor of a medium moving relative to the initial state $\mathring{\vartheta}_i$.

The finite deformation of the medium moving relative to a fixed basis $\overset{*}{\vartheta}_i$ is given by the tensor

$$\mathscr{E} = \varepsilon_{\alpha\beta}\overset{*}{\vartheta}{}^\alpha\overset{*}{\vartheta}{}^\beta, \qquad \text{where} \qquad \varepsilon_{\alpha\beta} = \hat{\varepsilon}_{\alpha\beta} - \overset{*}{\varepsilon}_{\alpha\beta}.$$

We will now show that the choice of $\overset{*}{\vartheta}_i$ as the initial state allows all the equations of the theory of elasticity to be fulfilled if the mass forces are defined by the relationships

$$\boldsymbol{F} = F^\alpha\hat{\vartheta}_\alpha = (\hat{F}^\alpha - \overset{*}{F}{}^\alpha)\hat{\vartheta}_\alpha + \frac{\overset{*}{p}{}^{\gamma\beta}}{\overset{*}{\rho}}(\hat{\Gamma}^\alpha_{\gamma\beta} - \overset{*}{\Gamma}{}^\alpha_{\gamma\beta})\hat{\vartheta}_\alpha, \tag{14.41}$$

where $\overset{*}{\Gamma}{}^\alpha_{\gamma\beta}$ and $\hat{\Gamma}^\alpha_{\gamma\beta}$ are the Christoffel symbols in the corresponding coordinate systems (the difference $\hat{\Gamma}^\alpha_{\gamma\beta} - \overset{*}{\Gamma}{}^\alpha_{\gamma\beta}$ may be different from zero if the deformation defined by tensor $\mathscr{E}$ is inhomogeneous), while the tensor of the internal stresses is written in the form

$$\boldsymbol{P} = p^{\alpha\beta}\hat{\vartheta}_\alpha\hat{\vartheta}_\beta, \qquad \text{where} \qquad \frac{p^{\alpha\beta}}{\rho} = \frac{\hat{p}^{\alpha\beta}}{\rho} - \frac{\overset{*}{p}{}^{\alpha\beta}}{\overset{*}{\rho}}. \tag{14 42}$$

The free energy in the new definition of the original state takes the form

$$\mathscr{F}_1 = \mathscr{F}(\mathring{g}_{\alpha\beta}, \varepsilon_{\alpha\beta} + \overset{*}{\varepsilon}_{\alpha\beta}, T) - \frac{\overset{*}{p}{}^{\alpha\beta}}{\overset{*}{\rho}}(\varepsilon_{\alpha\beta} + \overset{*}{\varepsilon}_{\alpha\beta}), \tag{14.43}$$

where $\mathscr{F}(\mathring{g}_{\alpha\beta}, \hat{\varepsilon}_{\alpha\beta}, T)$ is defined for the original unstressed initial state.

In fact we have the following equations of motion and equilibrium:

$$\overset{*}{\rho}\sqrt{\overset{*}{g}}(\hat{F}^\alpha - a^\alpha)\hat{\vartheta}_\alpha + \frac{\partial\overset{*}{\rho}\sqrt{\overset{*}{g}}(\hat{p}^{\alpha\beta}/\rho)\hat{\vartheta}_\alpha}{\partial\xi^\beta} = 0, \tag{14.44}$$

$$\overset{*}{\rho}\sqrt{\overset{*}{g}}\overset{*}{F}{}^\alpha\overset{*}{\vartheta}_\alpha + \frac{\partial\overset{*}{\rho}\sqrt{\overset{*}{g}}(\overset{*}{p}{}^{\alpha\beta}/\overset{*}{\rho})\overset{*}{\vartheta}_\alpha}{\partial\xi^\beta} = 0. \tag{14.45}$$

† This question has been investigated in more detail by V. D. Bondar.

In these equations we utilize the equality

$$\rho_0\sqrt{g_0} = \rho^*\sqrt{g^*}.$$

The vector equation (14.45) can be rewritten in the form of three scalar equations:

$$\rho^*\sqrt{g^*}\mathring{F}^\alpha + \frac{\partial\rho^*\sqrt{g^*}(\mathring{p}^{\alpha\beta}/\rho^*)}{\partial\xi^\beta} + \rho^*\sqrt{g^*}\frac{\mathring{p}^{\gamma\beta}}{\rho^*}(\mathring{\Gamma}^{*\alpha}_{\gamma\beta} - \hat{\Gamma}^\alpha_{\gamma\beta}) + \rho^*\sqrt{g^*}\frac{\mathring{p}^{\gamma\beta}}{\rho^*}\hat{\Gamma}^\alpha_{\gamma\beta} = 0$$

$$(\alpha = 1, 2, 3).$$

These equations are equivalent to one vector equation in the basis $\hat{\mathfrak{I}}_i$:

$$\rho^*\sqrt{g^*}\left[\mathring{F}^\alpha - \frac{\mathring{p}^{\gamma\beta}}{\rho^*}(\hat{\Gamma}^\alpha_{\gamma\beta} - \mathring{\Gamma}^{*\alpha}_{\gamma\beta})\right]\hat{\mathfrak{I}}_\alpha + \frac{\partial\rho^*\sqrt{g^*}(\mathring{p}^{\alpha\beta}/\rho^*)\hat{\mathfrak{I}}_\alpha}{\partial\xi^\beta} = 0. \tag{14.46}$$

Taking the difference of equations (14.44) and (14.46) and using the notations of (14.41) and (14.42), we obtain instead of (14.44) a new analogous equation with a changed reference origin for the components of the stress and deformation tensors:

$$\rho^*\sqrt{g^*}(\boldsymbol{F} - \boldsymbol{a}) + \frac{\partial\rho^*\sqrt{g^*}(p^{\alpha\beta}/\rho)\hat{\mathfrak{I}}_\alpha}{\partial\xi^\beta} = 0. \tag{14.47}$$

In this equation, the external mass forces are defined by the formula (14.41). It is curious to note that for an inhomogeneous deformation with respect to the new initial state, it is necessary to introduce the mass forces which are due to the presence of the original internal stresses. Such mass forces sometimes have to be introduced also in the case of an infinitesimal deformation defined by the tensor $\mathscr{E} = \varepsilon_{\alpha\beta}\hat{\mathfrak{I}}^\alpha\hat{\mathfrak{I}}^\beta$.

The equation of heat transfer

$$d\mathscr{F}(\mathring{g}_{ij}, \hat{\varepsilon}_{ij}, T) + S\,dT - \frac{\hat{p}^{\alpha\beta}}{\rho}d\hat{\varepsilon}_{\alpha\beta} = 0$$

can be rewritten as

$$d\left[\mathscr{F}(\mathring{g}_{ij}, \varepsilon_{ij} + \mathring{\varepsilon}_{ij}, T) - \frac{\mathring{p}^{\alpha\beta}}{\rho^*}(\varepsilon_{\alpha\beta} + \mathring{\varepsilon}_{\alpha\beta})\right] + S\,dT - \frac{p^{\alpha\beta}}{\rho}d\varepsilon_{\alpha\beta} = 0.$$

Hence we conclude that the expression (14.43) is valid. The tensors $\mathring{\varepsilon}_{ij}\hat{\mathfrak{I}}_i\hat{\mathfrak{I}}_j$, and $(\mathring{p}^{ij}/\rho^*)\hat{\mathfrak{I}}_i\hat{\mathfrak{I}}_j$ play the role of constant parametric tensors in equation (14.43).

In the case of small deformations, when a geometrically linear theory may be used (while dynamic theories are as a rule nonlinear), all the preceding final conclusions are simplified because the bases $\mathfrak{I}_i$, $\mathring{\mathfrak{I}}_i$, and $\hat{\mathfrak{I}}_i$ are coincident.

15. Thermoelastic isotropic media

A medium is called isotropic if the constants and parameters characterizing its physical-mechanical nature can be taken as scalars or as tensor functions of the fundamental metric tensor $\mathring{G}$ only.

Let us consider the relationships between the components of the deformation and stress tensors with mixed indices. We have

$$
\begin{aligned}
\mathring{\varepsilon}^{i\cdot}_{\cdot j} &= \mathring{g}^{i\alpha}\varepsilon_{\alpha j}\,, \\
\varepsilon^{i\cdot}_{\cdot j} &= g^{i\alpha}\varepsilon_{\alpha j}\,, \\
\mathring{p}^{\cdot i}_{j\cdot} &= \mathring{g}_{j\alpha}p^{\alpha i}\,, \\
p^{\cdot i}_{j\cdot} &= g_{j\alpha}p^{\alpha i}\,.
\end{aligned}
\tag{15.1}
$$

Any scalar invariants of the tensors $\mathscr{E}$ and G can be considered as functions of the invariants $\mathscr{I}_1$, $\mathscr{I}_2$, and $\mathscr{I}_3$ defined by the formulas

$$
\begin{aligned}
\mathscr{I}_1 &= \varepsilon^{\alpha\cdot}_{\cdot\alpha} = \varepsilon_1 + \varepsilon_2 + \varepsilon_3\,, \\
\mathscr{I}_2 &= \tfrac{1}{2}\left(\varepsilon^{\alpha\cdot}_{\cdot\alpha}\varepsilon^{\beta\cdot}_{\cdot\beta} - \varepsilon^{\alpha\cdot}_{\cdot\beta}\varepsilon^{\beta\cdot}_{\cdot\alpha}\right) = \varepsilon_1\varepsilon_2 + \varepsilon_1\varepsilon_3 + \varepsilon_2\varepsilon_3\,, \\
\mathscr{I}_3 &= \begin{vmatrix} \varepsilon^{1\cdot}_{\cdot 1} & \varepsilon^{1\cdot}_{\cdot 2} & \varepsilon^{1\cdot}_{\cdot 3} \\ \varepsilon^{2\cdot}_{\cdot 1} & \varepsilon^{2\cdot}_{\cdot 2} & \varepsilon^{2\cdot}_{\cdot 3} \\ \varepsilon^{3\cdot}_{\cdot 1} & \varepsilon^{3\cdot}_{\cdot 2} & \varepsilon^{3\cdot}_{\cdot 3} \end{vmatrix} = \varepsilon_1\varepsilon_2\varepsilon_3\,.
\end{aligned}
\tag{15.2}
$$

Consequently, the free energy of a particle, calculated for unit mass, can be considered as a function of the type

$$
\mathscr{F} = \mathscr{F}(\mathring{\mathscr{I}}_1, \mathring{\mathscr{I}}_2, \mathring{\mathscr{I}}_3, T, \mu_1, \mu_2, \dots, \mu_n, \xi^1, \xi^2, \xi^3)
$$

or

$$
\mathscr{F} = \mathscr{F}(\hat{\mathscr{I}}_1, \hat{\mathscr{I}}_2, \hat{\mathscr{I}}_3, T, \mu_1, \mu_2, \dots, \mu_n, \xi^1, \xi^2, \xi^3)\,.
\tag{15.3}
$$

The invariants $\mathring{\mathscr{I}}_1, \mathring{\mathscr{I}}_2, \mathring{\mathscr{I}}_3$ of tensor $\mathring{\mathscr{E}}$ and

$$
\hat{\mathscr{I}}_1 = \mathscr{I}_1, \qquad \hat{\mathscr{I}}_2 = \mathscr{I}_2, \qquad \hat{\mathscr{I}}_3 = \mathscr{I}_3
$$

of tensor $\mathring{\mathscr{E}}$ are related by formula (4.15) of Chapter II; $\mu_1, \mu_2, \dots, \mu_n$ are scalar physical parameters. An isotropic medium is homogeneous if the Lagrangian coordinates ξ_1, ξ_2, ξ_3 of the points in the medium do not appear in the free energy expression (15.3).

The equations of state (14.6) and (14.27) for an isotropic medium reduce to a simplified form. In order to derive these equations, we shall note the following auxiliary formula derived from (15.2):

$$\frac{\partial \mathcal{I}_1}{\partial \varepsilon^{j\cdot}_{\cdot i}} = \delta^{i\cdot}_{\cdot j}\,,$$

$$\frac{\partial \mathcal{I}_2}{\partial \varepsilon^{j\cdot}_{\cdot i}} = \mathcal{I}_1 \delta^{i\cdot}_{\cdot j} - \varepsilon^{i\cdot}_{\cdot j}, \tag{15.4}$$

$$\frac{\partial \mathcal{I}_3}{\partial \varepsilon^{j\cdot}_{\cdot i}} = \varepsilon^{i\cdot}_{\cdot \alpha}\varepsilon^{\alpha\cdot}_{\cdot j} - \mathcal{I}_1 \varepsilon^{i\cdot}_{\cdot j} + \mathcal{I}_2 \delta^{i\cdot}_{\cdot j} = \mathcal{I}_3 (\varepsilon^{-1})^{i\cdot}_{\cdot j},$$

where $(\varepsilon^{-1})^{i\cdot}_{\cdot j}$ is an element of the inverse matrix $\|\varepsilon^{i\cdot}_{\cdot j}\|^{-1}$. Recalling (15.4) and using (14.6) and (14.27) ,we obtain

$$\frac{1}{\rho}\mathring{p}^{\cdot i}_{j\cdot} = \frac{\partial \mathcal{F}}{\partial \mathring{\varepsilon}^{j\cdot}_{\cdot i}} = \left(\frac{\partial \mathcal{F}}{\partial \mathring{\mathcal{I}}_1} + \mathring{\mathcal{I}}_1 \frac{\partial \mathcal{F}}{\partial \mathring{\mathcal{I}}_2} + \mathring{\mathcal{I}}_2 \frac{\partial \mathcal{F}}{\partial \mathring{\mathcal{I}}_3}\right)\delta^{\cdot i}_{j\cdot}$$
$$- \left(\frac{\partial \mathcal{F}}{\partial \mathring{\mathcal{I}}_2} + \mathring{\mathcal{I}}_1 \frac{\partial \mathcal{F}}{\partial \mathring{\mathcal{I}}_3}\right)\mathring{\varepsilon}^{i\cdot}_{\cdot j} + \frac{\partial \mathcal{F}}{\partial \mathring{\mathcal{I}}_3}\mathring{\varepsilon}^{i\cdot}_{\cdot \alpha}\mathring{\varepsilon}^{\alpha\cdot}_{\cdot j} \tag{15.5}$$

and

$$\frac{1}{\rho}p^{\cdot i}_{j\cdot} = \frac{\partial \mathcal{F}}{\partial \varepsilon^{j\cdot}_{\cdot \mu}}(\delta^{i\cdot}_{\cdot \mu} - 2\varepsilon^{i\cdot}_{\cdot \mu}) = \left(\frac{\partial \mathcal{F}}{\partial \mathcal{I}_1} + \mathcal{I}_1 \frac{\partial \mathcal{F}}{\partial \mathcal{I}_2} + \mathcal{I}_2 \frac{\partial \mathcal{F}}{\partial \mathcal{I}_3} - 2\mathcal{I}_3 \frac{\partial \mathcal{F}}{\partial \mathcal{I}_3}\right)\delta^{i\cdot}_{\cdot j}$$
$$- \left(2\frac{\partial \mathcal{F}}{\partial \mathcal{I}_1} + \frac{\partial \mathcal{F}}{\partial \mathcal{I}_2} + 2\mathcal{I}_1 \frac{\partial \mathcal{F}}{\partial \mathcal{I}_2} + \mathcal{I}_1 \frac{\partial \mathcal{F}}{\partial \mathcal{I}_3}\right)\varepsilon^{i\cdot}_{\cdot j} + \left(\frac{\partial \mathcal{F}}{\partial \mathcal{I}_3} + 2\frac{\partial \mathcal{F}}{\partial \mathcal{I}_2}\right)\varepsilon^{i\cdot}_{\cdot \alpha}\varepsilon^{\alpha\cdot}_{\cdot j}. \tag{15.6}$$

It is obvious that in the space of the initial states the principal axes of tensors $\mathring{\mathscr{E}}$ and $\mathring{\boldsymbol{P}} = p^{\alpha\beta}\mathring{\boldsymbol{\vartheta}}_\alpha\mathring{\boldsymbol{\vartheta}}_\beta$ are coincident, and in the space of the deformed state, the principal axes of the tensors $\hat{\mathscr{E}}$ and $\hat{\boldsymbol{P}} = p^{\alpha\beta}\hat{\boldsymbol{\vartheta}}_\alpha\hat{\boldsymbol{\vartheta}}_\beta$ are coincident.

On the basis of general theory and formulas (7.16) and (7.17) of Chapter I, equations (15.5) and (15.6) can be represented in the form

$$\frac{\mathring{p}_i}{\rho} = \mathring{\sigma}_i = \frac{\partial \mathcal{F}}{\partial \mathring{\varepsilon}_i}, \qquad \frac{p_i}{\rho} = \sigma_i = (1 - 2\varepsilon_i)\frac{\partial \mathcal{F}}{\partial \varepsilon_i},$$

and

$$\frac{p^{\cdot i}_{j\cdot}}{\rho} = \sigma^{\cdot i}_{j\cdot} = \frac{\partial \mathcal{F}}{\partial h^{j\cdot}_{\cdot i}}, \tag{15.7}$$

where $h^{j\cdot}_{\cdot j}$ are the components of the Hencky tensor, defined in terms of the tensor $\mathscr{E}$ according to the formula

$$\boldsymbol{H} = -\ln\sqrt{\boldsymbol{G} - 2\mathscr{E}}.$$

The elementary work of the internal forces taking into account the solutions of relationships (14.24) with respect to $d\varepsilon_{\alpha\beta}$, can be written in the following forms:

$$\delta\mathscr{A}^i = -\frac{p^{\alpha\beta}}{\rho}\delta\varepsilon_{\alpha\beta} = -\frac{\mathring{p}_{\alpha\cdot}^{\cdot\beta}}{\rho}\delta\mathring{\varepsilon}_{\cdot\beta}^{\alpha\cdot} = -\frac{1}{\rho}\hat{p}_{\omega\cdot}^{\cdot\beta}\hat{q}_{\cdot\beta}^{\mu\cdot}\delta\hat{\varepsilon}_{\cdot\mu}^{\omega\cdot}. \tag{15.8}$$

Here $\hat{q}_{\cdot j}^{i\cdot}$ represents the elements of the matrix which is the inverse of the matrix $\|\delta_{\cdot j}^{i\cdot} - 2\hat{\varepsilon}_{\cdot j}^{i\cdot}\|$.

We will choose a coordinate system which at a given instant coincides for the point in question with the principal axes of the deformation tensor $\hat{\mathscr{E}}$. In this system of coordinates, we have the matrix equation

$$\begin{Vmatrix} (1-2\hat{\varepsilon}_1) & 0 & 0 \\ 0 & (1-2\hat{\varepsilon}_2) & 0 \\ 0 & 0 & (1-2\hat{\varepsilon}_3) \end{Vmatrix}^{-1} = \begin{Vmatrix} \dfrac{1}{1-2\hat{\varepsilon}_1} & 0 & 0 \\ 0 & \dfrac{1}{1-2\hat{\varepsilon}_2} & 0 \\ 0 & 0 & \dfrac{1}{1-2\hat{\varepsilon}_3} \end{Vmatrix}. \tag{15.9}$$

Along the principal axes of tensors $\mathring{\boldsymbol{P}}$ and $\hat{\boldsymbol{P}}$ in an isotropic body for the elementary work of the internal forces, using relationships (15.8) and (15.9), the following formulas can be written:

$$\delta\mathscr{A}^i = -\frac{1}{\rho}[\mathring{p}_1\,\delta\mathring{\varepsilon}_{\cdot 1}^{1\cdot} + \mathring{p}_2\,\delta\mathring{\varepsilon}_{\cdot 2}^{2\cdot} + \mathring{p}_3\,\delta\mathring{\varepsilon}_{\cdot 3}^{3\cdot}]$$

$$= -\frac{1}{\rho}\left[\frac{\hat{p}_1\,d\hat{\varepsilon}_{\cdot 1}^{1\cdot}}{1-2\hat{\varepsilon}_1} + \frac{\hat{p}_2\,d\hat{\varepsilon}_{\cdot 2}^{2\cdot}}{1-2\hat{\varepsilon}_2} + \frac{\hat{p}_3\,d\hat{\varepsilon}_{\cdot 3}^{3\cdot}}{1-2\hat{\varepsilon}_3}\right]. \tag{15.10}$$

In order to obtain the final formula, we note that the following are valid with an accuracy of the smallest order of magnitude:

$$\delta\mathring{\varepsilon}_{\cdot i}^{i\cdot} = \delta\mathring{\varepsilon}_i \quad \text{and} \quad \delta\hat{\varepsilon}_{\cdot i}^{i\cdot} = \delta\hat{\varepsilon}_i,$$

because for any symmetrical tensor in the principal coordinate system the following analogous relationship is valid:

$$\delta T_{\cdot i}^{i\cdot} = \delta T_i. \tag{15.11}$$

In fact, let T_i and $T_i - \delta T_i$ be the roots of the characteristic equations, which along the principal axes of tensor $\mathfrak{T} = T_{\cdot j}^{i\cdot}\mathfrak{Z}_i\mathfrak{Z}^j$ have the forms

$$\begin{vmatrix} \lambda - T_1 & 0 & 0 \\ 0 & \lambda - T_2 & 0 \\ 0 & 0 & \lambda - T_3 \end{vmatrix} = 0$$

and

$$\begin{vmatrix} \lambda - T_1 - \delta T^{1\cdot}_{\cdot 1} & -\delta T^{1\cdot}_{\cdot 2} & -\delta T^{1\cdot}_{\cdot 3} \\ -\delta T^{2\cdot}_{\cdot 1} & \lambda - T_2 - \delta T^{2\cdot}_{\cdot 2} & -\delta T^{2\cdot}_{\cdot 3} \\ -\delta T^{3\cdot}_{\cdot 1} & -\delta T^{3\cdot}_{\cdot 2} & \lambda - T_3 - \delta T^{3\cdot}_{\cdot 3} \end{vmatrix}$$

$$= (\lambda - T_1 - \delta T^{1\cdot}_{\cdot 1})(\lambda - T_2 - \delta T^{2\cdot}_{\cdot 2})(\lambda - T_3 - \delta T^{3\cdot}_{\cdot 3}) + \Delta, \qquad (15.12)$$

where Δ is an infinitesimal of the second order of magnitude.

If the principal components T_1, T_2, T_3 of tensor $\mathfrak{T}$ differ from one another, then from (15.12) it follows that for the roots of this equation, the following equations are valid:

$$\lambda_i = T_i + \delta T_i = T_i + \delta T^{i\cdot}_{\cdot i} + \Delta_i,$$

whence (15.11) follows as being true because the quantities Δ_i are infinitesimals of the second order [see also formula (7.12) of Chapter II].

If some of the terms in T_1, T_2, and T_3, are equal, then the principal axes of tensor $\mathfrak{T}$ are not uniquely defined.

The principal axes are defined so that in this case as well, the equations (15.11) would be fulfilled.* Thus, on the basis of (15.11), (15.10) can be written as

$$\delta\mathscr{A}^i = -\frac{1}{\rho}\sum_i \mathring{p}_i\,\delta\mathring{\varepsilon}_i = -\frac{1}{\rho}\sum_i \frac{\hat{p}_i\,\delta\hat{\varepsilon}_i}{1 - 2\hat{\varepsilon}_i}. \qquad (15.13)$$

The principal components $\mathring{\varepsilon}_i$ and $\hat{\varepsilon}_i$ are related by the formulas†

$$\mathring{\varepsilon}_i = \frac{\hat{\varepsilon}_i}{1 - 2\hat{\varepsilon}_i}, \qquad \text{hence} \qquad \delta\mathring{\varepsilon}_i = \frac{\delta\hat{\varepsilon}_i}{(1 - 2\hat{\varepsilon}_i)^2}.$$

Using the later relationship, we obtain from (15.13)

$$\hat{p}_i = \mathring{p}_i(1 - 2\hat{\varepsilon}_i) \qquad \text{or} \qquad \mathring{p}_i(1 + \mathring{E}_i) = \hat{p}_i(1 - \hat{E}_i), \qquad (15.14)$$

because

$$1 - 2\hat{\varepsilon}_i = (1 - \hat{E}_i)^2 \qquad \text{and} \qquad 1 + \mathring{E}_i = \frac{1}{1 - \hat{E}_i}.$$

On the basis of (15.7) it follows that

$$\delta\mathscr{A}^i = -\sum_i \frac{\partial\mathscr{F}}{\partial\mathring{\varepsilon}_i}\delta\mathring{\varepsilon}_i = -\sum_i \frac{\partial\mathscr{F}}{\partial\hat{\varepsilon}_i}\delta\hat{\varepsilon}_i = -\sum_i \frac{\partial\mathscr{F}}{\partial h_i}\delta h_i$$

$$= -\frac{\partial\mathscr{F}}{\partial h^{\cdot\beta}_{\alpha\cdot}}\delta h^{\cdot\beta}_{\alpha\cdot} = -\sigma^{\alpha\cdot}_{\cdot\beta}\,dh^{\cdot\beta}_{\alpha\cdot} = -(\delta\mathscr{F})_{T,\mu_i}. \qquad (15.15)$$

---

* We arrive at this conclusion by using a limiting transition from the case of unequal T_1, T_2, T_3 to the case when the roots of the characteristic equation are multiples.

† See formulas (4.14) of Chapter II.

Using this relationship, instead of an equation of state of the form (15.6), we obtain an equation of state solved with respect to $h^{i\cdot}_{\cdot j}$ with independent variables $\sigma^{i\cdot}_{\cdot j}$, T, and μ_i.

In fact, using (15.15), the equation of heat flow for reversible processes is

$$\delta\Psi^* = \frac{\partial\Psi^*}{\partial T}\delta T + \frac{\partial\Psi^*}{\partial\sigma^{\alpha\cdot}_{\cdot\beta}}\delta\sigma^{\alpha\cdot}_{\cdot\beta} + \frac{\partial\Psi^*}{\partial\mu_i}\delta\mu_i = -S\,\delta T - h^{\cdot\beta}_{\alpha\cdot}\,d\sigma^{\alpha\cdot}_{\cdot\beta}, \qquad (15.16)$$

where the potential Ψ^* is defined by the formula

$$\Psi^* = \mathscr{F} - h^{\cdot\beta}_{\alpha\cdot}\sigma^{\alpha\cdot}_{\cdot\beta}. \qquad (15.17)$$

From (15.16) it follows that the equation of state can be written as

$$h^{\cdot j}_{i\cdot} = -\frac{\partial\Psi^*}{\partial\sigma^{i\cdot}_{\cdot j}}. \qquad (15.18)$$

Let us consider some particular cases.*

We suppose that the free energy depends only on density ρ and temperature T. From the continuity equation (3.5), it follows that the free energy can be represented as a function of the following arguments T and $\chi = 1 - 2\hat{\mathscr{I}}_1 + 4\hat{\mathscr{I}}_2 - 8\hat{\mathscr{I}}_3$:

$$\mathscr{F} = \mathscr{F}(\chi, T).$$

In this case, formulas (15.6) reduce to the form

$$p^{\cdot i}_{j\cdot} = -2\frac{\partial\mathscr{F}}{\partial\chi}\chi\rho\delta^{\cdot i}_{j\cdot}.$$

Therefore, in the space of the deformed medium, the stress tensor is spherical. Such a medium can be considered as an ideal compressible liquid. In this case, the stress tensor $\mathring{\boldsymbol{P}}$ is not spherical in the space of the initial states (see § 4, Chapter II).

From (15.6) it is obvious that the necessary and sufficient conditions for a quasilinear relationship between tensors $\hat{\boldsymbol{P}}$ and $\hat{\mathscr{E}}$ are given by the expression

$$\frac{\partial\mathscr{F}}{\partial\hat{\mathscr{I}}_3} + 2\frac{\partial\mathscr{F}}{\partial\hat{\mathscr{I}}_2} = 0. \qquad (15.19)$$

The general solution of an equation with partial derivatives (15.19) can be written in the form

$$\mathscr{F}(\hat{\mathscr{I}}_1, 2\hat{\mathscr{I}}_3 - \hat{\mathscr{I}}_2, T)$$

---

* D. D. Ivlev considered the peculiarities of models of isotropic elastic bodies, for which the surface $\mathscr{F}$ = const is piecewise-continuous [11].

or in the following equivalent forms:

$$\mathscr{F} = \mathscr{F}(\hat{\mathscr{I}}_1, 1 - 2\hat{\mathscr{I}}_1 + 4\hat{\mathscr{I}}_2 - 8\hat{\mathscr{I}}_3, T)$$

and (15.20)

$$\mathscr{F} = \mathscr{F}(\hat{\mathscr{I}}_1, \rho, T).$$

From (15.6) and (15.20), it follows that

$$p_{j\cdot}^{\cdot i} = \left(\rho \frac{\partial \mathscr{F}}{\partial \mathscr{I}_1} - \rho^2 \frac{\partial \mathscr{F}}{\partial \rho}\right) \delta_{j\cdot}^{\cdot i} - 2\rho \frac{\partial \mathscr{F}}{\partial \mathscr{I}_1} \varepsilon_{\cdot j}^{i\cdot}. \tag{15.21}$$

If (15.21) is linear and homogeneous with respect to $\varepsilon_{\cdot j}^{i\cdot}$, then we must have

$$\rho\left(\frac{\partial \mathscr{F}}{\partial \mathscr{F}_1} - \rho \frac{\partial \mathscr{F}}{\partial \rho}\right) = \mathscr{A}\mathscr{I}_1, \qquad \rho \frac{\partial \mathscr{F}}{\partial \mathscr{I}_1} = \mathscr{B},$$

whence

$$\frac{\partial \mathscr{F}}{\partial \rho} = \frac{B - \mathscr{A}\mathscr{I}_1}{\rho^2}, \qquad \frac{\partial \mathscr{F}}{\partial \mathscr{I}_1} = \frac{\mathscr{B}}{\rho},$$

where $\mathscr{A}$ and $\mathscr{B}$ are scalar constants which can depend on temperature.

From the conditions of integrability, we obtain $\mathscr{A} = \mathscr{B}$, and therefore for function $\mathscr{F}$ we have

$$\mathscr{F} = \frac{\mathscr{A}(\mathscr{I}_1 - 1)}{\rho} + f(T). \tag{15.22}$$

The form of the functions (15.20) and (15.22) for the free energy defines the necessary and sufficient condition for the quasilinear and, correspondingly, linear relationships between tensors $\boldsymbol{P}$ and $\mathscr{E}$ in bases $\hat{\mathbf{Э}}_i$ or $\mathbf{Э}_i$.

From (15.15) it follows that the necessary and sufficient condition for quasilinearity for tensors $\mathring{\boldsymbol{P}}$ and $\mathring{\mathscr{E}}$ in bases $\mathring{\mathbf{Э}}_i$ are

$$\frac{\partial \mathscr{F}}{\partial \mathring{\mathscr{I}}_3} = 0, \qquad \mathscr{F} = \mathscr{F}(\mathring{\mathscr{I}}_1, \mathring{\mathscr{I}}_2, T), \tag{15.23}$$

and the condition for a homogeneous linear relationship* between tensors $(1/\rho)\mathring{\boldsymbol{P}}$ and $\mathring{\mathscr{E}}$ is

$$\mathscr{F} = \tfrac{1}{2}(a + b)\mathring{\mathscr{I}}_1^2 - a\mathring{\mathscr{I}}_2 + c, \tag{15.24}$$

where a, b, and c are scalar constants or functions of temperature.

---

* Because, in the general case $\mathring{\mathscr{I}}_3 \neq 0$, and the density depends on $\mathring{\mathscr{I}}_3$, it is obvious that using an exact nonlinear theory, a homogeneous linear relationship between $\mathring{\boldsymbol{P}}$ and $\mathring{\mathscr{E}}$ cannot be found for an elastic isotropic medium. The properties of the free energy of dynamically nonlinear isotropic bodies, for which Hooke's law applies for simple tension, for plane stresses or plane strain states, are dealt with by D. D. Ivlev [10] and M. E. Eglit [42].

It is obvious that the condition for the quasilinear relationships (15.20) and (15.23) are not the same. The quasilinear expression (15.21) is equivalent to some essentially nonlinear relationship between the components $\mathring{p}_{j\cdot}^{\cdot i}$ and $\mathring{\varepsilon}_{\cdot j}^{i\cdot}$, and conversely.

For infinitesimal deformations, (15.22) and (15.24) coincide within the accuracy of the second-order magnitude if

$$a = -\frac{2\mathscr{A}}{\rho_0} \quad \text{and} \quad b = \frac{4\mathscr{A}}{\rho_0}.$$

The quasilinear relationship (15.21) can be rewritten as an expression which shows explicitly the similarity between the stress deviators and deformation in the form

$$t_{j\cdot}^{\cdot i} = -2\rho \frac{\partial \mathscr{F}}{\partial \mathscr{I}_1} d_{\cdot j}^{i\cdot}, \tag{15.25}$$

where

$$t_{j\cdot}^{\cdot i} = p_{j\cdot}^{\cdot i} - \tfrac{1}{3}\mathscr{P}_1 \delta_{j\cdot}^{\cdot i} \quad \text{and} \quad d_{j\cdot}^{\cdot i} = \varepsilon_{\cdot j}^{i\cdot} - \tfrac{1}{3}\mathscr{I}_1 \delta_{\cdot j}^{i\cdot},$$

while $\mathscr{P}_1$ is the first invariant of the stress tensor for which according to (15.21) the following formula is valid:

$$\mathscr{P}_1 = p_{\alpha\cdot}^{\cdot\alpha} = (3 - 2\mathscr{I}_1)\rho \frac{\partial \mathscr{F}}{\partial \mathscr{I}_1} - 3\rho^2 \frac{\partial \mathscr{F}}{\partial \rho}. \tag{15.26}$$

$\varDelta_p$ and $\varDelta_\varepsilon$ indicate the second invariants of the deviators of the stress and deformation tensors defined by the formulas

$$\varDelta_p = \tfrac{1}{2}(t_{\alpha\cdot}^{\cdot\alpha} t_{\beta\cdot}^{\cdot\beta} - t_{\alpha\cdot}^{\cdot\beta} t_{\cdot\beta}^{\alpha\cdot}) = \mathscr{P}_2 - \tfrac{1}{3}\mathscr{P}_1^2$$

and

$$\varDelta_\varepsilon = \tfrac{1}{2}(d_{\cdot\alpha}^{\alpha\cdot} d_{\cdot\beta}^{\beta\cdot} - d_{\cdot\beta}^{\alpha\cdot} d_{\cdot\alpha}^{\beta\cdot}) = \mathscr{I}_2 - \tfrac{1}{3}\mathscr{I}_1^2, \tag{12.57}$$

where $\mathscr{P}_1$ and $\mathscr{P}_2$ are invariants of $\boldsymbol{P}$, and $\mathscr{I}_1$ and $\mathscr{I}_2$ the invariants of $\boldsymbol{\mathscr{E}}$.

From (15.25) it is obvious that

$$t_{j\cdot}^{\cdot i} = \sqrt{\frac{\varDelta_p}{\varDelta_\varepsilon}}\, d_{\cdot j}^{i\cdot} \quad \text{and} \quad \frac{\varDelta_p}{\varDelta_\varepsilon} = 4\rho^2 \left(\frac{\partial \mathscr{F}}{\partial \mathscr{I}_1}\right)^2. \tag{15.28}$$

From (15.28) and (15.26) we have

$$\frac{\partial \mathscr{F}}{\partial \mathscr{I}_1} = -\frac{1}{2\rho}\sqrt{\frac{\varDelta_p}{\varDelta_\varepsilon}} \quad \text{and} \quad \frac{\partial \mathscr{F}}{\partial \rho} = -\frac{\mathscr{P}_1}{3\rho^2} - \frac{3 - 2\mathscr{I}_1}{6\rho^2}\sqrt{\frac{\varDelta_p}{\varDelta_\varepsilon}}. \tag{15.29}$$

The condition of integrability (15.29) used to find the function $\mathscr{F}(\rho, \mathscr{I}_1, T)$ leads to the relationship

$$(3 - 2\mathscr{I}_1)\frac{\partial}{\partial \mathscr{I}_1}\sqrt{\frac{\varDelta_p}{\varDelta_\varepsilon}} - 3\rho \frac{\partial}{\partial \rho}\sqrt{\frac{\varDelta_p}{\varDelta_\varepsilon}} + \sqrt{\frac{\varDelta_p}{\varDelta_\varepsilon}} = -\frac{1}{3\rho^2}\frac{\partial \mathscr{P}_1}{\partial \mathscr{I}_1}. \tag{15.30}$$

This equation can be used for the experimental determination of the relationship between Δ_p and Δ_ε.

If we suppose that the first invariant of the stress tensor depends only on density ρ, equation (15.30) reduces to a partial differential equation with respect to ρ and $\mathscr{I}_1$ of the quantity $\sqrt{\Delta_p/\Delta_\varepsilon}$. Integrating this equation, we obtain

$$\sqrt{\frac{\Delta_p}{\Delta_\varepsilon}} = \sqrt{\mathscr{I}_1 - \tfrac{3}{2}}\, f\left(\frac{\rho^{\frac{1}{3}}}{\sqrt{\mathscr{I}_1 - \tfrac{3}{2}}}\right), \tag{15.31}$$

where f is an arbitrary function of its argument.

16. Notes on mechanical models with irreversible processes

Irreversible effects in continuum mechanics must be considered in connection with processes accompanied by an essential dissipation of mechanical energy, with structural changes of the physical-mechanical constitution due to the internal nonequilibrium of the particles of the continuum. This is also true in ideal media with reversible processes, but with irreversible losses at strong step discontinuities on certain surfaces (separating the regions of continuity) through which the particles of the medium are passing.

On the basis of the equation of mechanics and the first and second laws of thermodynamics, it has been shown that in order to describe reversible processes and motions in media with the aid of a closed system of equations, it is sufficient to specify in the function of corresponding variables, in addition to the external conditions, only one of the functions, for instance, the internal energy of the particle U calculated for a unit mass, or the free energy $\mathscr{F}$ of unit mass, or the thermal capacity $i = U - \sigma^{\alpha\beta}\varepsilon_{\alpha\beta}$, or the thermodynamic potential $\psi = \mathscr{F} - \sigma^{\alpha\beta}\varepsilon_{\alpha\beta}$.

These functions can be determined by considering the statistics of kinetic molecular models, by using experimental data, or by some hypotheses following as conclusions from the equations of motion. In certain cases, the determination of the functions of the state can be carried out using a combination of all three methods. To describe irreversible phenomena, a knowledge of one of these functions is not sufficient, because one must also know the supplementary equations that regulate the kinetics of the nonequilibrium variations of the defining parameters, or the supplementary laws that define the internal stresses due to mechanical energy losses occurring as a result of an entropy rise of the particles. The general methods mentioned above for the determination of the thermodynamic state functions for continuum models can also be used to derive the kinetic equations and to establish the properties of the internal stresses [7]. The thermodynamic investigation of irreversible processes must be carried out not only when the thermal effects are related to substantial temperature variations. Cases are possible when the temperature is constant in general (an isothermal process), and the thermodynamic effects are nevertheless important because, apart from temperature, other thermodynamic parameters of state can vary and strongly affect the process in question. In thermodynamic theories which involve entropy, the temperature also has to be taken into consideration, even if the temperature variations are insignificant, and consequently at first glance one would be tempted to omit temperature from the discussion.

In practice, for the study of different motions and the problems of strength of various structures, it is necessary to consider and describe a large number of effects which are due to thermodynamic irreversibility. Each fixed theoretical continuum model can describe only a particular class of phenomena applicable only to certain real bodies. It is important, however, that the physical and mechanical properties defining the theoretical model always obey the basic principles and laws of mechanics and thermodynamics.

Physical-mechanical problems also exist in which the solutions are obtained independently of the nature of the body, or in which they depend only on certain specific properties of the medium. In this case, an approximate correspondence between the model of the medium used and the real body is not always essential. However, for a detailed description of the behavior of the real body with the aid of a theoretical model, it is essential to have correspondence between the real body and the model.

The properties and behavior, under different conditions, of various structures such as steel, copper, glass, soil, rubber, polymers, liquids, gases, plasma, etc., are extremely diverse. Therefore many models are needed to describe the mechanical, and as a rule, thermodynamic irreversible macroscopic phenomena in such varied substances. In connection with this, many specific general problems on the relationship between theory and experiment arise, and also questions, important from the theoretical and practical points of view, on the methods of constructing the corresponding models.

As a rule, experimental data and theoretical hypotheses need supplementary treatment and simplification while retaining only the basic properties for a given class of phenomena, while innumerable properties of secondary importance are eliminated; these secondary properties are unimportant from the point of view of problems for whose solution the model is introduced.

The pecularities and properties which have to be studied are very diverse. The properties of bodies of practical importance are the subject of many contemporary investigations. Such properties (connected with thermodynamic irreversibility) as plasticity accompanied by residual deformations, hardening, the Bauschinger effect of plastic anisotropy, and such effects as creep and relaxation, fatigue of materials of different types, etc., still constitute a field for experimentation and introduction of new theoretical models of continua.

We will discuss in more detail below the theoretical models which are used to describe the phenomenon of plasticity in solids.

We shall now deal briefly with the basic experimental data on the plastic properties of metals.

Figure 10 shows a typical diagram for a simple tension or compression along the axis of a cylindrical steel specimen with external forces acting axially on the flat ends of the cylinder.

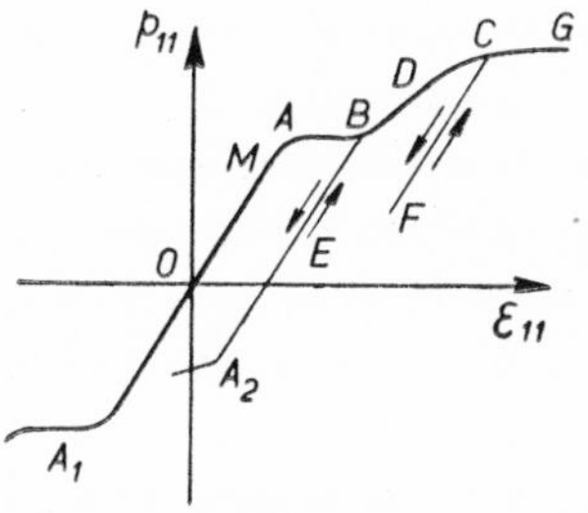

Figure 10

The abscissas are the components ε_{11} of the tensile strain along the axis of the cylinder (below we shall assume that the deformation can be taken as geometrically small) and the ordinates are the components p_{11} of the stress on an elementary area perpendicular to the axis of the cylinder.

The first section of the diagram A_1OA is nearly a straight line and represents a reversible elastic deformation for loading and unloading for the motion of an imaginary point M along this section.

If the external tensile load is increased, the representing point M passes through point A (see Fig. 10), which means that the function $p_{11} = f(\varepsilon_{11})$ becomes abruptly nonlinear, and irreversible plastic effects occur. After the point M passes through A to positions B or C and the subsequent removal of the external load (that is, gradual reduction of tension), as p_{11} decreases, the representing point will move along other curves BE or CF, which are almost straight lines whose slopes are approximately the same as OA. After unloading up to points E or F, and applying a new load, the representing point will move practically along the same curves EB or FC, and after reaching points B or C, further loading will cause the point to continue along the basic curve OAG.

If the external load is removed beginning with position B, then p_{11} becomes zero, and if the extension $\varepsilon_{11} = \varepsilon_{11}^p$ is different from zero, residual deformations will occur. The appearance of residual deformations is a characteristic property of plastic bodies. In plastic deformations the difference between the functions $p_{11} = f(\varepsilon_{11})$ for loading and unloading is also extremely important. The point A defines the origin of plastic properties in a body related to the residual deformation after unloading. The point A defines the elastic limit. It is essential that after plastic deformations occur, the elastic limit changes, and the points B and C also become the new elastic limits after applying the corresponding loads at subsequent unloading and new loadings.

The increase in the elastic limit is characterized by the curve $ABCG$ and is called a hardening effect. In the diagram in Fig. 10, the hardening effect in the region AB is not great, but it is stronger in the following region BDC.

The elastic limit, the plastic deformations, and the hardening effect must be considered both in tension and in compression. The elastic limit of the compression curve for the original state is designated by A_1. After an extension as far as point B with a subsequent unloading and compression, the compressive elastic limit on the elastic deformation curve BEA_2 is defined by point A_2. The magnitudes of the limiting values p_{11} at points A_1 and A_2 are generally different. The effect of the change of the compressive elastic limit after a preliminary elongation beyond the elastic limit is called the Bauschinger effect.

The quantitative behavior of curve $p_{11} = f(\varepsilon_{11})$ for simple tension is strongly dependent on the physical nature of the material. However, the indicated characteristic qualitative behavior of the plastic properties is typical of many materials.

In certain cases, along a large section of the curve AB the hardening due to plasticity is insignificant. In other cases, hardening beyond the elastic limit is always significant, and consequently, the sloping region of the hardening curve is practically nonexistent.

The indicated features also appear in other types of stress and deformation, for example, pure shear deformations, and in particular, in torsion of circular cylindrical pipe; in this case, an analogous relationship between the shearing stresses and the component of the deformation tensor characterizing the angle of twist is obtained.

The construction of mechanical models of plastic media involves two basic problems: (1) the generalization for arbitrary deformations of the condition of loading and the elastic limit, and (2) the establishment of the laws which define the growth of the residual plastic deformation.

Thus, for each element of a body for an arbitrary change in the external loading, a generalized diagram for a simple uniaxial tension, or for a simple torsion, etc., as presented in Fig. 10, must be given.

We shall mention two basic types of proposed continuum models in which the plastic properties of the body are considered.

1. The model of an ideal elastically plastic or rigidly plastic medium in which hardening and Bauschinger effects are not considered. These media can be obtained from the generalized ideal diagram developed by Prandtl for a uniaxial tension, as shown in Fig. 11.

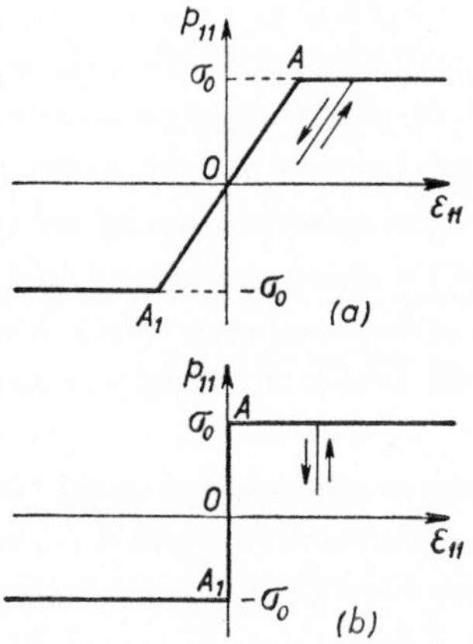

Figure 11

Figure 11(a) corresponds to an ideal elastically plastic medium. For a tensile stress less than some constant value σ_0, or a compressive stress more than σ_0, the material behaves as an ideally elastic body. In Fig. 11(b), for stresses less than the constant value σ_0 the deformation is neglected, and so the medium can be considered as an absolutely rigid solid. After increasing the stress to σ_0, flow is possible with a deformation increasing without limit for a constant stress σ_0. In this case, the actual deformations are not defined by the stresses as is the case for liquids.

2. Models of plastic bodies in which hardening and the resulting changes in elastic limit are considered. The basic problem of the mechanics of plastic bodies consists of establishing the general laws of plasticity for arbitrary deformations. Certain models of plastic bodies will be considered in the following sections.

17. Plastic, elastic, and complete deformations

In the following paragraphs we shall consider the fundamental ideas involved in contemporary theories of plasticity. On the basis of the general concepts formulated above, we can introduce into these theories in an explicit form the elements of thermodynamics and give generalizations for the case of finite deformations.

For the construction of models of plastic bodies in the case of finite deformations, and for the generalization of the developed theories of plasticity for arbitrarily small deformations in the case of arbitrary finite deformations, one has to consider certain additional geometric and kinematic methods of describing finite deformations, which can be elastic, residual plastic, or complete deformations [42].

We shall also consider using the theory of finite deformations, the stress tensor, and the means used to introduce individual infinitesimal increments of the deformation with time, and stress tensor components for a given small particle.

We shall consider a Lagrangian coordinate system $\xi^1\xi^2\xi^3$ frozen into the medium, and shall consider three positions of this continuum, defined with respect to a basic stationary coordinate system $x^1x^2x^3$ with basis vector $\boldsymbol{\text{Э}}_i$:

1. The initial position, in which there are no stresses, and with basis vectors in system $\mathring{\boldsymbol{\text{Э}}}_i$.

2. A position of complete deformation with basis vectors in system $\hat{\boldsymbol{\text{Э}}}_i$.

3. A new starting position with a residual plastic deformation and basis vectors $\overset{*}{\boldsymbol{\text{Э}}}_i$. This position corresponds to the state of a given small particle in which internal stresses are absent.

For the length of some small segment composed of one and the same points of the continuum in the three positions, we have

$$\begin{aligned} ds_0^2 &= \mathring{g}_{ij}\, d\xi^i\, d\xi^j, & \mathring{g}_{ij} &= (\mathring{\boldsymbol{\text{Э}}}_i, \mathring{\boldsymbol{\text{Э}}}_j), \\ d\overset{*}{s}{}_0^2 &= \overset{*}{g}_{ij}\, d\xi^i\, d\xi^j, & \overset{*}{g}_{ij} &= (\overset{*}{\boldsymbol{\text{Э}}}_i, \overset{*}{\boldsymbol{\text{Э}}}_j), \\ ds^2 &= \hat{g}_{ij}\, d\xi^i\, d\xi^j, & \hat{g}_{ij} &= (\hat{\boldsymbol{\text{Э}}}_i, \hat{\boldsymbol{\text{Э}}}_j). \end{aligned} \tag{17.1}$$

Because of these three fundamental forms, it is possible to consider the tensors for one and the same coordinates ξ^i in the three spaces* corresponding to the different bases $\mathring{\boldsymbol{\text{Э}}}_i$, $\overset{*}{\boldsymbol{\text{Э}}}_j$, and $\hat{\boldsymbol{\text{Э}}}_i$.

---

* In the consideration of the array of particles forming a finite body, the space corresponding to the quadratic forms ds_0^2 and ds^2 is Euclidean.

The space corresponding to the quadratic form $d\overset{*}{s}{}_0^2$ is generally non-Euclidean. This is due to the fact that after the plastic deformation of a finite body and after the removal of all external forces, one obtains a state of the body in which the internal stresses exist and in which elastic deformations are different from zero.

The equations of the law of motion of the points of the continuum

$$x^i = x^i(\xi^1, \xi^2, \xi^3, t) \tag{17.2}$$

define the coordinate transformation corresponding to a transition from basis $\hat{\mathbf{Э}}_i$ to basis $\mathbf{Э}_i$.

Therefore we can write

$$ds^2 = \hat{g}_{ij}\, d\xi^i\, d\xi^j = g_{ij}\, dx^i\, dx^j, \tag{17.3}$$

and consequently the tensors in $\mathbf{Э}_i$ and $\hat{\mathbf{Э}}_i$ can be considered as tensors in one and the same space.

In considering the actual process of deformation, each position can be defined as corresponding to some position corresponding to a basis $\overset{*}{\mathbf{Э}}_i$, in accordance with a conceived position or one determined by a specified manner of unloading.

We introduce three pairs of finite deformation tensors.

1. Plastic deformation tensors:

$$\mathscr{E}^p = \varepsilon^p_{ij} \overset{*}{\mathbf{Э}}{}^i \overset{*}{\mathbf{Э}}{}^j, \qquad \mathring{\mathscr{E}}^p = \varepsilon^p_{ij} \mathring{\mathbf{Э}}{}^i \mathring{\mathbf{Э}}{}^j, \tag{17.4}$$

where

$$\varepsilon^p_{ij} = \tfrac{1}{2}(\overset{*}{g}_{ij} - \mathring{g}_{ij}).$$

2. Elastic deformation tensors:

$$\mathscr{E}^e = \varepsilon^e_{ij} \hat{\mathbf{Э}}{}^i \hat{\mathbf{Э}}{}^j, \qquad \overset{*}{\mathscr{E}}{}^e = \varepsilon^e_{ij} \overset{*}{\mathbf{Э}}{}^i \overset{*}{\mathbf{Э}}{}^j, \tag{17.5}$$

where

$$\varepsilon^e_{ij} = \tfrac{1}{2}(\hat{g}_{ij} - \overset{*}{g}_{ij}).$$

3. Complete deformation tensors:

$$\mathscr{E} = \varepsilon_{ij} \hat{\mathbf{Э}}{}^i \hat{\mathbf{Э}}{}^j, \qquad \mathring{\mathscr{E}} = \varepsilon_{ij} \mathring{\mathbf{Э}}{}^i \mathring{\mathbf{Э}}{}^j, \tag{17.6}$$

where

$$\varepsilon_{ij} = \tfrac{1}{2}(\hat{g}_{ij} - \mathring{g}_{ij}).$$

For these different tensors, taken in different corresponding spaces, the following formula is fulfilled:

$$\varepsilon_{ij} = \varepsilon^e_{ij} + \varepsilon^p_{ij}. \tag{17.7}$$

Formula (17.7) is true in any Lagrangian coordinate system ξ^i, but in this equation the components of the tensors defined by the formula (17.4), (17.5), and (17.6) are taken for different bases.

Formula (17.7) can be considered as a tensor equation in one and the same base if along with the tensors (17.4) $\mathring{\mathscr{E}}^p$ and $\mathscr{E}^p$ we introduce the tensor $\hat{\mathscr{E}}^p = \varepsilon^p_{ij} \hat{\mathbf{Э}}{}^i \hat{\mathbf{Э}}{}^j$ ($\mathscr{E} = \mathscr{E}^e + \hat{\mathscr{E}}^p$). For the three tensors $\mathring{\mathscr{E}}^p$, $\mathscr{E}^p$, $\hat{\mathscr{E}}^p$, taken in different bases $\mathring{\ni}^i$, $\overset{*}{\ni}^i$, $\hat{\ni}^i$, there is one and the same system of covariant components definable by the residual plastic deformation. Tensors $\mathscr{E}^p$ and $\hat{\mathscr{E}}^p$ are defined by the same components and different vectors taken for bases which depend not only on the deformation, but also on the notation of the particles as a solid body.

Equation (17.7) is valid only for purely covariant components.

For components with mixed indices or for the contravariant components, we can write on the basis of (17.4) through (17.7) the following formulas:

$$\mathring{\varepsilon}^{i\cdot}_{\cdot j} = \mathring{\varepsilon}^{pi\cdot}_{\cdot j} + \mathring{g}^{i\omega}\varepsilon^{e}_{\omega j} = \mathring{\varepsilon}^{pi\cdot}_{\cdot j} + \mathring{g}^{i\omega}\cdot\overset{*}{g}_{\omega\alpha}\overset{*}{\varepsilon}^{e\alpha\cdot}_{\cdot j} = \mathring{\varepsilon}^{pi}_{\cdot j} + \mathring{g}^{i\omega}(\mathring{g}_{\omega\alpha} + 2\mathring{\varepsilon}^{p}_{\omega\alpha})\,\overset{*}{\varepsilon}^{e\alpha\cdot}_{\cdot j}$$

or

$$\mathring{\varepsilon}^{i\cdot}_{\cdot j} = \mathring{\varepsilon}^{pi\cdot}_{\cdot j} + \overset{*}{\varepsilon}^{ei\cdot}_{\cdot j} + 2\mathring{\varepsilon}^{pi\cdot}_{\cdot\alpha}\overset{*}{\varepsilon}^{e\alpha\cdot}_{\cdot j}. \qquad (17.8)$$

Whence we obtain the matrix identity

$$\|\mathring{\varepsilon}^{i\cdot}_{\cdot j}\| = \|\mathring{\varepsilon}^{pi\cdot}_{\cdot j}\| + \|\overset{*}{\varepsilon}^{ei\cdot}_{\cdot j}\| + 2\,\|\mathring{\varepsilon}^{pi\cdot}_{\cdot\alpha}\|\cdot\|\overset{*}{\varepsilon}^{e\alpha\cdot}_{\cdot j}\|.$$

In an analogous manner it is easy to obtain formulas giving the relationship between the pure contravariant components of the deformation tensors:

$$\mathring{\varepsilon}^{ij}_{\cdot\cdot} = \mathring{\varepsilon}^{pij}_{\cdot\cdot} + \overset{*}{\varepsilon}^{eij}_{\cdot\cdot} + 2\mathring{g}_{km}(\mathring{\varepsilon}^{pjm}_{\cdot\cdot}\overset{*}{\varepsilon}^{eik}_{\cdot\cdot} + \mathring{\varepsilon}^{pik}_{\cdot\cdot}\overset{*}{\varepsilon}^{ejm}_{\cdot\cdot}) + 4\mathring{g}_{rm}\mathring{g}_{kn}\mathring{\varepsilon}^{pim}_{\cdot\cdot}\mathring{\varepsilon}^{pjn}_{\cdot\cdot}\overset{*}{\varepsilon}^{erk}_{\cdot\cdot}. \qquad (17.9)$$

For a fixed particle, the increments in time dt of the covariant components of the complete deformation tensors ε'_{ij} and ε_{ij}:

$$\mathscr{E} = \varepsilon'_{ij}\ni^i\ni^j = \varepsilon_{ij}\hat{\ni}^i\hat{\ni}^j$$

according to formula (14.21) will be related by the expression

$$d\varepsilon'_{ij} = d\varepsilon_{ij} - \varepsilon_{\lambda j}\nabla_i v^\lambda\,dt - \varepsilon_{i\lambda}\nabla_j v^\lambda\,dt = \tfrac{1}{2}(\mathring{g}_{\lambda j}\nabla_i v^\lambda + \mathring{g}_{i\lambda}\nabla_j v^\lambda)\,dt,$$

where

$$d\varepsilon'_{ij} = \left[\left(\frac{\partial\varepsilon'_{ij}}{\partial t}\right)_{\xi^i} - \varepsilon'_{i\omega}\Gamma^{\omega}_{\lambda j}v^\lambda - \varepsilon'_{\omega j}\Gamma^{\omega}_{\lambda i}v^\lambda\right],$$

while

$$\begin{aligned} d\varepsilon_{ij} &= e_{ij}\,dt = \tfrac{1}{2}(\nabla_i v_j + \nabla_j v_i)\,dt, \\ \mathbf{v} &= v_i\ni^i = v_i\hat{\ni}^i = \frac{dw}{dt}, \end{aligned} \qquad (17.10)$$

where $dw = \mathbf{v}\,dt$ is the displacement vector of the points of the particle in time dt with respect to the reference system defined by the basis $\ni^i$.

It is obvious that for finite deformations

$$d\varepsilon_{ij} \neq d\varepsilon'_{ij},$$

where $d\varepsilon'_{ij} \neq 0$ for a particle which displaces as a solid. If the displacements are small, then using geometrically linear theory, we have

$$d\varepsilon_{ij} = d\varepsilon'_{ij}.$$

The complete displacement vector of each point of a small particle can be represented as the sum

$$\mathbf{w} = \mathbf{w}^e + \mathbf{w}^p,$$

where $\mathbf{w}^p$ is the displacement vector corresponding to a plastic distortion after an imaginary unloading, and $\mathbf{w}^e$ is the displacement vector corresponding to an elastic process. The subdivision of the complete displacement into the plastic and elastic cases is ambiguous, because plastic and elastic displacements can be defined accurately only for a displacement of all the medium as a solid. This circumstance is not important if we consider the characteristics of the motion which are independent of the motions of the medium as a solid body.

Just as for the complete deformation, we introduce for the plastic and elastic cases the individual increments in the covariant components of tensors $\mathcal{E}^p$ and $\mathcal{E}^e$ according to the formulas

$$d\varepsilon_{ij}^p = \tfrac{1}{2}(\nabla_i v_j^p + \nabla_j v^p)\,dt \qquad \mathbf{v}^p = v_i^p \mathbf{\Im}^i = \frac{d\mathbf{w}^p}{dt} \tag{17.11}$$

and

$$d\varepsilon_{ij}^e = \tfrac{1}{2}(\nabla_i v_j^e + \nabla_j v_i^e)\,dt \qquad \mathbf{v}^e = v_i^e \mathbf{\Im}^i = \frac{d\mathbf{w}^e}{dt}. \tag{17.12}$$

The increments $d\varepsilon_{ij}^p$ and $d\varepsilon_{ij}^e$ are defined uniquely at the same time as the displacements $\mathbf{w}^p$, $\mathbf{w}^e$ and velocities $\mathbf{v}^p$ and $\mathbf{v}^e$ are defined ambiguously.

The quantities $d\varepsilon_{ij}^p$ are defined by an infinitesimal deformation, due to a movement of the basis $\hat{\mathbf{\Im}}_i$ with respect to the reference system which is stationary and has an initial basis $\mathring{\mathbf{\Im}}_i$. The quantities $d\varepsilon_{ij}^p$ are also due to an infinitesimal deformation caused by a movement of basis $\hat{\mathbf{\Im}}_i$ with respect to another reference system which is stationary and has a basis $\hat{\mathbf{\Im}}_i$.

Because

$$\mathbf{v} = \mathbf{v}^e + \mathbf{v}^p,$$

it is obvious that in one and the same arbitrary coordinate system the infinitesimal tensors $d\varepsilon_{ij}$, $d\varepsilon_{ij}^e$, $d\varepsilon_{ij}^p$ defined by (17.10), (17.11), and (17.12) in one and the same space, are related by the tensor expression

$$d\varepsilon_{ij} = d\varepsilon_{ij}^e + d\varepsilon_{ij}^p. \tag{17.13}$$

This equation also comes from the matrix expression (17.7). It is necessary, however, to bear in mind the fact that by differentiating ε_{ij}^e and ε_{ij}^p in the right-hand side of (17.7), one can also in a certain sense obtain formulas of the type (17.13), which, similarly to (17.7), are matrix equations connecting the components of infinitesimal tensors defined in different spaces.*

The elementary work of the internal stresses can be represented in the form

$$\delta \mathscr{A}^i = -\frac{1}{\rho} p^{\alpha\beta} \delta \varepsilon_{\alpha\beta} = -\frac{p^{\alpha\beta}}{\rho} \delta \varepsilon^e_{\alpha\beta} - \frac{p^{\alpha\beta}}{\rho} \delta \varepsilon^p_{\alpha\beta} . \tag{17.14}$$

In accordance with formula (17.14) one can introduce into consideration of the elementary work of the stresses based on elastic deformations

$$\delta \mathscr{A}^e = -\frac{p^{\alpha\beta}}{\rho} \delta \varepsilon^p_{\alpha\beta} ,$$

and correspondingly for plastic deformations

$$\delta \mathscr{A}^p = -\frac{p^{\alpha\beta}}{\rho} \delta \varepsilon^p_{\alpha\beta} .$$

By utilizing the covariant components of the deformation tensors, for which equations (17.7) and (17.13) hold, in the formulas which subdivide the work into elastic and plastic parts, we introduce contravariant components of the stress tensor.

From a consideration of the expression for the elementary work and from the general theory of reversible processes as applied to elasticity, it follows that instead of considering the stress tensor $\boldsymbol{P}$ with components p^{ij}, it would be more convenient to consider tensor $\boldsymbol{\sigma}$ with components $\sigma^{ij} = p^{ij}/\rho$.

In the theory of small deformations, the difference between σ^{ij} and p^{ij} is not important, because the density ρ can be considered as a constant within the accuracy of formulas (17.14) and (14.6).

To simplify the theory without losing generality, it is assumed that the reference system in basis $\boldsymbol{\mathrm{Э}}_i$ is cartesian. In this system, components of the tensor $\boldsymbol{\sigma} = \sigma'^{ij} \boldsymbol{\mathrm{Э}}_i \boldsymbol{\mathrm{Э}}_j$ with different forms of indices are the same, and their increments are also the same $d\sigma'^{ij} = d\sigma'^{i\cdot}_{\cdot j} = d\sigma'^{\cdot\cdot}_{ij}$. If the system $\hat{\boldsymbol{\mathrm{Э}}}_i$ is cartesian at a given instant, then $\sigma^{ij} = \sigma^{i\cdot}_{\cdot j} = \sigma_{ij}$.

However, if the system $\hat{\boldsymbol{\mathrm{Э}}}_i$ at a given instant is cartesian, then at following instants, because of the deformation, it becomes curvilinear. Therefore the

---

* It is obvious that the components of tensors ε^e_{ij} and $d\varepsilon^e_{ij}$ in the deformed space with the fundamental form $\hat{g}_{ij}$ will, in general, not satisfy the compatibility equations of Chapter II. This also will apply to components of tensors ε^p_{ij} and $d\varepsilon^p_{ij}$ connected with the fundamental form g^p_{ji}.

increments $d\hat{\sigma}^{ij}$, $d\hat{\sigma}^{i\cdot}_{\cdot j}$, and $d\hat{\sigma}_{ij}$ over time dt, defined on the basis of (10.11) of Chapter I by the formulas

$$d\sigma^{ij} = (d\sigma^{ij})' - (\sigma^{\omega j}\nabla_\omega v^i + \sigma^{i\omega}\nabla_\omega v^j)\,dt, \tag{17.15a}$$

$$d\sigma^{i\cdot}_{\cdot j} = (d\sigma^{i\cdot}_{\cdot j})' - (\sigma^{\omega\cdot}_{\cdot j}\nabla_\omega v^i - \sigma^{i\cdot}_{\cdot\omega}\cdot\nabla_j v^\omega)\,dt, \tag{17.15b}$$

$$d\sigma_{ij} = (d\sigma_{ij})' + (\sigma_{\omega j}\nabla_i v^w + \sigma_{i\omega}\nabla_j v^\omega)\,dt, \tag{17.15c}$$

give different tensors. These tensors can be taken to be approximately the same if the second terms within the parentheses of (17.15) are small in comparison with the derivatives of components of the tensor of stresses $d\sigma'^{ij}/dt$.

Formulas (17.15b) define the mixed components of a generally unsymmetrical tensor $d\sigma^{i\cdot}_{\cdot j}/dt$. Formula (17.15a) defines the contravariant components of the symmetrical tensor $d\sigma^{ij}/dt$, and (17.15c) defines the covariant components of another symmetrical tensor $d\sigma_{ij}/dt$. This formula for the derivative $d\sigma_{ij}/dt$ is analogous to the formula (17.10) for the derivative $d\varepsilon_{ij}/dt$ defining the tensor of rates of deformation.

In accordance with (17.14) for the elementary work and with a definition for $\delta\varepsilon_{\alpha\beta}$ from (17.10), and for a transformation of $\delta\mathscr{A}^i$ to the form

$$\delta\mathscr{A}^i = -\,\sigma^{\alpha\beta}\delta\varepsilon_{\alpha\beta} = -\,\delta(\sigma^{\alpha\beta}\varepsilon_{\alpha\beta}) + \varepsilon_{\alpha\beta}\delta\sigma^{\alpha\beta},$$

the increments of $\sigma^{\alpha\beta}$ must be taken in the sense defined by formula (17.15a). With the tensors

$$\boldsymbol{\sigma} = \frac{1}{\rho}\boldsymbol{P} = \sigma^{ij}\hat{\mathfrak{I}}_i\hat{\mathfrak{I}}_j = \sigma^{i\cdot}_{\cdot j}\hat{\mathfrak{I}}^i\hat{\mathfrak{I}}_j = \sigma_{ij}\hat{\mathfrak{I}}^i\hat{\mathfrak{I}}^j = \sigma'_{ij}\mathfrak{I}^i\mathfrak{I}^j$$

we define a nine-dimensional space Π, in which the cartesian coordinates of the points are equal to the components σ^{ij}. Consequently the quantities σ^{ij} will be considered as vector components in nine-dimensional space. We can determine three such spaces corresponding to the bases $\mathring{\mathfrak{I}}_i$, $\check{\mathfrak{I}}_i$, and $\hat{\mathfrak{I}}_i$, in which σ^{ij} will have the some value. All possible transformations of coordinates ξ^1, ξ^2, ξ^3 define the transformation groups for σ^{ij} in the corresponding nine-dimensional spaces, in which the following quantities are respectively invariant:

1. $$\hat{\mathscr{I}}_1 = \hat{g}_{\omega\alpha}\sigma^{\omega\alpha},$$
$$\hat{\mathscr{I}}_2 = \tfrac{1}{2}(\sigma^{\alpha\cdot}_{\cdot\alpha}\sigma^{\beta\cdot}_{\cdot\beta} - \sigma^{\alpha\cdot}_{\cdot\beta}\sigma^{\beta\cdot}_{\cdot\alpha}) = \tfrac{1}{2}\hat{g}_{\alpha p}\hat{g}_{\beta q}(\sigma^{p\alpha}\sigma^{q\beta} - \sigma^{p\beta}\sigma^{q\alpha}),$$
$$\hat{\mathscr{I}}_3 = \hat{g}\,|\sigma^{ij}|, \qquad \text{where} \qquad \hat{g} = |\hat{g}_{ij}|;$$

2. $$\mathring{\mathscr{I}}_1 = \mathring{g}_{\omega\alpha}\sigma^{\omega\alpha},$$
$$\mathring{\mathscr{I}}_2 = \tfrac{1}{2}\mathring{g}_{\alpha p}\mathring{g}_{\beta q}(\sigma^{p\alpha}\sigma^{q\beta} - \sigma^{p\beta}\sigma^{q\alpha}),$$
$$\mathring{\mathscr{I}}_3 = \mathring{g}\,|\sigma^{ij}|, \qquad \text{where} \qquad \mathring{g} = |\mathring{g}_{ij}|;$$

3. $$\mathring{\mathscr{J}}_1 = \mathring{g}_{\omega\alpha}\sigma^{\omega\alpha};$$
$$\mathring{\mathscr{J}}_2 = \tfrac{1}{2}\mathring{g}_{\alpha p}\mathring{g}_{\beta q}(\sigma^{p\alpha}\sigma^{q\beta} - \sigma^{p\beta}\sigma^{q\alpha}),$$
$$\mathring{\mathscr{J}}_3 = \mathring{g}\,|\sigma^{ij}|, \qquad \text{where} \qquad \mathring{g} = |\mathring{g}_{ij}|.$$

It is obvious that in the space Π, the invariants of group 3 depend only on the tensor components σ^{ij}, but the invariants of groups 1 and 2 depend also on the components of the complete or the plastic deformation tensors, respectively.

The transformation groups in nine-dimensional spaces corresponding to bases $\hat{\mathfrak{Э}}_i$ and $\mathfrak{Э}_i$ have the same invariants. The coordinates of the corresponding points σ^{ij} and σ'^{ij} are different, because the coordinate systems ξ^i and x^i are generally different.

It is easy to prove that if the derivatives $d\sigma^{ij}/dt$ (17.15a) become zero, the invariants $\mathscr{J}_1$, $\mathscr{J}_2$, $\mathscr{J}_3$ are constant. If, for the complete deformation, the derivatives $d\sigma^{i}_{\cdot j}/dt$ from (17.15a) become zero, then the invariants $\hat{\mathscr{J}}_1$, $\hat{\mathscr{J}}_2$, and $\hat{\mathscr{J}}_3$ are constant. If, for the plastic deformation, these derivatives become zero, then the invariants $\mathring{\mathscr{J}}_1$, $\mathring{\mathscr{J}}_2$, and $\mathring{\mathscr{J}}_3$ all remain constant.

Because tensor σ^{ij} is symmetric, and the derivatives $d\sigma^{ij}/dt$ defined in (15.1) form a symmetrical tensor, the nine-dimensional space Π can be replaced by a six-dimensional space, and if the tensor σ^{ij} and its derivative $d\sigma^{ij}/dt$ are deviators, the space Π can become five dimensional.

All the conclusions of this section have a purely geometric or kinematic significance. The concepts of elasticity and plasticity are used only to establish the terminology, which will be used in the applications to be discussed in the following section.

18. The elastic region and loaded surface

Let us consider a small particle of an elastic-plastic body, and examine the effects which are observed at constant temperature, when, starting from zero, the components of the tensor of the internal stress vary in this particle.

In accordance with experiment and the definition of the phenomena of plasticity for sufficiently small values of all the components of the stress tensor,* the particle will have all the properties of an elastic body. In the nine-dimensional space Π of the components of the stress tensor σ'^{ij}, we shall consider a region $\mathscr{D}_p$ in which the plastic body can be considered as

* In order to make the terminology in the theory of small deformations applicable to the theory of plasticity for finite deformation, we shall term the quantities $p^{ij}/\rho = \sigma^{ij}$ the components of the stress tensor.

an elastic one. We shall denote by Σ_p the surface which encloses the volume $\mathscr{D}_p$. The set of stresses corresponding to points on the surface Σ_p forms a set of elastic limits. The region Σ_p can extend to infinity in certain directions.

Continuous processes in which stresses correspond to points on surface Σ_p are called loading processes. Processes in which the stress passes from the boundary Σ_p into region $\mathscr{D}_p$ are called unloading processes. For processes taking place within volume $\mathscr{D}_p$, the particle possesses all the characteristics of an elastic body. We shall assume that for a change in temperature within some limited range, the volume $\mathscr{D}_p$ and its boundary Σ_p change continuously. In the general case, after the loading process on surface Σ_p takes place, the elastic properties of the particle in region $\mathscr{D}_p$ and the form of the region $\mathscr{D}_p$ itself can change. This also means that the free energy and other thermodynamic functions may change after the process of loading.

According to the established definition, a medium is called ideally plastic if the region $\mathscr{D}_p$ and its boundary Σ_p remain fixed during the process of isothermal loading. For an ideally plastic body, the stresses cannot be arbitrary. In the elastic region, they correspond to points of region $\mathscr{D}_p$, and in the plastic state, they correspond to points on the fixed surface Σ_p.

The medium is called a plastic body with hardening if the surface Σ_p changes during the loading process.

During loading processes with hardening, for which plasticity occurs at every moment of time, the stressed state corresponds to movable points on surface Σ_p.

The surface Σ_p is defined as a set of elastic limits. It is possible to construct models of plastic bodies in which the plastic states may correspond to any point on the given surface Σ_p, or models in which the appearance of plasticity is related to the supplementary limitations imposed on the stress tensor. Because of this, the transition from the elastic to plastic region may correspond only to certain sets of points of the surface Σ_p. In the latter case, one must define the additional conditions of the stress forces on the surface S which separates the elastic region from the region of plastic flow.

In dynamic problems, surface S can be a surface of strong discontinuity moving through the particle. On this surface the well-known compatibility conditions [29] should be fulfilled. In static problems, certain conditions dealing with the continuity of the internal stresses must be satisfied on surface S.

The auxiliary conditions on the surface S may serve as conditions determining this surface.

From this, the plastic properties in certain cases can be related to the restrictions imposed on the stress tensor. In particular, one can consider cases analogous to the equilibrium of an elastic body, ice (the stress tensor must have a general form), and an ideal liquid, water (the stress tensor is spherical), which are separated by a surface S.

If all the points lie in the plastic region, as in the case of a liquid,* the stress tensor cannot be arbitrary, and therefore the equilibrium becomes possible only for a special system of external forces.

Every small particle of the body can, generally speaking, undergo an arbitrary deformation, and therefore, for a given particle, the deformation tensor both in the elastic and plastic regions can have arbitrary components.

It follows that in essence the space of the possible values of the deformation tensor is always six dimensional, and in the case of an incompressible medium, five dimensional.

In the elastic region, the space of the possible stresses is also usually six dimensional. For the plastic region, models can be constructed in which the stress space can, in essence, have a smaller number of dimensions. For example, for an ideal liquid, the stress space is essentially one dimensional.

Thus, for certain plastic models of bodies, a reciprocally unique continuous relationship between stresses and deformations is not possible, in general.

Moreover, in the case of an ideal plastic body, it is not possible to consider the isomorphism of the stresses and deformations. Such isomorphism is also not possible for all the models of plastic bodies with hardening.

The second basic property of the phenomenon of plasticity is that residual deformations occur for unloading until the stress is zero, after the loading processes take place on surface Σ_p.

It is obvious that after plastic deformation, the particle, considered as a physical system in a stressed state, will be, in general, different from the original particle prior to the loading process.

The residual plastic deformations are obtained as a result of internal processes related to relative displacements and reconstruction in the crystal lattice of molecules or atoms in the original structure of the solid body.

The changes in the elastic and plastic properties of a plastically stressed particle can be characterized by the various parameters of the plastic loading. According to the concept expressed in § 6, it must be assumed that the number of these parameters is finite.

If we assume that the difference in the mechanical and thermal properties before and after loading is due to the residual deformation, we can choose the covariant components of the residual deformation tensor to be parameters which define the change in the properties of the particle: ε_{ik}^p.

---

* Of course, a liquid is a statically overdeterminate mechanical system.

The components of the tensor of the complete deformation ε_{ik} in the stressed state at any point in region $\mathscr{D}$ or on surface Σ can be represented as a sum

$$\varepsilon_{ik} = \varepsilon_{ik}^{p} + \varepsilon_{ik}^{e},$$

where ε_{ik}^{e} are the components of the tensor of deformation, defined as a deformation obtained according to the laws of elasticity for a transition from an unstressed state to a stressed one. The unstressed deformation, corresponding to $\boldsymbol{P} = 0$, is defined by the laws of elastic theory, which in turn depend on an ideal loading process, generally speaking.

In addition to the components of the tensor of residual deformations, or along with these components, we can also take another system of parameters

$$\chi_1, \chi_2, \ldots, \chi_n,$$

which can be related to the residual deformations or to unloading processes in particular, by nonholonomous differential expressions. The quantities χ_s generally depend on loading processes in a functional form. If ε_{ik}^{p} and $\chi_1, \ldots, \chi_n$ are chosen as defining parameters, one can delete from the subsequent closed system the equations which contain functional relationships.

Thus, we shall assume that the system of defining parameters for particles of elastic-plastic models has the form

$$\sigma^{ik}, T, \varepsilon_{ik}^{p}, \chi_1, \chi_2, \ldots, \chi_n, k_1, k_2, \ldots, k_m \qquad (i, k = 1, 2, 3), \tag{18.1}$$

where $k_1, k_2, \ldots, k_m$ are physical constants.

The concept of the elastic region $\mathscr{D}_p$ and loaded surface Σ_p can be extended to a ten-dimensional space; correspondingly we obtain $\mathscr{D}$ and Σ when we add a new dimension for the temperature T, which varies within a certain range.*

In defining an elastic-plastic medium, it is also assumed that parameters ε_{ik}^{p} and χ_s have constant values inside region $\mathscr{D}$. It therefore follows that the elastic properties of a particle can change because of the relationships of the thermodynamical functions of these parameters† after the loading processes accompanied by plastic deformations.

In the loading processes on surface Σ, the parameters ε_{ik}^{p} and χ_s can be variable.

---

* W. Prager [26] has recently dealt with the effect of temperature on the elastic limits and the load function.

† We note that if a closed-cycle process has a region of plastic deformation, the work of the internal stress forces in the elastic deformation, even for isothermal processes, taken through this closed cycle, can be different from zero.

We also suppose that the possible hardening, characterized by the deformation and motion of surface Σ, is also defined by a system of parameters (18.1). It therefore follows that in a ten-dimensional space, the points of which are defined by the components of the stress tensor and temperature T, the surface Σ for a given particle can be represented as

$$f(\mathring{g}_{ij}, \sigma^{ij}, T, \varepsilon^p_{ij}, \chi_1, \chi_2, \ldots, \chi_n, k_1, k_2, \ldots, k_m) = 0. \qquad (18.2)$$

Without losing generality, we shall in the following consider that the function f depends in a symmetrical way on the components of the symmetrical tensors σ^{ij} and $\varepsilon^p_{\cdot j}$.

We shall further assume that the function f is defined so that in the region $\mathscr{D}$, corresponding to thermoelastic processes, the following inequality is valid:

$$f < 0. \qquad (18.3)$$

The function $f(\mathring{g}_{ij}, \sigma^{ij}, T, \varepsilon^p_{ij}, \chi_s, k_1, k_2, \ldots, k_m)$ is called the loading function.

The medium is ideally plastic if the equation (18.2) in cartesian coordinates has the form

$$f(\sigma^{ij}, T, k_1, k_2, \ldots, k_m) = 0. \qquad (18.4)$$

Consequently, surface Σ is fixed in the space σ^{ij} and T. In the case of an ideally plastic body, surface Σ with equation $f = 0$ is called a flow surface.

If, for an ideally plastic body, the physical constants k_1, k_2, ..., k_m are scalars, the medium is isotropic. In this case, the function f will depend only on the invariants of tensor $\boldsymbol{\sigma}$.

In a plastic medium in which hardening is possible, the loading process corresponds to the inequality

$$d'f = \frac{\partial f}{\partial T} dT + \frac{\partial f}{\partial \sigma^{ij}} d\sigma^{ij} > 0. \qquad (18.5)$$

By definition, on surface Σ we have

$$d'f = 0,$$

while the corresponding process is thermoelastic, in which the parameters ε^p_{ij} and χ_s keep their constant value.

For an ideally plastic medium, equation (18.4) is satisfied, and therefore for plastic loading we have*

$$df = \frac{\partial f}{\partial T} dT + \frac{\partial f}{\partial \sigma^{ij}} d\sigma^{ij} = 0. \qquad (18.6)$$

From the definition of the medium with hardening, it follows that $d\chi_s = 0$

* The differentials $d\sigma^{ij}$ are defined in the sense of formulas (17.15a).

for $d'f = 0$, and therefore the differential relationships for the determination of χ_s should have the form

$$d\chi_s = \mathscr{A}_s d'f,$$

where $\mathscr{A}_s$ can depend on the system of parameters (18.1), taken on surface Σ, i.e., related by the expression (18.2). For a plastic body with hardening, it is also obvious that if $d'f = 0$, then it is also true that

$$df = d'f + \frac{\partial f}{\partial \varepsilon_{ik}^p} d\varepsilon_{ik}^p + \frac{\partial f}{\partial \chi_s} d\chi_s = 0,$$

because in this case $d\varepsilon_{ik}^p = 0$, and $d\chi_s = 0$.

The transition from surface Σ into the elastic region $\mathscr{D}$ for unloading processes is defined by the inequality $df = d'f < 0$.

Apart from specifying region $\mathscr{D}$ and consequently the functions f, the specification of models of plastic bodies is concerned with fixing the elastic properties in region $\mathscr{D}$ and to the formulation of additional laws for irreversible processes defining the values of the components of the tensor of the residual deformations ε_{ik}^p and the parameters χ_s.

It is normally assumed that thermoelastic properties in region $\mathscr{D}$ do not depend on ε_{ij}^p and χ_s, while for isothermal deformations in the region $\mathscr{D}$, the elastic deformation and the stress tensor are related linearly by Hooke's law.

19. The basic laws in the theories of plastic bodies

The bases for building the various models for plastic bodies are the laws governing the determination of ε_{ij}^p and χ_s, and along with this, the data on the load function f.

We will now show that from the formulation of the basic properties of plastic bodies it follows that at any instant the residual deformations ε_{ik}^p and the parameters χ_s for any plastic loading process cannot be defined at that instant by the values of the components of the stress tensor. In other words, the laws of plasticity for arbitrary loading laws cannot be represented in the form of finite single-valued functions of the type

$$\varepsilon_{ij}^p = \varepsilon_{ij}^p(\sigma^{ij}, T, k_1, k_2, \ldots, k_m)$$

and

$$\chi_s = \chi_s(\sigma^{ij}, T, k_1, k_2, \ldots, k_m), \qquad (19.1)$$

where σ^{ij} and T are for a plastic-loading process.

The formulas of the form of (19.1), when the parameters χ_s are absent, are the basis of the so-called deformation theories of plasticity, which may be regarded as a natural generalization of nonlinear elastic theory.

Let us first consider the case of an ideally plastic body. Let M and N be two arbitrary different points on the loaded surface Σ, corresponding to two different plastic states for $T =$ const. For any two processes, which originate in one and the same state in the elastic region $\mathscr{D}$, the residual deformation and the values of the parameters χ_s on approaching M and N are zero or equal. The isothermal process of the transition from N to M along Σ for plastic loading produces a further residual deformation and causes a change in ε_{ij}^p, so that, to a point M with given values of σ^{ij} and T, will correspond different values of ε_{ij}^p. On the other hand, if the stress σ^{ij} on Σ is fixed, various values of ε_{ij}^p can correspond to this stress. From this it follows that these quantities cannot be related by finite relationships of the type (19.1). In other words, in the case of an ideally plastic body, isomorphism of the correspondence between ε_{ij}^p and σ^{ij} is not possible.

In the case of plastic deformations with hardening, for loading along the loaded surface, we have $d'f = 0$ and $df = 0$, and therefore, for any fixed temperature and at every instant of time, at all the points on the corresponding surface $f = 0$ (surface Σ is different at different instants and will trace out a certain volume), the quantities ε_{ij}^p and χ_s, are constant, and σ^{ij} can vary over quite a wide range. Thus, the same constant values ε_{ij}^p and χ_s can correspond to different values of σ^{ij} along the fixed surface Σ; but, on the other hand, along different surfaces Σ the constant values of ε_{ij}^p and χ_s can be different.

It is therefore clear that if for any two states the residual deformations are different, then in the presence of relationship (19.1) the corresponding loaded surfaces Σ_1 and Σ_2 can have no common points. If Σ_1 and Σ_2 have common regions, then the relationships (19.1) are impossible.

Each of the equations (19.1), and the equation $f = 0$ in the space of stresses, and temperature, define one and the same surface Σ. Therefore all the quantities ε_{ij}^p and χ_s can be considered as universal functions of one of them, for example, ε_{11}^p. Consequently, the supposition that a finite relationship of the type (19.1) exists imposes essential and unacceptable restrictions on the residual deformation tensors.

Thus it was shown that for plastic bodies with hardening, finite relationships of the type (19.1) are impossible* for arbitrary loading systems.

On the other hand, it is clear that for each completely defined loading

* An analogous supposition has been made by Handelman and Warner using the special laws of the theory of plasticity established by Prager and Drucker [49]. We note that the discussion we have given uses only very general ideas about plastic bodies. The conclusions arrived at are valid also when sharp corners are present on the loaded surface.

law, relationships of the type (19.1) can be used. In connection with this, we can ask whether there are various particular loading systems for which one and the same finite relationship (19.1) is fulfilled. For certain models, this question can be answered affirmatively.

The construction of models of plastic bodies is related to the specification of certain general properties of the irreversible loading process and the properties of the loaded surface Σ which are derived herefrom.

In accordance with the definition given in (17.14), we shall consider the elementary work of the internal stresses for a loading process accompanied by an increment in the plastic deformations $d\varepsilon_{\alpha\beta}^{p}$. We have

$$d\mathscr{A}^{p} = -\frac{p^{\alpha\beta}}{\rho} d\varepsilon_{\alpha\beta}^{p}.$$

For a given deformed state and given increments $d\varepsilon_{\alpha\beta}^{p}$, the work of the internal stresses $p^{*\alpha\beta}$ corresponding to any point of the elastic region $\mathscr{D}$, is given by the expression

$$d\overset{*}{\mathscr{A}}{}^{p} = -\frac{\overset{*}{p}{}^{\alpha\beta}}{\rho} d\varepsilon_{\alpha\beta}^{p}.$$

The hypothesis expressed by the inequality

$$d\overset{*}{\mathscr{A}}{}^{p} - d\mathscr{A}^{p} = \frac{p^{\alpha\beta} - \overset{*}{p}{}^{\alpha\beta}}{\rho} d\varepsilon_{\alpha\beta}^{p} \geq 0 \tag{19.2}$$

has a thermodynamic nature. This inequality present already in an implicit form in the work of Mises [72] was formulated as a thermodynamic principle in the work of many contemporary authors, and at present is the basis for the construction of models of plastic bodies. This inequality is called the principle of Bishop-Hill, who made it the theoretical basis of monocrystals and certain polycrystalline aggregates of monocrystals.

In considering tensors $d\varepsilon_{\alpha\beta}^{p}$ and $d\overset{*}{p}{}^{\alpha\beta} = p^{\alpha\beta} - \overset{*}{p}{}^{\alpha\beta}$ for a given deformation as elementary vectors in the nine-dimensional space of tensor p^{ij} or σ^{ij}, the postulate (19.2) can be considered as the condition of the positiveness of the scalar product of vectors $d\overset{*}{p}{}^{\alpha\beta}$ and $d\varepsilon_{\alpha\beta}^{p}$ or $d\overset{*}{\sigma}{}^{\alpha\beta}$ and $d\varepsilon_{\alpha\beta}^{p}$:

$$d\overset{*}{p}{}^{\alpha\beta} d\varepsilon_{\alpha\beta}^{p} \geq 0 \qquad \text{or} \qquad d\overset{*}{\sigma}{}^{\alpha\beta} d\varepsilon_{\alpha\beta}^{p} \geq 0\,; \tag{19.3}$$

whence it follows that the angle between the vectors $d\overset{*}{\sigma}{}^{\alpha\beta}$ and $d\varepsilon_{\alpha\beta}^{p}$ is always acute ($\leq 90°$), and stress $\overset{*}{\sigma}{}^{\alpha\beta}$ can correspond to the points of surface Σ_p. If a surface perpendicular to $d\overset{*}{\varepsilon}{}_{\alpha\beta}^{p}$ is passed through point $\overset{*}{\sigma}_{\alpha\beta}$, then from (19.3) it follows that the entire loaded surface Σ_p is disposed along one side of this plane. From this it follows that the surface Σ_p is convex on the side of the elastic region $\mathscr{D}_p$.

If at point $\sigma^{\alpha\beta}$ surface Σ_p has only one tangent plane, this plane would be perpendicular to the vector $d\varepsilon^p_{\alpha\beta}$. Hence it follows that in the presence of a unique normal to surface Σ, we have the following equations:

$$\begin{aligned} d\varepsilon^p_{\alpha\beta} &= d\lambda \frac{\partial f}{\partial \sigma^{\alpha\beta}} \qquad (f = 0), \\ d\varepsilon^p_{\alpha\beta} &= 0 \qquad (df < 0), \end{aligned} \tag{19.4}$$

where $d\lambda$ is a certain positive quantity, because by virtue of (19.3), a vector with components $d\varepsilon^p_{ij}$ is directed along the external normal to $\mathscr{D}$. For an ideally plastic body, the quantity $d\lambda$ is determined from the condition of loading.* For an elastic body with hardening, we have $d\lambda = 0$ for $d'f = 0$, and therefore we may write $d\lambda = h\, d'f$, where h is a function of the defining parameters. Consequently, in this case, we have

$$\begin{aligned} d\varepsilon^p_{\alpha\beta} &= h \frac{\partial f}{\partial \sigma^{\alpha\beta}} d'f \qquad (f = 0) \quad (d'f > 0), \\ d\varepsilon^p_{\alpha\beta} &= 0 \qquad (d'f \leq 0). \end{aligned} \tag{19.5}$$

Equations (19.4) and (19.5) can be considered as auxiliary kinetic relationships for determining the increments $d\varepsilon^p_{\alpha\beta}$ produced by irreversible processes.

It is obvious that for hardening processes, the increment $d\chi_s$, which reduces to zero simultaneously with $d'f$, can be written as

$$\begin{aligned} d\chi_s &= \mathscr{A}_s d'f \qquad (d'f > 0), \\ d\chi_s &= 0 \qquad (d'f \leq 0). \end{aligned} \tag{19.6}$$

In order to determine the functions f, h, and $\mathscr{A}_s$, additional hypotheses by which the properties of the models can be related to experimental observations are necessary. If $\varepsilon^p_{\alpha\beta}$ is taken in basic $\Im_i$, then for infinitesimal deformations when $d\varepsilon_{\alpha\beta} = d\varepsilon'_{\alpha\beta}$, we obtain from (18.2), (19.5), and (19.6) the formula

$$1 + h \frac{\partial f}{\partial \sigma^{\alpha\beta}} \frac{\partial f}{\partial \varepsilon^p_{\alpha\beta}} + \mathscr{A}_s \frac{\partial f}{\partial \chi_s} = 0, \tag{19.7}$$

which establishes one relationship between h, f, and $\mathscr{A}_s$. According to the conditions and generalizations assumed, we can suppose that (19.7) is also valid for finite deformations.

---

* In static problems for bodies of finite dimensions in the plastic region, the scalar field $d\lambda$ is determined from a complete system of equations to the accuracy of the multiplicative constant. This circumstance is related to the additional arbitrary choice of the time scale.

Relationships (19.4) and (19.5), which are derived from (19.3) and from the supposition about the smoothness of surface Σ, are called the associative law. Such a law in the theory of ideally plastic bodies was first established and applied in a general form by Mises.

In the applied concrete theories of plastic media with hardening, the parameters of type χ are either entirely absent, or only one parameter χ is present, and the load function f and the function h in (19.5) are dependent upon this parameter.

Let us cite examples:

1. $d\chi = p^{ij} d\varepsilon^p_{ij}$ (Taylor and Quinney, 1931 and Schmidt, 1932).
2. $d\chi = +\sqrt{\frac{2}{3} d\varepsilon^p_{ij} d\varepsilon^p_{ij}}$ (Odguist, 1933).

These authors considered only isothermal processes and assumed that the equation of the loaded surface has the form

$$f = F(p^{ij}) + \omega(\chi).$$

The following suppositions are generally accepted:

1. $f = \mathscr{D}_2 - \omega(\chi)$, where
$$\mathscr{D}_2 = (p^{ij} - \tfrac{1}{3}\mathscr{I}_1 \delta^{ij})(p^{ij} - \tfrac{1}{3}\mathscr{I}_1 \delta^{ij}) = F(p^{ij})$$

(the coordinate system is cartesian, $\delta^{ij} = 0$, $i \neq j$, and $\delta^{ij} = 1$ for $i = j$; $\mathscr{D}_2$ is the second invariant of the deviator of the stress tensor). This is the theory of Mises.

From this form of function f and from (19.5), it follows that the volume deformation is elastic.

2. $f = \tau_{\max} - k_0$ where $\tau_{\max}$ (p_1, p_2, p_3) is the maximal shearing stress, p_1, p_2, p_3 are the principal stresses, and k_0 is a constant or a function of some parameter χ. This is Tresca's theory.

In the general case, the invariant scalar function f depends only on the joint system of invariants of the tensors σ^{ij}, ε^p_{ij}, and of other tensors defined by the parameters χ_s and the constants k_j.

If the load function is represented as

$$f = F(\sigma^{ij}) + \omega(\varepsilon^p_{ij}),$$

then this function must have the form

$$f = F(\mathscr{I}^\sigma_1, \mathscr{I}^\sigma_2, \mathscr{I}^\sigma_3) + \omega(\mathscr{I}^e_1, \mathscr{I}^e_2, \mathscr{I}^e_3),$$

where $\mathscr{I}^\sigma_i$ and $\mathscr{I}^e_i$ are the respective invariants of the stress and residual deformation tensors. A further particular function f can be obtained if it is assumed that the volumetric deformations are always elastic or that the material is incompressible. In the literature, this latter supposition has frequently been used together with assumptions about the smallness of the deformation. The assumptions and certain additional ones lead one to the conclusion that plastic processes can be described with the aid of the foregoing formulas, in which only the stress deviator appears, while the tensor of the residual deformations is also a deviator. We shall consider these suppositions in more detail below.

The investigation of different particular forms of load function dependent only on p^{ij} and ε_{ij}^{p}, was carried out by Edelmann and Drucker [50], who explained how to take into account various experimentally observed substantial effects, e.g., the Bauschinger effect, the anisotropy occurring after plastic deformation, etc.

In particular, Reuss [84], Prager [79], and other authors have considered load functions dependent only on the tensor

$$\mathring{\boldsymbol{P}} - m\mathring{\mathscr{E}},$$

where m is some constant.

It is obvious that in this case the loaded surface Σ and the elastic region $\mathscr{D}$ for isothermal hardening are displaced successively in nine-dimensional space.

This idea of the nature of hardening was used and developed by various authors [13, 16, 91].

The use of particular forms of function f allows satisfactory descriptions of many important physical effects to be given. However, up to the present time there has been no comprehensive listing of plastic properties formulated with the aid of experiments. At present, further theoretical developments of new models with various properties which have been observed and various experiments are being carried out.

Apparently these theoretical investigations can help in the basic experimental problem concerning the formulation of the properties of the various plastic materials which have to be considered.

In developing the concepts of the internal mechanisms and the properties of continuum models, the simplest mechanical systems with one or a small number of degrees of freedom played an important role.

Elements of such systems may be moving loads, springs, appliances for obtaining forces of dry frictional type, viscous drag, certain nonlinear interaction forces, etc.

The basic static and dynamic effects involved in elasticity, viscosity, and plasticity can be described both quantitatively and qualitatively with simple schematic devices.

To describe the various effects of plastic hardening in certain particular cases, moving and deformable frames representing the loaded surfaces can be utilized. The laws governing the displacement and deformation of the frame can characterize the residual deformations. The shape of the frame, the presence on it of sharp points, and the possibility of its deformation allow one to investigate the effect of peculiarities of the loaded surface on the process of plastic deformation, and to discover the dependence of the results on the manner of loading or deforming.

The Prager model [27], which takes the form of an I-beam, subject to tensile forces and bending moments so arranged that the stressed state is reduced to tensioning the upper flange with a force p_1 and the lower one with a force p_2, is simple, interesting, and instructive. If we assume that the stress diagrams of the flanges are the same and are represented by Prandtl's law, then in the plane $\mathscr{P}$ with rectilinear cartesian coordinates p_1 and p_2, the loaded surface will be represented in the form of a rigid rectangular frame. We will now introduce a plane $\mathscr{E}$ with cartesian coordinates equal to the tension coefficients ε_1 and ε_2 of the flanges. If we now place the frame of the plane $\mathscr{P}$ in the plane $\mathscr{E}$ so that the coordinate axes are parallel, then for plastic deformations the frame of the stress surface in the plane $\mathscr{E}$ is displaced successively. The displacement of the center of the frame defines the vector of the plastic deformation. This model easily explains such facts as the possibility of obtaining different stresses for the same general deformation.

On the other hand, it is obvious that for plastic deformation with stress corresponding to a sharp point, it is possible to obtain the same finite stresses for various manners of developing the deformation.

A broken deformation path can correspond to a simple linear loading process.

The more difficult example of the bending of round pipe [29] (with a Prandtl diagram for the tension of the generators of the pipe) was considered by Yu. N. Rabotnov in an analogous situation. In this case, the original loaded surface is circular. During the deformation the loaded surface deforms, and it is curious to note in this case the established effect of appearance of a corner point at the point of application of load.

Thus, the simplest models exhibit properties which form the basis of the model, also simple, of a small particle of elastic-plastic medium.

The concept of plastic medium is related to the representation of the initial state. For a given particle, the original state actually realized or defined with the aid of mental processes is a state in which there are no internal surface stresses (a state for which the stress tensor becomes zero).

For a plastic body, the original state and basic mechanical properties of the particles can be different before and after the loading. Among such initial states one state with essentially simple properties may sometimes be singled out, and this state can be taken as the original state. Obviously, in building models of plastic bodies, it is useful if the essential mechanical properties of various original states are characterized by a minimum number of loading parameters, because each intermediate loaded state can be related by a removal of load to a corresponding initial state.

In the process of loading, different residual deformations correspond to the various initial states. A change in the mechanical properties of the initial states can be ascribed to residual deformations and to a difference in the other characteristic quantities. In the simplest cases, such as the I-beam example of Prager, the effect of plastic deformations is reduced only to a change in the reference origin for the deformation, but all the mechanical properties of the particle are preserved.

A change in the mechanical properties with a change in the initial state is possible because of the appearance, due to plastic effects, of anisotropy in the elastic properties and of nonsymmetry of the loaded surface with respect to the initial point. It is convenient to take the parameters characterizing these effects as characteristics of the initial properties.

In general theories intended for mass investigations, it is essential that the mechanical "questionnaires" and "passports," containing data about materials, provide at least a minimum amount of information conveniently obtained from experiment, which at the same time is adequate for practical purposes. The use of detailed "genealogies" and "biographies" is expedient only in special problems. In connection with this, the introduction of the basic theoretical concepts of plastic theory, and in particular, concepts about the initial state can be based on intermediate states. In considering mechanical processes with repeated plastic loading and unloading, the original ideal state need no longer serve as the reference base and as the fixed characteristic of the problem.

In other words, the closed set of principles which describe the mechanical processes can have a local character with respect to time and particles. In connection with this, the equations in which these principles are formulated must be finite or differential.

Correspondingly, we must utilize the concepts which are completely defined at a given instant and for a given particle as the determining characteristics.

Let us now consider the properties of the loaded surface in connection with certain general requirements and observations.

1. The material is plastically incompressible.

Elastic changes in volume are permissible. In cartesian coordinates this means that the equation

$$d\varepsilon_{11}^p + d\varepsilon_{22}^p + d\varepsilon_{33}^p = 0 \tag{19.8}$$

is satisfied.

Let us write tensor $\boldsymbol{\sigma}$ in the form of a sum

$$\boldsymbol{\sigma} = pG + \mathscr{D}, \qquad \mathscr{D} = d^{ik}\mathbf{Э}_i\mathbf{Э}_k,$$

$$\sigma^{ik} = d^{ik} + p\delta^{ik}, \qquad p = \frac{\sigma_{11} + \sigma_{22} + \sigma_{33}}{3}.$$

After replacing in the argument of load function the quantities σ^{ik} by d^{ik} and p, taking into account (19.8) and the associated laws (19.5), we obtain

$$\frac{\partial f}{\partial p} = \frac{1}{3}\left(\frac{\partial f}{\partial \sigma^{11}} + \frac{\partial f}{\partial \sigma^{22}} + \frac{\partial f}{\partial \sigma^{33}}\right) = 0.$$

Consequently, the hypothesis of plastic incompressibility leads to the conclusion that the function f depends only on the components of the deviator d^{ik}, and that for infinitesimal deformations, the residual deformation tensor is also a deviator.

For finite deformations, the tensor of finite residual deformations is not a deviator, but its invariants are related by a known expression which guarantees constant density.

In plastic materials, the property of incompressibility is not always fulfilled; for example, residual volume deformations can occur in soils. It is also possible to construct corresponding models suitable for studying the spatial movements, taking into account volume plasticity, for example, in applications to soils [6].

2. Rectilinear loading paths.

Within the assumed range of small deformations we shall consider the conditions under which the following relationships for proprotional loading [62, 87] will be fulfilled, when the two following equations are simultaneously satisfied:

$$d^{ij} = \lambda d_0^{ij} \quad \text{and} \quad \varepsilon_{ij} = \mu\varepsilon_{0ij}^p, \tag{19.9}$$

where λ and μ are scalars.

From equations (19.9) it follows that if in the space of the stress deviator the components of the latter during loading change along a straight line, then the corresponding residual deformation will also change along a straight line. If the directions of these two straight lines coincide, then

$$d^{ij} = k\varepsilon_{ij}^p, \tag{19.10}$$

where k is generally a variable scalar.

From the associated law (19.5) it follows that if the equations (19.9) and (19.10) can be simultaneously applied to all lines radiating from the coordinate origin, the initial loaded surface in the space of deviator d^{ij} can only be a sphere. If this equation also applies after unloading, the loaded surface after hardening must also remain spherical. However, the center of the sphere can be displaced and the radius can change.

Consequently, if the loaded surface is initially not spherical, then the equation (19.10) cannot be satisfied. However, it will be satisfied approximately for small deviations of the loaded surface from a sphere.

If the sphere is deformed during loading, the equation (19.10) for intermediate initial states cannot be satisfied for all directions after unloading. It can, however, be satisfied in certain specific directions.

Expression (19.9) can be fulfilled along all the loading directions if the initial loaded surface is any convex surface which changes in a similar way during hardening. This means that in this case, the load function f must be a homogeneous function of the components of the deviator d^{ij} and the components of the residual deformations ε_{ij}^{p}.

3. Acquired anisotropy.

A particle which is physically isotropic before loading can become physically anisotropic after plastic loading. The anisotropy properties can occur both in the elastic and in the plastic regions. According to the concepts that we have assumed, the anisotropic properties can be regarded as properties defined by the parameters ε_{ij}^{p} and χ_s. To determine the elastic anisotropic properties, it is sufficient to establish the dependence of free energy on these parameters.

The actual number of the characteristics of elastic anisotropy can be reduced if we consider small deformations, and if Hooke's law is valid in the elastic region. The property of plastic incompressibility and the absence of additional tensors defined by parameters χ_s, allow further simplifications to be made.

To determine the anisotropic plastic properties of a hardening material, it is sufficient to know how the load function depends on these parameters. The anisotropy which occurs is due to the fact that the load function depends essentially on invariant scalars containing combinations of the components of σ^{ij}, ε^{ij}, and χ_s. The development of plastic anisotropy gives rise to an unsymmetrical displacement or deformation of the surface Σ with respect to the origin of coordinates in the nine-dimensional space of the components of the stress tensor.

In special cases, the anisotropy of plastic properties can be considered with the aid of a successive displacement of the loaded surface Σ. Other very simple complications which arise during the deformation of surface Σ have been analyzed by a number of authors [58].

4. The work of the internal stresses for plastic deformations.

The elementary work of the internal stress forces, acting on unit mass for plastic deformation, is represented by the expression

$$d\mathscr{A}^p = -\frac{1}{\rho} p^{ij}\, d\varepsilon_{ij}^p,$$

where ρ is the density, which for finite deformations is a known function of the invariants of the components of the tensor of $\varepsilon_{ij}^e + \varepsilon_{ij}^p$. In accordance with the laws of the theory of elasticity, the tensor of elastic deformations ε_{ij}^e can be replaced by the stress tensor and the other quantities which appear in the equation of state.

If the deformations are small, the density can be considered as a constant.

The equation of heat flow leads to the expression

$$d\mathscr{F} + S\,dT - \frac{p^{ij}}{\rho} d\varepsilon_{ij}^e - \frac{p^{ij}}{\rho} d\varepsilon_{ij}^p = dQ - T\,dS, \tag{19.11}$$

where $\mathscr{F}$ $(\mathring{g}_{ij}, \varepsilon_{ij}^e, T, \varepsilon_{ij}^p, \chi_s, k_j)$ is the free energy. For finite deformations, we suppose that all the components of the tensors are arguments of function $\mathscr{F}$ taken with basis $\mathring{g}_{ij}$ (a Lagrangian coordinate system in the space of the initial state), $k_1, k_2, \ldots, k_m$ are the physical constants of the particle, S is the entropy, and dQ the actual external flow of heat.

Because the process of plastic deformation is irreversible, from the second law of thermodynamics it follows that

$$dQ - T\,dS = -\,dQ' \leq 0, \tag{19.12}$$

where dQ' is the noncompensated heat.

At every moment of time the stresses p^{ij} and the entropy S, both in the elastic region $\mathscr{D}$ and on its boundary Σ, can be determined with the aid of laws of elasticity using the formulas

$$p^{ij} = \rho \frac{\partial \mathscr{F}}{\partial \varepsilon_{ij}^e}, \qquad S = -\frac{\partial \mathscr{F}}{\partial T}. \tag{19.13}$$

From (19.11), taking into account (19.12) and (19.13), we shall obtain

$$-\,d\mathscr{A}^p = \frac{p^{ij}}{\rho} d\varepsilon_{ij}^p \geq \left(\frac{\partial \mathscr{F}}{\partial \varepsilon_{ij}^p} d\varepsilon_{ij}^p + \frac{\partial \mathscr{F}}{\partial \chi_s} d\chi_s\right). \tag{19.14}$$

From the inequality (19.14), it follows that the work of the internal forces in plastic deformations is always negative ($d\mathscr{A}^p < 0$) if the increment in internal energy

$$d'\mathscr{F} = \frac{\partial \mathscr{F}}{\partial \varepsilon_{ij}^p} d\varepsilon_{ij}^p + \frac{\partial \mathscr{F}}{\partial \chi_s} d\chi_s$$

is positive. If $d'\mathscr{F} < 0$, the second law of thermodynamics in the presence of dissipation of mechanical energy can be satisfied even in the case when $d\mathscr{A}^p > 0$.

If we suppose that the deformations are small and that the thermoelastic laws in region $\mathscr{D}$ do not depend on the plastic deformations, the free energy must take the form

$$\mathscr{F} = \mathscr{F}(\mathring{g}_{ij}, \varepsilon_{ij}^e, T, k_j) + \omega(\mathring{g}_{ij}, \varepsilon_{ij}^p, \chi_s, k_j)\,; \tag{19.15}$$

the function ω depends only on the characteristics of the plastic deformation. In this case, (19.14) assumes the form

$$-\,d\mathscr{A}^p = \frac{p^{ij}}{\rho} d\varepsilon_{ij}^p \geq \frac{\partial \omega}{\partial \varepsilon_{ij}^p} d\varepsilon_{ij}^p + \frac{\partial \omega}{\partial \chi_s} d\chi_s\,. \tag{19.16}$$

In studying the motions of a plastic body with a given heat flow, expression (19.11) must be used to close the system of equations; and therefore in defining a model of a plastic medium it is necessary to specify the dependence of the free energy on ε_{ij}^p and χ_s; and in the case of (19.15), the function ω must be specified.

Equation (19.11) can be used to calculate the necessary heat flow in isotropic processes. To solve mechanical problems, it is sufficient to know equations of state (19.13), the associated laws (19.5) and (19.6) for ε_{ij}^p and χ_s, and the universal equations of mechanics for continua.

Function ω need not be given for investigations of isothermal motions in case (19.15). However, in all cases, the sign of the work of the internal forces on residual deformations depends on the way in which the free energy $\mathscr{F}$ or function ω depends on ε_{ij}^p and χ_s. It should be noted that as a rule residual deformations always occur in ideal liquids or gases. However, in this case, the work of the stress forces on the residual deformations is always zero (this is because of the reversible character of the residual deformations in an ideal liquid). Irreversible phenomena are possible in which the sign for the increments $d'\mathscr{F}$ or $d\omega$ can be arbitrary. Consequently, the problem of the sign of the plastic work cannot be regarded as a simple consequence of the irreversibility condition (19.12). Analogous irreversible effects in chemical reactions can occur both as a result of the absorption of external energy as well as the result of the transfer of energy to external bodies. The stress at the elastic limit plays the role of the critical temperature which stimulates chemical reaction in plastic processes.

Let us now consider the complete work of the internal stresses for plastic deformations, which, on the basis of the associated law (19.5), can be written as

$$\mathscr{A}^p = -\int \frac{p^{ij}}{\rho} d\varepsilon_{ij}^p = -\int \frac{h}{\rho} p^{ij} \frac{\partial f}{\partial p^{ij}} d'f$$

$$= -\int \frac{h}{\rho} p^{ij} \frac{\partial f}{\partial p^{ij}} \frac{\partial f}{\partial p^{\alpha\beta}} dp^{\alpha\beta} + \frac{h}{\rho} p^{ij} \frac{\partial f}{\partial p^{ij}} \frac{\partial f}{\partial T} dT. \tag{19.17}$$

In the general case, the magnitude of the work $\mathscr{A}^p$ depends on the loading path. Handelman and Warner [57] considered the case of small plastic deformations, when $p =$ const and f has the form

$$f = f_0(p^{ij}) + \omega(\varepsilon_{ij}^p, \chi_s),$$

and also h is dependent only on f_0.

In this case, for isothermal processes, the condition for the work $\mathscr{A}^p$ being independent from the loading path leads to the conclusion that the function f_0 should have the form

$$f_0 = F(\Phi), \tag{19.18}$$

where F is an arbitrary function of its argument, and $\Phi(p^{ij})$ is an arbitrary first-order homogeneous function of its arguments.

In fact, from (19.17) we have

$$d\mathscr{A}^p = -\frac{h}{\rho} p^{ij} \frac{\partial f_0}{\partial p^{ij}} df_0$$

if $\mathscr{A}_p$ is independent of the loading path; and since $d\mathscr{A}^p$ and df_0 are simultaneously zero, $\mathscr{A}^p = \mathscr{A}^p(f_0)$, i.e., the work of the plastic deformations, depends only on f_0. Therefore we must have

$$\frac{h(f_0)}{\rho} p^{ij} \frac{\partial f}{\partial p^{ij}} = \frac{h(f_0)}{\rho} g(f_0), \tag{19.19}$$

where $g(f_0)$ may be an arbitrary function. Replacing $g(f_0)$ by $\Omega(f_0)$ in accordance with

$$g(f_0) = \Omega(f_0) \int \frac{df_0}{\Omega(f_0)} = \Omega(f_0)\Phi(f_0),$$

the relationship (19.19) reduces to the form

$$p^{ij} \frac{\partial \Phi}{\partial p^{ij}} = \Phi;$$

whence it follows that function $\Phi(f_0)$ is an arbitrary homogeneous first-order function of the components of the tensor of p^{ij}, and as a result, formula (19.18) is valid.

20. Models of plastic media whose loaded surfaces have angular points

Recently much work has been published on the construction and use of models of plastic bodies whose loaded surfaces have sharp ridges and angular or conical points.

In the first classical model of a plastic body first proposed by Tresca, the loaded surface was defined by the condition that the shearing stresses for plastic deformation are a maximum and have a given value. This surface is formed by intersecting planes and has sharp edges.

In the nine-dimensional space of the stress tensor, the loaded surface Σ is a surface with plane facets.

In the three-dimensional space of the principal stress axes, this is an equilateral six-sided prism whose axis is equally inclined to the principal stress axes. The cross section of this prism formed by the deviator plane

$$p_1 + p_2 + p_3 = 0$$

is an equilateral hexagon; the distance of its vertexes from the center is equal to $2\tau_{\max}$, where $\tau_{\max}$ is the shearing stress for which plastic flow is initiated.

In the space of the principal stresses, the loaded surface in the deviator plane according to Mises' condition (the second invariant of the stress deviator on the loaded surface is constant) is a circle inscribed within the Tresca hexahedron.

The Mises circle and the Tresca hexahedron are symmetrical with respect to the origin and the projections of the principal coordinate axes onto the deviator plane.

In both cases, the physical isotropy conditions are satisfied. In general, however, these conditions will not necessarily lead to a loaded surface which is symmetrical about the origin. For example, it is known that the loaded surface in the deviator plane would not be symmetrical about the origin if the tensile and compressive elastic limits are different. Nevertheless, the conditions of symmetry of the loaded surface with respect to straight lines which are projections of the principal strain axes onto the deviator plane will be satisfied.

Thus, the deviations of the elastic limits from Mises condition do not violate the physical isotropy conditions.

Experimental data do exist which may serve as a basis for introducing elastic limits different from Mises conditions and which stimulate the examination of loaded surface with angular points.

The residual deformation must remain constant in accordance with Mises conditions for a loading path coinciding with the Mises circumference. Experimental data exist [71] which point in a definite manner to the change for a loading path which follows the Mises circumference.

The laws of theory of elasticity must to some extent be observed for strain-hardened plastic media at smooth points of the loaded surface when the motion is along the tangent to the loaded surface. However, it has been noted [22, 40] that in this case, deviations from elastic theory do arise, while it is also noted that in this case, the plastic deformation trajectory becomes a broken line. These effects can be explained by assuming that at the loaded point the loaded surface has angular or conical points.

At the same time, complications arise because experimental data exist which do not indicate the effects mentioned above. At regular points of the loaded surface with a single normal, the sense of increment in the residual deformations is fixed. The direction of the vector $d\varepsilon^p_{ij}$, according to (19.3) can change within certain limits at angular points of the loaded surface. Thus, the plastic deformation has a high degree of freedom when loading takes place at an angular point of the loaded surface.

We therefore need additional data in order to establish plastic deformations for loading at angular points.

Koiter [67], in 1953, gave the generalized associated law for this case. At present, Koiter's theory is the basis of all work devoted to the investigation of plasticity when the loaded surface has angular points.

Koiter's basic assumptions are in agreement with the principle included in the inequality (19.3), which considers the minimum work of the stresses for plastic deformations. The essence of this theory is as follows.*

Let the boundary of the elastic region in the space of tensor of stresses p^{ij}, and let the particular loaded points be formed by several intersecting regular planes defined by the equations

$$f_k(p^{ij}, \varepsilon^p_{ij}, T, \chi_s, k_j) = 0 \qquad (k = 1, 2, \ldots), \tag{20.1}$$

while the number of these planes is arbitrary.

---

* In the case of a plastic body subject to hardening, which will be discussed below, in our development of Koiter's theory we assume that f_i can depend in an arbitrary way on the residual deformation and parameter χ_s. These suppositions were not used by Koiter in the cited work, but have been utilized by other authors who extended this theory.

In certain cases, the loaded surface may be regarded as the envelope of multitude (20.1) with an infinite number of surfaces.

Functions f_k are defined such that displacements in the elastic region obey the inequalities

$$f_k < 0 \qquad \text{and} \qquad d'f_k = \frac{\partial f_k}{\partial T}\, dT + \frac{\partial f_k}{\partial p^{\alpha\beta}}\, dp^{\alpha\beta} < 0 . \tag{20.2}$$

In the case of an ideal plastic body for which arguments ε_{ij}^p and χ_s are absent in (20.1), the following equations correspond to a plastic loading process:

$$df_\omega = d'f_\omega = 0 , \qquad df_\nu = d'f_\nu = 0 , \tag{20.3}$$

where indices ω and ν are different and cover exhaustively the set $k = 1,2, \ldots$.

In an analogous manner, the following expressions correspond to a loading process with strain hardening:

$$d'f_\omega > 0 , \qquad df_\omega = 0 , \qquad df_\nu = d'f_\nu \leq 0 . \tag{20.4}$$

If the index ω coincides with several indices, the stress tensor for an infinitesimal loading path will still correspond to particular points on the loaded surface Σ. If $\omega = j$, where j is a unique fixed index, the loaded point is displaced from a particular point to a regular point of surface Σ.

If the indices ω coincide with all the indices $k = 1,2, \ldots$, such loading is called complete loading.

Koiter's generalization of the associated Mises law (19.4) is given by the equation

$$d\varepsilon_{ij}^p = \sum_\omega d\lambda_\omega \frac{\partial f_\omega}{\partial p^{ij}} , \tag{20.5}$$

where $d\lambda_\omega$ are positive. For ideally plastic bodies, the values of multipliers $d\lambda_\omega$ are related to the fulfillment of the conditions of plasticity:

$$f_\omega = 0 . \tag{20.6}$$

For plastic bodies subject to strain hardening, one can write for multipliers $d\lambda_\omega$

$$d\lambda_\omega = \kappa_\omega h_\omega d'f_\omega , \tag{20.7}$$

where h_ω are functions of the parameters defining the physico-mechanical characteristics of the particle, and κ_ω is a positive quantity less than unity. The functions h_ω are analogous to the function h, which occurs in formula (19.5). The specification of the function h_ω plays a part in determining the model of a plastic body. The factors κ_ω are defined in the basic problems which deal with bodies as a whole [11].

If the system of functions in (20.1) is infinite, the sum in (20.5) can be replaced by an integral whose limits of integration are defined by the conditions (20.3) and (20.4). If the loading conditions are satisfied, formula (20.5) can be used to close the system of mechanical equations.

The additional parameters χ_s can be introduced by formulas of the following type in the case of strain-hardened materials:

$$d\chi_s = \sum_\omega \mathscr{A}_{s\omega}\, d'f_\omega$$

and (20.8)

$$d\chi_s = \mathscr{B}_s^{\alpha\beta}\, d\varepsilon^p_{\alpha\beta},$$

where $\mathscr{A}_{s\omega}$ or $\mathscr{B}_s^{\alpha\beta}$ are known functions of the defining parameters.

For plastic materials with strain hardening, formulas (20.5) can be written in the form

$$d\varepsilon^p_{ij} = \sum_\omega \kappa_\omega h_\omega \frac{\partial f_\omega}{\partial p^{ij}} d'f_\omega. \tag{20.9}$$

For a given system of indices ω defined by the increments in the tensor of the stresses dp^j and temperature T, formula (20.9) gives a linear relationship between $d\varepsilon^p_{ij}$, dp^{ij}, and dT. However, in the stress space around a particular loading point, we can point out different regions of variations of dp^{ij} and dT, in each of which the system of indices ω will be different. Corresponding to this we will find that the linear relationships (20.9) differ in such regions. Thus, (20.9) may be regarded as essentially a nonlinear relationship between $d\varepsilon^p_{ij}$, dp^{ij}, and dT.

Sanders [90] has discussed the nonlinear effects at angular loaded points, and Hodge [53] has investigated the cases when surfaces Σ_i defined by the equations $f_i = 0$ are plane.

In this case, one can find a finite relationship between stresses and deformations which is the same for certain corresponding classes of loading paths, but different for other classes.

Koiter has shown that the conditions for yielding with an irregular surface in Tresca's theory can be found within the limits of expressions (20.5), in which surface Σ is taken as an envelope of an infinite number of planes of the form

$$f_{ab} = \tfrac{1}{2} p^{ij}(n_i^a n_j^b + n_j^a n_i^b) - k = 0,$$

where n_i^a and n_i^b are the components of two mutually perpendicular unit vectors. The symbols a and b define two perpendicular directions which may be arbitrary.

Koiter has also shown that the Batdorf and Budiansky theory is obtained with the aid of (20.9) on the supposition (equivalent to hypotheses of Batdorf and Budiansky) that the flow surface is the envelope of an infinite number of planes. In this theory, the loaded point is conical, and the relationship between the increments in stress and deformation has a complicated integral form.* A. K. Malmeister and co-workers [21] have developed analogous theories.

The relationship between h_ω and f_ω, and the parameters of the loading path, can be extremely complex, and because of this, the loaded surface may change considerably under plastic deformation.

In considering active loading (i.e., without any intermediate unloading), only the local properties at the loaded points are important, and therefore the theory of plastic deformation with strain hardening can be developed using formula (20.9), in which the functions f_ω may be considered as linear functions of the stress components.

Despite the nonlinear effects and the very complicated situation for arbitrary loading paths, the special feature of the theory of loading at angular points is the fact that the theory can be simplified for a certain set of loading paths which pass through each point within the region of complete loading.

Budiansky [46] has shown that finite relationships between stress and deformation can exist for certain sets of paths passing through the region of complete loading.

In the theory of ideal plasticity, the direct and closest generalization of Prandtl's diagram for uniaxial deformation in the general case of volumetric plastic motion may be served by the hypothesis on fixing the deviator of a stress tensor different from zero with arbitrary orientation with respect to axes of principal stresses. Such an assumption may be regarded as a natural generalization of the concept of an ideal liquid, which for arbitrary motions is determined by the condition that the stress deviator becomes zero.

It is within the last ten years that the general notions about building models of plastic bodies have been developed. In connection with this, the problems concerned with the determination of specific functions corresponding to the experimental data of certain materials and mechanical problems have not yet been resolved. However, we possess models which are rationally constructed and are based on a theoretical analysis. Further

---

* Recently Joshimaru's [63] work appeared in which critical comments were given on the concordance of the Batdorf and Budiansky theory with experimental data.

development of the theory of plasticity should be based on existing theories which, however, require further simplification and critical comparison with experiment.

It is also obvious that we should study in more detail the temperature and thermal effects as related to dynamical problems.

The physical concepts involved in construction of solids, and the general statistical and thermodynamic principles must be invoked to a greater extent than hitherto.

BIBLIOGRAPHY

1. Bondar, V. D., "O tenzornykh kharakteristikakh konechnykh deformstsii sploshnoi sredy" [The tensor characteristics of finite deformation of a continuous medium], *Prikl. matem. i mekhan.*, **25**, 3 (1961).
2. Bondar, V. D., "Nekotorye tochnye resheniya uravnenii sovmestnosti dlya komponent tenzora deformatsii pri prostom nagruzhenii" [Certain exact solutions to the equations of compatibility for the tensor components of deformations with simple loading], *Doklady Akad. Nauk SSSR*, **130**, 6 (1960).
3. Batchelor, G. K., *Theory of homogeneous turbulence,* Cambridge University Press, Cambridge (1953).
4. Gantmakher, F. R., *Teoryia matrits* [Theory of matrices], Gostekhizdat, Moscow (1953).
5. Gol'denblat, I. I., *Nekotorye voprosy mekhaniki deformiruemykh sred* [Some problems in the mechanics of deformed media], Gostekhizdat, Moscow (1955).
6. Grigoryan, S. S., "Ob osnovnykh predstavleniyakh dinamiki gruntov" [Basic concepts in the dynamics of soils], *Prikl. matem. i mekhan.*, **24**, 6 (1960).
7. Groot, S. R. de, *Thermodynamics of irreversible processes,* North-Holland Publishing Company, Amsterdam (1951).
8. Zhukov, A. M. and Rabotnov, Yu. N., *Issledovanie plasticheskikh deformatsii slozhnom nagruzhenii* [Investigation of plastic deformation of steel with complex loading].
9. Sommerfield, A., *Termodinamika i statisticheskaya fizika* [Thermodynamics and statistical physics] (translations from German), Izdat Inostr. Liter., Moscow (1955).
10. Ivlev, D. D., "K postroeniyu teorii uprugosti" [The construction of a theory of elasticity], *Doklady Akad. Nauk SSSR*, **138**, 6 (1961).
11. Ivlev, D. D., "O matematicheskom opisanii povedeniya uprugogo izotropnogo tela pri pomoshchi kusochno-lineinogo potentsiala" [Mathematical description of the behavior of an elastic isotropic body in terms of a segmented linear potential], *Prikl. matem. i mekhan.*, **25**, 5 (1961).
12. Il'yushin, A. A., *Plastichnost'* [Plasticity], Gostekhizdat, Moscow (1948).
13. Ishlinskii, A. Yu., "Obshchaya teoriya plastichnosti s lineinym uprochneniem" [General theory of plasticity with linear simplification], *Ukr. matem. Zhurnal*, **6**, 3 (1954).
14. Kachanov, L. M., *Osnovy teorii plastichnosti* [Fundamentals of the theory of plasticity], Gostekhizdat, Moscow (1956).
15. Kachanov, L. M., *Teoriya polzuchesti* (Theory of creep), Fizmatgiz, Moscow (1960).
16. Kadashevich, Yu. I. and Novozhilov, V. V., "Teoriya plastichnosti uchityvayushchaya effekt Baushingera" [The theory of plasticity with consideration of the Bauschinger effect], *Doklady Akad. Nauk SSSR*, **117**, 4 (1957).
17. Kochin, N. E., *Vektornoe ischislenie i nachalo tenzornogo ischisleniya* [Vector analysis and elementary tensor analysis], 6th ed., GONTI (1938).
18. Landau, L. D. and Lifshitz, E. M., *Mekhanika sploshnykh sred* [Mechanics of continuous media], 2nd ed., Gostekhizdat, Moscow (1954).

19. Lorentz, H. A., *Lektsii po termodinamike* [Lectures on thermodynamics] (translations from German), Gostekhizdat, Moscow (1941).
20. Love, A. E. H., *A treatise on the mathematical theory of elasticity*. 4th rev. ed. (1927); repr. Dover Publishing Company, New York.
21. Malmeister, A. K., *Uprugost' i neuprugost' betona* [Elasticity and inelasticity of concrete], Riga (1957). See "Issledovaniya po betonyy i zhelezobetony" [Investigation of concrete and reinforced concrete], *Sborniki statei Latviiskoi Akad. Nauk.*
22. Naghdi, P. and Rowley, J. J., "An experimental study of biaxial stress-strain relations in plasticity," *J. Mech. Phys. Solids,* **3,** No. 1 : 63–80 (1954).
23. Novozhilov, V. V., *Osnovy nelineinoi teorii uprugosti* [Fundamentals of non-linear elasticity theory], Gostekhizdat, Leningrad and Moscow (1947).
24. Novozhilov, V. V., *Teoriya uprugosti* [Theory of elasticity], Sudpromgiz, Leningrad (1958).
25. Prager, W., "Ob elementarnyi analiz opredeleniya skorosti izmeneniya napry-azheni" [Elementary analysis of the determination of rate of stress change], Mekhanika [Mechanics], Translations from the foreign periodical literature, No. 3 (1960). [Paper presented at the first Soviet Russian Congress on Mechanics, January 28, 1960.]
26. Prager, W., "Non-isothermal plastic deformation," *Proc. Kon. Ned. Akad. Wetenschap.* **61,** 3, 176–182 (1958).
27. Prager, W. *An introduction to plasticity,* Addison-Wesley Publishing Company, Reading, Mass. (1959).
28. Rabotnov, Yu. N., "'Model' illyustriruyushchaya nekotorye svoistva uprochnyayushchegosya plasticheskogo tela" [A model illustrating certain properties of a strain-hardening plastic body], *Prikl. matem. i mekhan.,* **23,** 1 (1959).
29. Sedov, L. I., *Ploskie zadachi gidrodinamiki i aerodynamiki* [Plane hydrodynamic and aerodynamic problems], Gostekhizdat, Moscow and Leningrad (1950).
30. Sedov, L. I., "Ponyatie raznykh skorostei izmeneniya tenzora" [The concept of different rates of change in a tensor], *Prikl. matem. i mekhan.,* **23,** 3 (1960).
31. Sedov, L. I., "O ponyatiyakh prostogo nagruzheniya i o vozmozhnykh putyakh deformatsii" [Concepts of simple leading and possible paths of deformation], *Prikl. matem. i mekhan.,* **23,** 2 (1959).
32. Sedov, L. I., *Metody podobiya i razmernosti v mekhanike* [Similitude and dimensional analysis methods in mechanics], 4th ed., Gostekhizdat, Moscow (1957).
33. Sedov, L. I., "Ob obshchem vide uravnenii kinematiki khimicheskikh reaktsii v gazakh" [General form of equations of the kinematics of chemical reactions in gases], *Doklady Akad. Nauk SSSR,* **60,** 1 (1948).
34. Sedov, L. I., "K teorii postroeniya mekhanicheskikh modelei sploshnykh sred" [Theory of construction of mechanical models of continuous media], *Vestn. Akad. Nauk SSSR,* No. 7 (1960).
35. Sedov, L. I., "Ob osnovnykh kontseptsiyakh mekhaniki sploshnoi sredy" [Basic concepts of the mechanics of a continuous medium], in: *Some Problems of Mathematics and Mechanics. Jubilee volume on 60th birthday of Academician M. A. Lavrent'ev.* Izdat. Sibirskogo otd. Akad. Nauk SSSR, Novosibirsk (1961).

36. Sedov, L. I., "Ob osnovnykh printsipakh mekhaniki sploshnoi sredy" [Basic principles of the mechanics of a continuous medium], Izdat. MGU (1961).
37. Sedov, L. I. and Eglit, M. E., "Postroenie negolonomnykh modelei sploshnykh sred s uchetom konechnosti deformatsii i nekotorykh fizikokhi-micheskikh effektov" [Construction of nonholonomic models of continuous media with consideration of the finiteness of the deformations and of certain physioco-chemical effects], *Doklady Akad. Nauk SSSR,* **142,** 1 (1962).
38. Skripkin, V. A., "Priblizhennye formuly dlya vektora povorota pri maloi deformatsii" [Approximative formulas for the rotation vector with slight deformation], *Prikl. matem. i mekhan.,* **21,** 5 (1957).
39. Timoshenko, S., *History of strength of materials,* McGraw-Hill Book Company, New York (1953).
40. Feigen, M., "Inelastic behavior under combined tension and torsion", *Proc. 2nd U.S. Nat. Congr. Appl. Mech.* (1954), pp. 469–476.
41. Yakimov, Yu. A., "Raspredelenie udarnykh voln v ideal'nykh sredakh s proizvol'nymi fizicheskimi svoistvami" [The distortion of shock waves in ideal media with arbitrary physical properties], Dissertation defended at Moscow State University in 1959, *Mekhanika* [Mechanics], Journal of Abstracts, No. 8, 8507D (1959).
42. Eglit, M. E., "O tenzornykh kharakteristikakh konechnykh deformatsii" [The tensor characteristics of finite deformations], *Prikl. matem. i mekhan.,* **24,** 5 (1960).
43. Eglit, M. E., "Ob opredelenii uprugikh potentsialov iz opyta" [The determination of elastic potentials from experiment], *Prikl. matem. i mekhan.,* **25,** 4 (1961).
44. Biot, M. A., "Theory of elasticity with large displacements and rotations," *Proc. 5th Intern. Congr. Appl. Mech.* (1939).
45. Biot, M. A., "Non-linear theory of elasticity and the linearized case for a body under initial stress," *Phil. mag.,* **27,** No. 183 (1939), pp. 449–452, 468–489.
46. Budiansky, B., "A reassessment of deformation theories of plasticity." *Trans. ASME, Series E, Journ. of Appl. Mech.,* **26,** No. 1–2 (March–June, 1959), pp. 259–246.
47. Cotter, B. A. and Rivlin, R. S., "Tensors associated with time-dependent stress," *Quart. Appl. Math.,* **13,** No. 2 (1955), pp. 177–182.
48. Donder, Theophile de, *Thermodynamic theory of affinity,* Stanford University Press, Stanford (1936).
49. Drucker, D. C. and Prager, W., *J. Math. and Phys.,* **23,** No. 2 (1953).
50. Edelmann, F. and Drucker, D. C., "Some extensions of elementary plasticity theory," *J. Franklin Inst.* (1951), pp. 581–607.
51. Ericksen, J. L. and Rivlin, R. S., "Large elastic deformations of homogeneous anisotropic elastic materials," *J. Rational Mech. and Anal.,* **3,** No. 3 (1954), pp. 281–301.
52. Ericksen, J. L. and Rivlin, R. S., "Stress-deformation relations for isotropic materials," *J. Rational Mech. and Anal.,* **4,** No. 2 (1955).
53. Goodier, J. H. and Hodge, P. G., *Elasticity and plasticity,* John Wiley and Sons, New York (1958).
54. Green, A. E. and Zerna, W., *Theoretical elasticity,* Oxford University Press, Oxford (1954).

55. Gibbs, J. W., *Collected works,* Vol. I: *Thermodynamics,* Longmans, Green and Co., New York (1928).
56. Hirschfelder, J. O., Curtiss, C. F., and Bird, R. B., *Molecular theory of gases and liquids,* John Wiley and Sons, New York (1954).
57. Handelman, G. H. and Warner, W. H., "Loading paths and the incremental strain law." *J. Math. Phys.,* **33,** No. 2 (1954).
58. Hodge, Ph. G., "A general theory of piece-wise linear plasticity based on maximum shear," *J. Mech. Phys. Solids,* **5,** No. 4 (1957).
59. Hanin, M. and Reiner, M., "On isotropic tensor functions and the measure of deformation," *J. Appl. Math. Phys. (ZAMP),* **2,** Fasc. 5 (1956), pp. 377–393.
60. Hill, R., *The mathematical theory of plasticity,* Clarendon Press, Oxford (1956).
61. Jaumann, G., *Grundlagen der Bewegungslehre,* Leipzig (1950). See also *Sitzungsberichte Akad. Wiss. Wien* **(110) 120** (1911).
62. Joshimaru Joshimura, "On the definition of stress in the finite deformation theory," *J. Phys. Soc. Japan.* **8,** No. 5 (1953).
63. Joshimaru Joshimura, "Comment on the slip theory of Batdorf and Budiansky," *Bull. JSME,* **1,** No. 2 (1958), pp. 109–113.
64. Kappus, R., "Über Elastizitätstheorie endlicher Verschiebungen," *ZAMM,* **19,** Hft. 5 (1939), pp. 271–285.
65. Kirchhoff, G., "Über die Gleichungen des Gleichgewichts eines elastischen Körpers bei nichtunendlich kleinen Verschiebungen seiner Teile," *Sitzungsberichte Akad. Wiss. Wien,* **9,** (1883).
66. Kirchhoff, G., *Vorlesungen über mathematische Physik,* Bd. I: *Mechanik,* 2. Aufl., Leipzig (1877); 3. Aufl. (1883).
67. Koiter, W. T., "Stress-strain relations, uniqueness and variational theorems for elastic-plastic materials with a singular field surface." *Quart. Appl. Math.,* **9,** No. 3 (1953), pp. 350–354.
68. Koiter, W. T., "General theorems for elastic-plastic solids," *Progress in Mechanics,* **1,** (1960).
69. Lagally, M., *Vorlesungen über Vektorrechnung,* Leipzig (1928).
70. Lodge, W., *Forschungsarbeiten a. d. Gebiete d. Ingeniurwesens,* No. 303, VDI-Verlag, Berlin (1928).
71. Marin, J. and Hu. L. W., "Biaxial plastic stress-strain relations of a mild steel for variable stress ratios, *Trans. ASME,* **78,** No. 3 (1956).
72. Mises, R., "*Mechanik der plastischen Formänderung von Kristallen,*" *ZAMM* **8,** Hft. 3 (1928), pp. 161–185.
73. Murnaghan, F. D., *Finite deformation of an elastic solid,* John Wiley and sons, New York (1951).
74. Murnaghan, F. D., "Finite deformations of an elastic solid," *Am. J. Math.,* **59,** No. 3 (1937), pp. 235–260.
75. Oldroyd, J. G., "On the formulation of rheological equations of state," *Proc. Roy. Soc. (A),* **200,** No. 1063 (1950), pp. 523–541.
76. Onsager, Lars, "Reciprocal relations in irreversible processes – 1", *Phys. Rev.,* **37,** No. 2 (1931), pp. 405–426.
77. Onsager, Lars, "Reciprocal relations in irreversible processes – 2," *Phys. Rev.,* **38,** No. 12 (1931), pp. 2265–2279.
78. Penner, J. J., *Introduction to the study of chemical reactions in flow systems,* Butterworths, London (1955).

79. Prager, W., "Der Einfluss der Verformung auf die Fliessbedingung zäh-plastischer Körper," *ZAMM,* **15,** Hft. 1–2 (1935), pp. 76–80.
80. Prager, W., *Einführung in die Kontinuumsmechanik,* Birkhäuser Verlag, Basel und Stuttgart (1961).
81. Prigogine, I., *Etude thermodynamique des processus irreversibles* (Thesis), Dunod, Paris-Liège (1947).
82. Reiner, M., "The theory of non-Newtonian liquids." *Physics,* **5,** No. 11 (November 1934).
83. Reiner, M., "A mathematical theory of dilatancy," *Am. J. Math.,* **67,** No. 3 (1945), pp. 350–362.
84. Reuss, E., *Abstracts 4th Internat. Congr. Appl. Mech.,* Cambridge (1934), p. 91.
85. Rivlin, R. S., "The constitutive equations for certain classes of deformations," *J. Rational Mech. and Anal.,* **3,** No. 4 (1959), pp. 304–311.
86. Rivlin, R. S., *Some topics in finite elasticity, structural mechanics,* Pergamon Press, London (1960).
87. Roy, M., "Transformations faiblement irreversibles et relations de Onsager; Echanges thermiques et resistances passives," *C. R. Acad. Sci. Paris,* **250,** No. 4 (1960), pp. 639–642.
88. Roy, M., *Mécanique des millieux continus et deformables,* Vols. 1–2, Gauthier-Villars (1950).
89. Roy, M., "Sur les notions d'effluence et de production d'entropie et sur loi de Fourier," *C. R. Acad. Sci. Paris,* **250,** No. 1 (1960), p. 35.
90. Sanders, J. L., "Plastic stress-strain relations based on linear loading functions, *Proc. 2nd U.S. Nat. Congr. Appl. Mech.* (1954), pp. 455–460.
91. Shield, R. T. and Ziegler, H., "On Prager's hardening rule," *J. Appl. Math. Phys.,* **9a,** No. 3 (1958), pp. 260–275.
92. Signorini, A., *Questioni di elasticità non linearezzata,* Roma (1960).
93. Sokolnikoff, I. S., *Mathematical theory of elasticity,* 2nd ed., McGraw-Hill Book Company, New York (1956).
94. Seth, B. R., "Finite strain in elastic problems," *Phil. Trans. Roy. Soc. (London),* **A 234** (1935), pp. 231–264.
95. Taylor, G. I. and Quinney, H., "The plastic distortion of metals," *Phil. Trans. Roy. Soc. (London),* **A 230** (1932), pp. 323–362.
96. Truesdell, C., "The mechanical foundations of elasticity and fluid dynamics," *J. Rational Mech. and Anal.* **1** (1952), p. 125; **2** (1953), pp. 593–616.

INDEX

Alternation of tensors, 16
Angular points, 148, 150
Anisotropy
  elastic, 250
  plastic, 250

Basis
  contravariant, 5
  corresponding to the initial state 216
  corresponding to the state of deformation, 216
  covariant, 5
Bauschinger effect, 228
Bishop-Hill principle, 243

Chemical potential, 183
Christoffel symbols, 6, 61
Clapeyron's equation, 184
Closed system, 140
Coefficient
  of elongation, 91, 135
  poisson, 163
  of specific heat, 159
  of thermal conductivity, 169
  of viscosity, 197
Compatibility conditions, 112
Components
  contravariant, 6
  covariant, 6
  principal, of the stress tensor, 132
  principal, of a tensor, 23
Concentration of components in a mixture, 179
Constant
  Boltzmann, 150
  gas, 161
  Planck's, 116
Continuity equation, 120, 179
Coordinate systems
  Cartesian, 2
  Euclidean, 2, 6
  Lagrangian, 87
  Spherical, 6
Creep, 227

Dalton's law, 184
Defining parameters for a gaseous mixture, 179
Deformation
  affine, 81
  complete, 230
  elastic, 230
  plastic, 230
Density
  of air under various conditions, 116
  of gaseous mixtures, 176
  of interstellar gas, 116
  of iron, 116
  of nuclear matter, 116
Deviator, 21
Differentiation
  by Jaumann's method, 76
  of nonlinear tensor functions, 106
  of tensors in the reference system, 73
  of tensors with respect to coordinates, 57
  of tensors with respect to a parameter, 65
  total, 72
Diffusion, 118, 179
Dimensions, 170
Dissipation of energy, 197
Dissociation, 184, 187
Dynamic equations of Newton's law, 127

Effect
Bauschinger, 228
Kelvin, 40
Poynting, 40
Elastic limit, 228
Elastic region, 236
Energy
free, 215
free of elastic body, 215
internal, 146
kinetic, 137
potential, 188
Enthalpy, 188
Entropy, 149
Entropy flow, 192
Equation
Clapeyron, 161
of continuity, in an arbitrary coordinate system, 121
of continuity, in the Lagrangian form, 120
of diffusion, 179
of an equilibrium phase, 184
for gaseous mixtures, 179
Guldberg-Waage, 186
of heat flow, 147
Lagrange, 25
of mass balance in mixtures with physico-chemical reactions, 178
of motion for a continuous medium in a curvilinear coordinate system, 134
of motion for a continuous medium in the Eulerian form, 156
of motion for a continuous medium in the Langrangian form, 135
Navier-Stokes, 200
Newton, 127
Reynolds, 200
of state for a continuum, 180
of state for an elastic body, 203, 208
of state for an elastic isotropic body, 218
of state for an ideal two-parameter medium, 173
van der Waals, 163

First law of thermodynamics, 147
Forces
external surface, 126
gravitational, 137
internal surface, 127
mass, 126
Formula
Gibbs, 193
Lagrange-Sylvester, 38, 42
Oldroyd, 72
Formulas
for thermodynamic functions in gaseous mixtures, 184
for thermodynamic functions in real gases, 162
Functions
isotropic, 32
stress, 240
tensor, 32

Gas
ideal, 156
real, 162
van der Waals, 163
Gauss' divergence theorem, 134
Generalized forces, 144
Gibbs formula, 193
Guldberg-Waage law, 186

Hamilton-Cayley identity, 37
Hardening, 228
Heat
Joule, 166
specific, 159
uncompensated, 151, 180
Hooke's law, 215

Invariants
of deformation tensor, 224

of deviator, 28
of stress tensor, 18
of tensor, 224
Isotropy, 32, 218

Jacobian transformation, 8

Kelvin effect, 40
Kinetic energy theorem, 136

Lagrange
coordinates, 78, 88
equation, 25
Law
of action and reaction, 124
associative, in plastic theory, 245
of conservation of energy, 147
of conservation of mass, 120
of conservation of momentum, 129
of conservation of motion, 129
of heat transmission, 168
Liquid
compressible, 159
ideal, 155
incompressible, 160
viscous, 195
Lode parameter, 28

Mass, 115
of a liquid, 176
molecular, 161
Material
anisotropy, 250
cont inuum, 117, 118
Medium
elastic-plastic, 229
homogeneous isotropic, 218
ideal plastic, 236, 240
ideal two-parameter, 171
isotropic, 218
plastic with hardening, 236, 240
Model
of elastic body, 201
of ideal liquid, 156
of plastic body, 229
of viscous liquid, 195
Motion
of an ideal incompressible liquid, 160
laminar, 198
potential, 197
turbulent, 197

Navier-Stokes equation, 200
Newton's dynamic equation, 126, 151
Newton's law, 196

Onsager's principle, 149, 194

Phase transitions, 165
Photon momentum, 116
Plastic theory
of Mises, 245
of Reuss and Prager, 246
of Tresca, 245
Poynting effect, 40
Principal components
of a deformation tensor, 92
of stress tensor, 220
of a tensor, 23
Principal vector
of mass forces, 127
of the momentum of the external surface forces, 128
of surface forces, 130
Process
adiabatic, 150, 166
irreversible, 149, 151, 166
isothermal, 167, 214
loading, 237
polytropic, 168
reversible, 149, 151, 183
Properties
of affine deformations, 85
of internal stresses, 128, 130

Radiation, 118, 165
Radius
 of electron, 116
 of proton, 116
Recombination, 184, 187
Relaxation, 227
Reuss' theory, 246
Reynolds equation, 200
Rules
 Gibbs phase, 180
 for the summation of indices, 5
 for tensor addition, 14

Scale of deviator, 29
Second law of thermodynamics, 148, 152, 187, 225
Self-similar solution, 174
Simple tension diagram, 227
Stoichiometric coefficients, 178
Stress
 internal, 118, 128
 normal, 128
 shearing, 128
Surface
 flow, 240
 loaded, 236, 248

Temperature, 148
Temperature gradient, 168
Tensor
 acceleration, of pure deformation, 104
 concepts, 11
 finite deformation, 91
 Hencky, 219
 linearly dependent, 48
 linearly independent, 48
 Riemann-Christoffel, 61
 similar, 27
 skew-symmetric, 20
 spherical, 22
 stress, 132
 symmetric, 20
 velocity deformation, 104
 viscous stress, 195
Tensor products (scalar, vector, mixed), 4
Theory of finite deformations, 205
Theory of small deformations, 205, 206
Thermal conductivity, 165
Thermodynamic potential, 158
Thermodynamic systems, 139
Turbulence, 197

Vector
 displacement, 205
 rotation, of deformation axis, 99
Vector of
 diffusion flow, 177
 energy flow, 192
 entropy flow in gaseous mixtures, 192
Viscosity, 118
Viscosity coefficients, 197

Work
 of external surface and volume forces, 137
 of gravitational forces, 137
 of internal surface forces, 138
 of internal volume forces, 137